Laboratory Studies of Chick, Pig, and Frog Embryos

Laboratory Studies of Chick, Pig, and Frog Embryos

Guide and Atlas of Vertebrate Embryology

Sixth Edition

Gary C. Schoenwolf, Ph.D.

Associate Professor
University of Utah
School of Medicine
Salt Lake City, Utah

Ray L. Watterson, Ph.D.

Formerly Professor
University of Illinois
Urbana, Illinois

Macmillan Publishing Company
New York
Collier Macmillan Publishers
London

Front cover: Scanning electron micrograph of a transverse cryofracture through a 33-hour chick embryo.

Back cover: Light micrograph of a dorsal view of the head of a living 33-hour chick embryo.

Macmillan Publishing Company
866 Third Avenue, New York, New York 10022

Collier Macmillan Canada, Inc.

ISBN 0-02-408011-X

Printing: 2 3 4 5 6 7 8   Year: 9 0 1 2 3 4 5 6 7 8

PREFACE

Six major changes have been made in the sixth edition. First, exercises on experimental embryology of the frog and chick have been added to allow students to gain some hands-on experience with living embryos. Instructors may choose to have students do all the exercises or only selected ones. Additionally, instructors may choose to do all or some of the exercises as demonstrations with various degrees of student participation. Furthermore, students may consider doing selected exercises as independent study or research projects. It is difficult to schedule experiments in a typical quarter or semester course format when embryos develop over hours or days. However, the pedagogic value of working with living embryos far outweighs the scheduling difficulties. Probably the best way to schedule the experiments to yield maximum results is to have the instructor (or teaching assistants) set up the experiment at selected periods *prior* to the scheduled laboratory. Then, during the scheduled periods, students can do two things: (1) repeat the experiment trying the described techniques, and (2) observe the results of the experiment set up by the instructor. If students are sufficiently stimulated by this experience they may be willing to come to the laboratory in off-hours to view their results. Second, additional references have been added to the "Useful References and Audiovisual Aids" section. Now listed are many of the textbooks used currently in courses in developmental biology/embryology. Third, a new section comparing the early development of amphibian and avian embryos has been added. This section should help students better understand that vertebrate embryos develop similarly, even though they have very different structural features. Fourth, a text figure has been added to the section on the circulatory system of the 10-mm pig embryo. This illustration should help students better understand the three-dimensional patterns of the major veins associated with the liver. Fifth, the index has been expanded. Now it lists every term designated in the text by **boldface** and every page on which the boldfaced term appears, as well as terms illustrated by both text figures and plates. Sixth, an abridged, illustrated Hamburger and Hamilton (1951) stage series has been added (Appendix III) to allow students to gain practice staging avian embryos according to the criteria used in most research publications. Finally, several minor changes have been made in the text to update it and to improve its clarity.

As in previous editions, it is possible for students to start their studies with either frog embryos or chick embryos, depending on the instructor's preference. Study of the early embryo begins with the 33-hour stage. Students then examine *earlier* stages in detail to learn how the structural relationships in the 33-hour embryo originated. They then study *later* stages in detail to learn how the structural relationships in the 33-hour embryo are progressively modified during further development. Drawings of whole mounts (or midsagittal sections) appear on plate legends to indicate the levels of certain transverse sections, slices, or fractures shown in the plates.

The sixth edition, like previous editions, is designed to help students study developmental anatomy quickly and independently. Material is presented concisely, clearly, and logically. The text is supplemented with over 200 illustrations. Because of this approach, minimal time is required for "just learning the parts." Time thus freed can be used to study embryos experimentally. We highly encourage instructors to use the new experimental exercises or to provide students with brief instructions for a few of their favorite experiments (if such instructions are sent to the author they will be considered for inclusion, with appropriate acknowledgment, in subsequent editions). In doing so, students will be directly exposed to the joy and excitement that comes from working with living embryos.

Special appreciation is due to several individuals who helped in the preparation of this edition: Dr. Robert E. Waterman, for graciously providing illustrations for Plates 5 and 6; Brenda Sahr, for secretarial assistance; Maggie Kasten, for technical assistance; and Philip Sheard and Jodi Smith, for editorial assistance. The following illustrations have been modified from figures that have appeared in research publications: Plate 10, Figs. 2 and 3, and Plate 19, Fig. 1 (*American Journal of Anatomy* 155:445-466); Plate 12, Fig. 3 (*Scanning Electron Microscopy,* 1978, Vol. 2, pp. 739–745); Plate 28, Fig. 2, and Plate 40 (G.M. Hodges and R.C. Hallowes, eds., *Biomedical Research Applications of Scanning Electron Microscopy,* New York: Academic Press, 1979, Chap. 1); Appendix III, Stage 15 (*Developmental Biology* 110:467–479).

Finally, it is my sad duty to inform the readers of the death of one of the authors, Dr. Ray L. Watterson. Dr. Watterson was the sole author of the first edition and remained actively involved in the preparation of the second through fifth editions. In the second and third editions he collaborated with the late Dr. Robert M. Sweeney; in the fourth and fifth editions he collaborated with me. The sixth edition has been revised with his standards and goals in mind. I trust that he would have approved of the revisions and, accordingly, the present edition is proudly dedicated to his memory.

G. C. S.

CONTENTS

TEXT FIGURES xi

USEFUL REFERENCES AND AUDIOVISUAL AIDS xiii

EXERCISES xv

PART I LABORATORY GUIDE FOR VERTEBRATE EMBRYOLOGY 1

Chapter 1 INTRODUCTION 3

Chapter 2 EARLY EMBRYOLOGY OF THE FROG 6

    A. Oogenesis and Fertilization 6
    B. Formation of the Gray Crescent 7
    C. Cleavage and Blastulation 8
    D. Gastrulation 10
    E. Neurulation 12
EXERCISE 1: Spawning of Eggs and Observations of Living Embryos 12
EXERCISE 2: Mapping of Morphogenetic Movements 15
EXERCISE 3: Exogastrulation 17
EXERCISE 4: Neural Crest Ablation 19
    F. 4-mm Frog Embryos 21
      1. Introduction 21
      2. Serial transverse sections 21
        a. Ectodermal derivatives 21
        b. Endodermal derivatives 22
        c. Mesodermal derivatives 23
      3. Summary of the contributions of the germ layers to structures present in the 4-mm frog embryo 24
    G. Scanning Electron Microscopy 24

Chapter 3 EARLY EMBRYOLOGY OF THE CHICK 25
    A. The Part of the Egg to Be Studied 26
    B. 33-Hour Chick Embryos 26
      1. Whole mounts 26
EXERCISE 5: Preparation of graphical reconstruction 28
      2. Serial transverse sections 28
      3. Serial sagittal sections 34

4. Summary of the contributions of the germ layers to structures present in the 33-hour chick embryo   35
5. Scanning electron microscopy   35
C. Structure and Function of the Reproductive System of the Adult Hen   36
D. Oogenesis, Fertilization, and Cleavage   38
E. Formation of the Hypoblast   39
F. Gastrulation   41
1. Location and migration of the prospective endoderm   42
2. Location and migration of the prospective mesoderm   42
3. Summary of epiblast ingression during gastrulation   42
4. Location and changes of the prospective ectoderm   43
5. Location of epiblast areas prior to gastrulation   43
G. 18-Hour Chick Embryos   43
1. Whole mounts   43
2. Scanning electron microscopy   44
H. 24-Hour Chick Embryos   46
1. Whole mounts   46
2. Serial transverse sections   46
3. Serial sagittal sections   47
4. Scanning electron microscopy   48
I. Summary of Development of the Young Chick Embryo   48
1. Regional specialization of the mesoderm   48
2. Formation of the neural tube   48
3. Formation and consequences of the body folds   49
EXERCISE 6: Observations of Living Embryos (18-to 33-Hour Stage)   49
EXERCISE 7: Blastoderm Development in Culture   52
EXERCISE 8: Mapping of Morphogenetic Movements   55
EXERCISE 9: Separation of Gastrulating and Neurulating Regions   57
EXERCISE 10: Formation of a Double Heart   59
J. Comparison of Amphibian and Avian Development   61
K. 48-Hour Chick Embryos   63
1. Whole mounts: injected and uninjected   63
EXERCISE 11: Observations of living embryos (48-Hour Stage)   65
2. Serial transverse sections   66
3. Serial sagittal sections   72
4. Summary of the contributions of the germ layers to structures present in the 48-hour chick embryo, but not present in the 33-hour chick embryo   72
5. Scanning electron microscopy   72
EXERCISE 12: Chemical dissection of organ rudiments   73
L. 72-Hour Chick Embryos   75
1. Whole mounts: injected and uninjected   75
EXERCISE 13: Observations of living embryos (72-Hour Stage)   75
2. Serial transverse sections   76
3. Serial sagittal sections   80
4. Summary of the contributions of the germ layers to structures present in the 72-hour chick embryo, but not present in the 48-hour chick embryo   81
5. Scanning electron microscopy   81
EXERCISE 14: Extraembryonic membrane development in culture   81

Chapter 4   10-MM PIG EMBRYOS   83

A. Whole Specimens   83
B. Serial Transverse Sections   85
1. Nervous system   85

a. Brain 85
b. Cranial nerves 87
c. Spinal cord and spinal nerves 90
2. Respiratory and digestive systems 91
3. Urogenital system 95
4. Circulatory system 96
a. Arterial system 96
b. Heart 99
c. Venous system 100
C. Summary of the Contributions of the Germ Layers to Structures Present in the 10-mm Pig Embryo, but Not Present in the 72-Hour Chick Embryo 103

APPENDIX I. BRIEF TECHNIQUES FOR PREPARING EMBRYOS FOR LIGHT MICROSCOPY 104

A. Whole Mounts 104
B. Serial Sections 105

APPENDIX II. BRIEF TECHNIQUES FOR PREPARING EMBRYOS FOR SCANNING ELECTRON MICROSCOPY 107

A. Intact Specimens 107
B. Slices 108
C. Cryofractures 108
D. Sectioned Blocks 108

APPENDIX III. ABRIDGED HAMBURGER AND HAMILTON STAGE SERIES FOR MAJOR STAGES COVERED IN THIS GUIDE 109

PART II ATLAS FOR VERTEBRATE EMBRYOLOGY 113

PLATES 1–6 EARLY FROG EMBRYOS 115

PLATES 7–40 EARLY CHICK EMBRYOS 129

PLATES 41–54 10-MM PIG EMBRYOS 199

INDEX 229

TEXT FIGURES

Figure A. Drawings illustrating the relationships between a preserved 4-mm frog embryo viewed from the left side and four representative transverse sections through this embryo.   4

Figure B. Schematic drawing of a section through three ovarian follicles of a mature female frog.   7

Figure C. Drawings of early developmental stages of the frog.   8

Figure D. Prospective fate map of the frog blastula.   10

Figure E. Drawings of the cut surfaces of right halves of blastula and gastrula stages of the frog.   11

Figure F. Schematic drawing of a midsagittal section of a 4-mm frog embryo.   21

Figure G. Drawing of a 33-hour chick embryo whole mount.   25

Figure H. Graphical reconstruction of a 33-hour chick embryo showing relationships of parts to one another along the craniocaudal axis.   29

Figure I. Drawing of the functional reproductive system of the mature hen.   37

Figure J. Drawings of early cleavage stages of the chick blastoderm removed from the yolk and viewed from the upper surface.   38

Figure K. Schematic drawings of the area pellucida showing the formation of the ingressed endoderm and the displacement of the hypoblast.   40

Figure L. Schematic drawings of the area pellucida showing the formation of the subdivisions of the ingressed mesoderm.   41

Figure M. Prospective fate map of the chick epiblast.   44

Figure N. Drawing of the cranial half of a blastoderm at the definitive primitive streak stage.   45

Figure O. Drawing of the right side of the cranial half of a 48-hour chick embryo.   63

Figure P. Schematic drawings of midsagittal sections of the caudal ends of chick embryos between 48 and 72 hours of incubation.   70

Figure Q. Schematic drawings of transverse sections of 48-hour chick embryos showing the formation of the amnion, chorion, and yolk sac.   71

Figure R. Drawing of the right side of a preserved 10-mm pig embryo.   84

Figure S.   Schematic drawing of the cranial nerves and ganglia in the 10-mm pig embryo.   86

Figure T.   Schematic drawing of the digestive and urogenital systems in the 10-mm pig embryo.   93

Figure U.   Drawing of a reconstruction of the aortic arches of the 10-mm pig embryo.   97

Figure V.   Schematic drawing of the arteries in the head of the 10-mm pig embryo.   98

Figure W.   Schematic drawing of the major veins associated with the liver in the 10-mm pig embryo.   101

Figure X.   Drawing of a reconstruction of the major veins associated with the liver in the 10-mm pig embryo.   102

USEFUL REFERENCES
AND AUDIOVISUAL AIDS

Although this manual is thoroughly illustrated by photomicrographs, scanning electron micrographs, and line drawings, certain textbooks and atlases provide additional helpful illustrations. Each textbook or atlas will be referred to by the letters listed in parentheses. Because textbooks vary in terminology, the student should follow the terminology used in this manual to avoid confusion.

(A)   Arey, L. B. 1974. *Developmental Anatomy*. Rev. 7th ed. Philadelphia: Saunders.

(B)   Balinsky, B. I. 1981. *An Introduction to Embryology*. 5th ed. Philadelphia: Saunders.

(BR)   Browder, L. W. 1980. *Developmental Biology*. Philadelphia: Saunders.

(G)   Gilbert, S. F. 1988. *Developmental Biology*. 2nd ed. Sunderland, MA: Sinauer.

(H)   Hamilton, H. L. 1952: *Lillie's Development of the Chick*. New York: Holt, Rinehart and Winston.

(HU)   Huettner, A. F. 1949. *Comparative Embryology of the Vertebrates*. Rev. ed. New York: Macmillan.

(HV)   Ham, R. G., Veomett, M. J. 1980 *Mechanisms of Development*. St. Louis: C. V. Mosby.

(L)   Loomis, W. F. 1986. *Developmental Biology*. New York: Macmillan.

(M)   Mathews, W. W. 1986. *Atlas of Descriptive Embryology*. 4th ed. New York: Macmillan.

(P)   Patten, B. M. 1971. *Early Embryology of the Chick*. 5th ed. New York: McGraw-Hill.

(PA)   Patten, B. M. 1948. *Embryology of the Pig*. 3rd ed. New York: McGraw-Hill.

(S)   Saunders, J. W. 1982. *Developmental Biology*. New York: Macmillan.

Audiovisual aids are also very useful for studying developmental anatomy, especially in helping students to visualize developmental events three-dimensionally and changes in morphology with time. The following audiovisual aids are highly recommended. Each aid will be referred to by the letters and numbers listed in parentheses.

(A–V#1)   *Color 35-mm Slides for Laboratory Studies of Chick, Pig, and Frog Embryos*. 254 color slides with instructor's guide. Burgess Publishing Co., Minneapolis, MN 55435. Available from: Gary C. Schoenwolf, Department of Anatomy, University of Utah School of Medicine, Salt Lake City, Utah 84132. Phone: (801) 581-6453.

(A–V#2)   *Amphibian Embryo (Frog, Toad, and Salamander)*. 16 min., color, sound. Available from: Encyclopedia Britannica Education Corp., 425 North Michigan Ave., Department 10 P/R, Chicago, IL 60611. Phone: (312) 321–7311.

(A–V#3)   *Development of the Cardiovascular System of the Chick: The Heart*. 20 min., color, sound. Available from: Indiana University, Audio-Visual Center, Bloomington, IN 47405. Phone: (812) 337–8087.

(A–V#4)   *Development of the Cardiovascular System of the Chick: The Blood Vessels*. 23 min., color, sound. Available from: Indiana University, Audio-Visual Center (address given above).

(A–V#5)   *Development of the Chick: Extra-embryonic Membranes*. 20 min., color, sound. Available from: Indiana University, Audio-Visual Center (address given above).

(A–V#6)   *Congenital Malformations of the Heart. Part I. Development of the Normal Heart*. 15 min., color, sound. Available from Instructional Media Services, DG-10, University of Washington, Seattle, WA 98195. Phone: (206) 543–9909.

(A–V#7)   *Fetal and Neonatal Circulation*. 15 min., color, sound. Available from: E.R. Squibb and Sons, Inc., P.O. Box 4000, Princeton, NJ 08540. Phone: (609) 921–4000.

EXERCISES

EXERCISE 1.   Spawning of Eggs and Observations of Living Embryos (Amphibian Embryos)   12

EXERCISE 2.   Mapping of Morphogenetic Movements (Amphibian Embryos)   15

EXERCISE 3.   Exogastrulation (Amphibian Embryos)   17

EXERCISE 4.   Neural Crest Ablation (Amphibian Embryos)   19

EXERCISE 5.   Preparation of Graphical Reconstruction (Avian Embryos)   28

EXERCISE 6.   Observations of Living Embryos (Avian Embryos at 18 to 33 Hours)   49

EXERCISE 7.   Blastoderm Development in Culture (Avian Embryos)   52

EXERCISE 8.   Mapping of Morphogenetic Movements (Avian Embryos)   55

EXERCISE 9.   Separation of Gastrulating and Neurulating Regions (Avian Embryos)   57

EXERCISE 10.   Formation of a Double Heart (Avian Embryos)   59

EXERCISE 11.   Observations of Living Embryos (Avian Embryos at 48 Hours)   65

EXERCISE 12.   Chemical Dissection of Organ Rudiments (Avian Embryos)   73

EXERCISE 13.   Observations of Living Embryos (Avian Embryos at 72 Hours)   75

EXERCISE 14.   Extraembryonic Membrane Development in Culture (Avian Embryos)   81

Laboratory Studies of Chick, Pig, and Frog Embryos

PART I

Laboratory Guide for Vertebrate Embryology

Chapter 1

INTRODUCTION

Laboratory work in introductory courses in developmental biology and embryology usually includes studies of *developmental anatomy*. Suppose you obtained some preserved frog embryos at the stage illustrated by Fig. Aa and wanted to study their anatomy. With a microscope, you could identify a few poorly defined external features as well as the body axes (*cranial-caudal, dorsal-ventral, right-left*). To study internal features in detail, you could slice (section) the entire embryo into thin sections of a given thickness. One or more slides containing every section from the first one (the most *anterior* one) to the last one (the most *posterior* one) is called a *set of serial sections*. The most anterior section of this set (#1) is mounted at the upper left-hand corner of the slide, and successive sections are mounted in the following way (the numbers shown are for illustrative purposes only; the actual numbers of sections in each row, and the number of rows per slide, vary):

1	2	3	4	5	6	7	8	9	10
11	12	13	14	15	16	17	18	19	20
21	22	23	24	25	26	27	28	29	30

If there are too many sections to mount on one slide, the more posterior ones are mounted on slide #2 of the series in the following way:

31	32	33	34	35	36	37	38	39	40
41	42	43	44	45	46	47	48	49	50
and so forth.									

Fig. Ab illustrates four representative *transverse sections* (that is, sections cut perpendicularly to the cranial-caudal axis). Fig. Ac illustrates these same sections after they were transferred to a glass slide and mounted from left to right in the order in which they were cut. Exactly how much of the anatomy of the embryo can one expect to see in any one representative section? Suppose that your set of serial sections contained a total of 100 sections. The sixth section of the set might cut through the level of the developing *eyes*; in this section you could determine the relationship of the eyes to other structures (Figs. Ab, Ac). You might then examine a more posterior section, such as #15 through the *heart*, or still more posterior sections (#50, #80). Unfortunately, the study of individual sections provides only a two-dimensional picture of the embryo. To understand the anatomy of the embryo in *three* dimensions you must visualize each section as again part of the whole embryo. For example, the *notochord* can be identified in sections #15, #50, and #80. By connecting the section of the notochord at the level of section #15 with the section of the notochord at the next level (section #50) and those at successive levels, you get an accurate picture of the craniocaudal extent of the notochord, as well as its relationship to other structures. In the same way, you can get an accurate picture of the craniocaudal extent of the *neural tube* (*brain* and *spinal cord*) and *digestive tube*, as well as their relationships to each other and to other structures. *The most difficult*

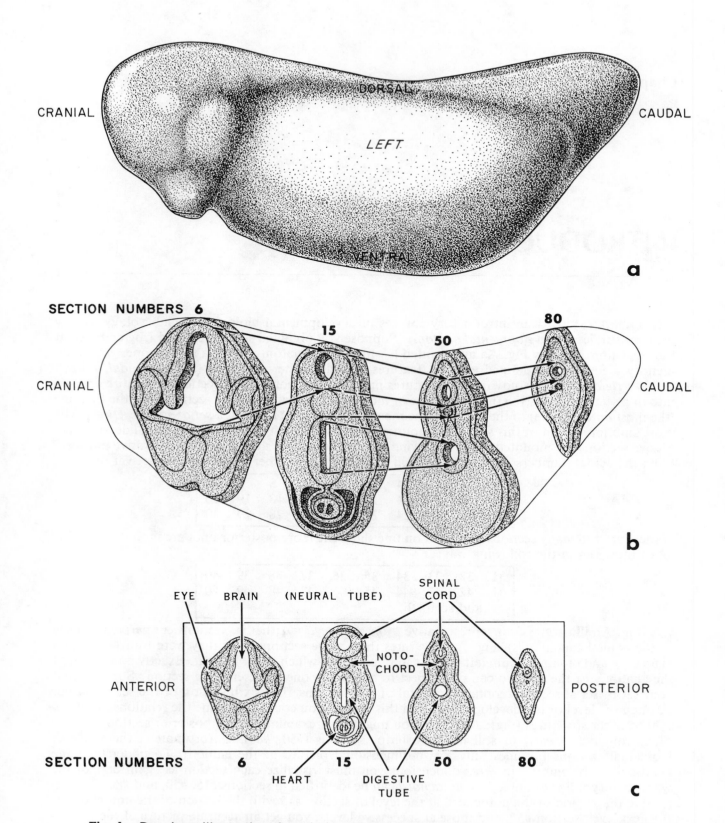

Fig. A. Drawings illustrating the relationships between a preserved 4-mm frog embryo viewed from the left side (Fig. Aa) and four representative transverse sections through this embryo (Figs. Ab, Ac).

task facing the beginning student is to learn to visualize relationships of parts of an embryo to one another in three dimensions. We have attempted to help you do this difficult task by providing three types of visual aids in this laboratory manual: (1) text figures (reconstructions, drawings showing the relationships of sections to whole embryos, and so forth); (2) drawings of intact or sagittally sectioned embryos placed on certain plate legends (such drawings show the exact levels where embryos were sectioned, sliced, or cryofractured transversely); and (3) scanning electron micrographs, which portray a more three-dimensional image than do flat, two-dimensional serial sections.

Methods have been included in the appendices to help you understand how embryos are prepared for light microscopy (Appendix I) and scanning electron microscopy (Appendix II) and to help you understand why different processing procedures result in different types of images.

Chapter **2**

EARLY EMBRYOLOGY OF THE FROG

Amphibian eggs are relatively large and can be readily obtained. Many outstanding experimental embryologists (including Hans Spemann, Ross Harrison, and their several students) took advantage of these facts when they began to experiment on developing vertebrate embryos by removing parts, adding parts, and recombining parts by microsurgery. Because so much of classical experimental embryology involved experiments on early amphibian embryos, it is essential that you have an understanding of the structure of these embryos and how this structure originated in order to appreciate experimental analyses. The study of early amphibian development will also demonstrate the basic similarities in developmental events and processes in amphibian, birds, and mammals.

A. OOGENESIS AND FERTILIZATION

Aids: Fig. B; A–V#2.

Oogenesis (development of the ovum) begins in the paired **ovaries** of the mature female frog. During the breeding season (which begins in the spring), each ovary consists of a sac containing a cluster of spherical structures called **follicles** (Fig. B). Each follicle consists of a large central cell containing a lot of **yolk** in its cytoplasm, the **primary oocyte**, surrounded by a layer of much smaller, flattened cells called **follicle cells**. The primary oocyte contains a large nucleus, the **germinal vesicle**. The **vitelline membrane** lies between the follicle cells and the **plasmalemma** of the primary oocyte. A thin sheath of connective tissue, the **theca folliculi externa**, forms the surface layer of the ovary. Another sheath, the **theca folliculi interna**, partially surrounds each follicle but is lacking in the region where the follicle contacts the theca folliculi externa; at this region **ovulation** (the rupture of the follicle and release of its contained oocyte) occurs.

Each ovary also contains cells called **oogonia**. These cells undergo rapid mitotic divisions, increasing in number. After the breeding season is completed (that is, in the autumn), several hundred oogonia within each ovary lose the ability to divide mitotically. Each enlarges slightly as a **primary oocyte** and becomes surrounded by a single layer of **follicle cells**, forming an ovarian **follicle**, which slowly enlarges due to the accumulation of yolk. Primary oocytes enter the **prophase** stage of the **first meiotic division** but remain there until the following spring.

The fully grown oocytes undergo **ovulation**, in response to hormones secreted by the **anterior pituitary gland (adenohypophysis)**, when spring arrives. Each oocyte is slowly squeezed through the follicular wall at the region where the theca folliculi interna is lacking (Fig. B) and enters the body cavity (coelom) of the female. Many oocytes (2,000–20,000, depending upon the species) are ovulated by a single female each spring. Primary oocytes complete the **first meiotic division** during ovulation, with each forming a **first polar body** and **secondary oocyte**. Both these structures are contained within the vitelline membrane formed earlier, while the primary oocyte was in the ovary. Cilia on the lining of the coelom beat toward the **ostium** of the **oviduct** and propel the secondary oocytes into this opening. The **second meiotic division** is *initiated* by each secondary oocyte at about the time that it enters the oviduct but then arrests in the **metaphase** stage. As the secondary oocytes pass through the oviduct, a multilayered, gelatinous **egg capsule** is secreted outside of the vitelline membrane by the cells lining the oviduct.

 Fertilization occurs externally as the **secondary oocytes** are spawned (shed) by the female into the water. The **second meiotic division** is completed as a successful **sperm** contacts and penetrates each secondary oocyte, resulting in formation of a **second polar body** and a **mature ovum** containing the **female pronucleus.** The nucleus of the successful sperm enlarges within the ovum as the **male pronucleus,** and the male and female pronuclei unite to complete the process of fertilization.

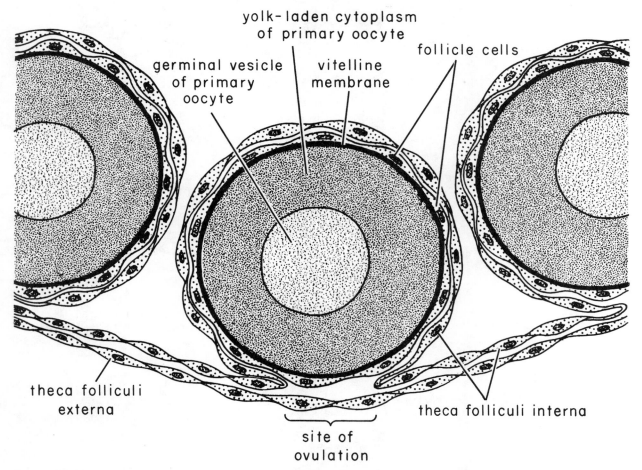

Fig. B. Schematic drawing of a section through three ovarian follicles of a mature female frog.

B. FORMATION OF THE GRAY CRESCENT

 Aids: Fig. C; A–V#2; H, Fig. 46.

 The outer portion of the egg (the **cortex**) contains a distinct pattern of pigmentation at the time of ovulation (Fig. Ca). About two-thirds of the cortex is heavily pigmented; the remainder contains almost no pigment. The uppermost part of the pigmented portion is the **animal pole**. This pole corresponds to the *cranial* end of the future embryo. The half of the egg that contains the animal pole is the **animal hemisphere**. The **vegetal pole** lies directly opposite the animal pole. This pole corresponds to the *caudal* end of the future embryo. The half of the egg that contains the vegetal pole is the **vegetal hemisphere**.

Following contact by and entrance of the successful **sperm**, the pigmented cortex shifts toward and past the site of sperm entrance and away from the side of the egg opposite the sperm entrance point (Fig. Cb). This reduces the pigmentation of a crescent-shaped area opposite the point of sperm entrance. This crescent-shaped area between the heavily pigmented cortex above and the essentially nonpigmented cortex below constitutes the **gray crescent** (Figs. Cb, Cc). A plane passing through the animal and vegetal poles and through the center of the gray crescent corresponds to the *mid-sagittal plane* of the future embryo (Fig. Cc).

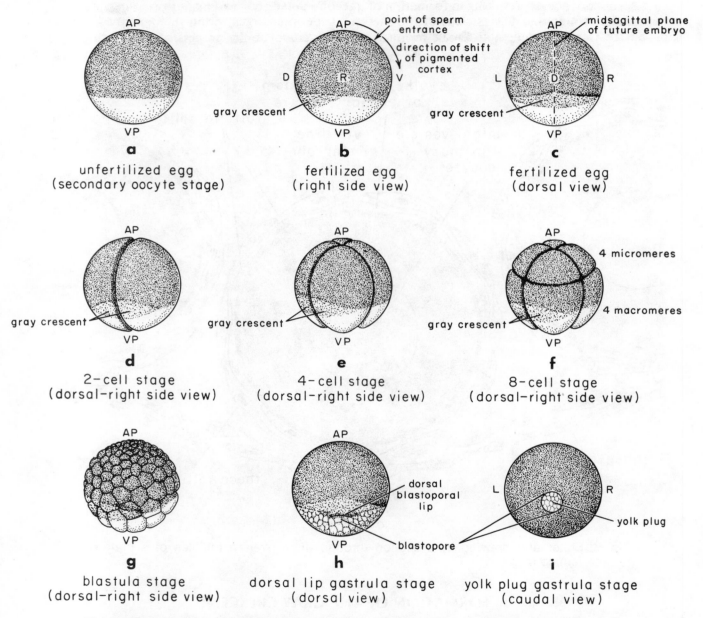

Fig. C. Drawings of early developmental stages of the frog. AP, animal pole; D, dorsal side; L, left side; R, right side; V, ventral side; VP, vegetal pole.

C. CLEAVAGE AND BLASTULATION

Aids: Figs. C, D; Plate 1, Fig. 1; A–V#1, #2; H, Figs. 46, 47; M, Figs. 83–85.

Cleavage consists of a series of rapid mitotic divisions that result in **blastulation** (that is, the formation of a **blastula**, which consists of a group of cells called **blastomeres** surrounding a cavity, the **blastocoel**). **Cleavage furrows** pass through the entire egg, so cleavage is classified as **total**

(**holoblastic**). However, furrows pass through the vegetal hemisphere much more slowly than through the animal hemisphere, presumably because the former contains far more yolk than the latter. A rough timetable of the first three cleavages for the frog, *Rana pipiens*, is as follows (Figs. Cd-Cf): (1) first cleavage: meridional (that is, passes through both animal and vegetal poles), usually bisecting the gray crescent (that is, passes through the midsagittal plane of the future embryo), 2.5 hours postfertilization; (2) second cleavage: meridional, at right angles to the first, 3.5 hours postfertilization; and (3) third cleavage: horizontal, displaced toward the animal pole due to the yolk content of the vegetal hemisphere, producing four smaller animal hemisphere cells, the **micromeres**, and four larger vegetal hemisphere cells, the **macromeres**, 4 hours postfertilization. The egg reaches the **blastula** stage near the end of cleavage (approximately 16 hours postfertilization) (Fig. Cg). Numerous small blastomeres occupy the animal hemisphere, whereas the vegetal hemisphere consists of a lesser number of larger blastomeres. The blastula is only slightly larger at the end of cleavage than is the newly fertilized egg.

Examine models, or preferably living eggs (see Exercise 1), showing early cleavage stages. Note the position of early cleavage furrows (that is, whether meridional or horizontal), the difference in size of the micromeres and macromeres, and the difference in pigmentation of animal and vegetal hemisphere cells. Try to identify the **gray crescent**; the region of the gray crescent that is broadest will become the *dorsal* surface of the embryo, and the opposite side, the *ventral* surface.

Examine a section of the frog blastula that closely resembles Plate 1, Fig. 1. Identify the main cavity, the **blastocoel**. Note that it is displaced toward one side of the blastula, the **animal pole**; thus, it is contained within the **animal hemisphere**. The blastocoel is filled with a fluid that coagulated during preparation of your slide. Note that the wall of the blastula is composed of distinct cells, the **blastomeres**. Identify their **nuclei**. Spaces between blastomeres in the **vegetal hemisphere** are shrinkage spaces produced during preparation of your slides.

Examine the **animal hemisphere**. It has the following characteristics: (1) there is a heavily pigmented cortex, with pigmentation being most intense at the animal pole and grading off progressively toward the vegetal pole; (2) it is four or five cells thick, with smaller cells and fewer cell layers at the animal pole and with a progressive increase in cell size and number of cell layers toward the vegetal pole; and (3) the blastomeres contain very little yolk.

Examine the **vegetal hemisphere**. Its characteristics are exactly the opposite: (1) a pigmented cortex, if present at all, is much less evident than in the animal hemisphere; (2) the blastomeres are very large and few in number, indicative of less frequent cleavage; and (3) the blastomeres are packed with yolk.

Try to identify the **gray crescent**. In your sections it usually lies either to the left or right side of the blastocoel and also slightly ventral to it. It has the following characteristics (compare sides indicated by letters *D* and *V* in Plate 1, Fig. 1): (1) the pigmented cortex is thinner in the gray crescent than on the opposite side; and (2) the blastocoel lies nearer the surface on the gray crescent side than on the opposite side (that is, the wall of the blastula is thinner on the gray crescent side than on the opposite side).

The blastula consists of a mosaic of cellular areas, each of which will normally produce a certain structure during subsequent development. In other words, each area of cells has a certain **prospective fate** that will be realized during normal development. In blastulae of some chordates (Urochordata or tunicates) the outlines of these cellular areas can be determined directly because the cytoplasm of cells within certain areas is colored differently. But in most cases it is necessary to determine the prospective fate of each cellular area indirectly by marking experiments. **Vital dyes** have been used most frequently for this purpose in amphibians. Several areas of the blastula are stained with a vital dye. It is then observed what structure or structures are formed from each stained area (see Exercise 2). Another technique has been used more recently. A **cell marker** (for example, the enzyme **horseradish peroxidase**, which can be demonstrated histochemically by incubating tissue containing the enzyme with the appropriate substrate; or **fluorescein-** or **rhodamine-labeled dextran**, which can be demonstrated with a fluorescence microscope after illumination with the proper wavelength of light) is injected into a single cell or groups of cells at the blastula stage. As injected cells cleave, the marker is passed to their descendants. A **prospective fate map** is constructed, with the aid of the information gained by these techniques, such as the one in Fig. D. The amphibian fate map should be carefully compared with the one for the chick (Fig. M). A prospective fate map indicates the location of specific groups of cells prior to the onset of

gastrulation. These groups of cells are shifted in an orderly way into appropriate positions during gastrulation, which will enable them to cooperate and interact in formation of tissues and organs. The blastocoel appears to be essential in many species to provide a space into which certain groups of cells can move either *en masse* or individually during gastrulation.

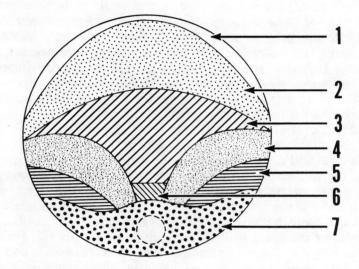

Fig. D. Prospective fate map of the frog blastula. The approximate site of blastopore formation is indicated by a circular dashed line.

1. Prospective ectoderm
2. Prospective neural plate
3. Prospective notochord
4. Prospective segmental plate mesoderm
5. Prospective lateral plate mesoderm
6. Prospective head mesenchyme
7. Prospective endoderm

D. GASTRULATION

Aids: Figs. C–E; Plate 1, Figs. 2, 3; A–V#1, 2; B, Fig. 143; BR, Fig. 12.19; G, Chap. 4, Figs. 14, 15, 23, 24; H, Figs. 48, 49, 53; HV, Figs. 2–15, 2–20; L, Figs. 1.10, 9.5, 9.6; M, Figs. 86–92; S, Figs. 9.12, 9.13, 9.67.

During gastrulation some of the cells originally located on the surface of the blastula turn inward or undergo **involution** to move into the interior. These cells will give rise to two **germ layers**: the **endoderm**, or innermost layer, and the **mesoderm**, or middle layer; cells that remain on the surface form the outermost germ layer, the **ectoderm**. A depression, the **blastopore**, begins to form just below the **gray crescent** as cells initiate involution (Fig. Ch). Simultaneously, a liplike structure, the **dorsal blastoporal lip**, forms just above the blastopore. With formation of the blastopore and dorsal blastoporal lip, the blastula is transformed into a **gastrula**. Cells continue to involute over the dorsal blastoporal lip with further development, and involution progressively occurs laterally and ultimately ventrally as well. This results in formation of a circular blastopore containing a mass of yolk-filled endodermal cells called the **yolk plug** (Fig. Ci). The circular blastopore is surrounded by continuous **dorsal, lateral,** and **ventral blastoporal lips**. The directions of gastrulation movements can be altered experimentally, resulting in **exogastrulation**, a process during which surface cells move but fail to involute over the blastoporal lips (see Exercise 3).

The locations of several areas (designated arbitrarily as areas 1–10 and 25–27) before and during their involution over the **dorsal** and **ventral blastoporal lips** are shown in Fig. E. All these areas are located on the surface at the blastula stage. Areas 1–5 have undergone involution over the *dorsal* blastoporal lip by the dorsal lip gastrula stage. Similarly, Areas 1–8 have undergone involution over the *dorsal* blastoporal lip by the yolk plug gastrula stage, and Areas 27 and 26 have undergone involution over the *ventral* blastoporal lip. The remaining numbered areas will undergo involution

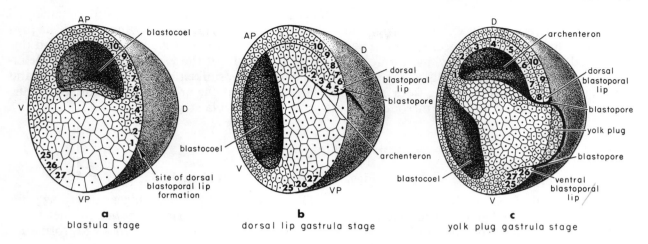

Fig. E. Drawings of the cut surfaces of right halves of blastula and gastrula stages of the frog. AP, animal pole; D, dorsal side; V, ventral side; VP, vegetal pole; numbers 1-10 indicate specific areas of the blastula that undergo involution over the dorsal blastoporal lip; numbers 25-27 indicate specific areas that undergo involution over the ventral blastoporal lip.

during subsequent development. Other cellular areas undergo involution over the *lateral* blastoporal lips in a similar manner.

Fig. D shows the locations of several prospective areas, some of which undergo involution during gastrulation. Some of the cells of the **prospective endoderm** and all the cells of the **prospective head mesenchyme** and **prospective notochord** involute over the *dorsal* blastoporal lip. Similarly, some of the cells of the **prospective endoderm**, some of the cells of the **prospective lateral plate mesoderm**, and all the cells of the **prospective segmental plate mesoderm** involute over the *lateral* lips of the blastopore. The remaining cells of the **prospective lateral plate mesoderm**, as well as some of the cells of the **prospective endoderm**, involute over the *ventral* blastoporal lip. Only a relatively small number of prospective endodermal cells undergo involution over the blastoporal lips. Most prospective endodermal cells remain relatively stationary during gastrulation stages forming the **yolk plug** and floor of the **archenteron** (Fig. E). As areas involute, the **prospective neural plate** and **prospective ectoderm** undergo spreading, or **epiboly**, toward the blastopore to replace areas that have moved into the interior of the gastrula.

Obtain a slide containing sagittal sections of the dorsal lip gastrula and select a section closely resembling Plate 1, Fig. 2. Identify the **blastopore, dorsal blastoporal lip,** and **blastocoel.** The blastopore represents the future *caudal* end. The future *cranial* end lies directly opposite. The blastopore opens into a narrow cavity, the primitive gut, or **archenteron.** The floor of the archenteron is formed by yolk-filled endodermal cells. The cranial end of the archenteron roof is formed from endoderm because the first cells to involute over the dorsal and lateral blastoporal lips, and thus contribute to the wall of the archenteron, are the cells of the **prospective endoderm** (Fig. D). The remainder of the archenteron roof at the gastrula stage is formed by mesoderm, which involutes over the dorsal and lateral blastoporal lips following involution of prospective endoderm. The mesoderm of the archenteron roof will *later* be covered by endoderm, which migrates upward over the inner surface of the mesoderm (see below). Thus the archenteron is ultimately lined entirely by endoderm. Note that the ectoderm in the frog consists of two layers: an **outer (superficial) ectodermal layer** and an **inner (deep) ectodermal layer.**

Obtain a slide containing sagittal sections of a yolk plug gastrula and select a section closely resembling Plate 1, Fig. 3. Identify the **yolk plug,** a protruding mass of yolk-filled endodermal cells located between the very prominent **dorsal blastoporal lip** above and the less prominent **ventral blastoporal lip** below. Also identify the **archenteron** located above the mass of poorly defined endodermal cells forming its floor. The yolk plug fills the entrance to the archenteron, the **blastopore.** Beneath the archenteron and separated from the latter by endodermal cells is the irregularly shaped **blastocoel**. This cavity is later squeezed out of existence. Note that the pigmented cortex now covers all cells except those of the yolk plug. The more rapidly dividing cells of the **prospective ectoderm** and **prospective neural plate** undergo epiboly between the blastula stage and this advanced gastrula stage, growing down over the yolk-filled cells of the vegetal hemisphere. Meanwhile the large endodermal cells of the vegetal hemisphere have sunken inward to some extent and become rearranged to form the floor and ventrolateral walls of the archenteron. Most of the archenteron roof still consists of mesoderm at the yolk plug gastrula stage.

E. NEURULATION

Aids: Plate 1, Figs. 4, 5; Plate 2, Figs. 1, 2; A–V#1, 2; BR, Fig. 12.32; H, Fig. 56.

The ectodermal cells directly overlying the archenteron roof at the yolk plug gastrula stage constitute the **neural ectoderm**. The mesodermal cells of the archenteron roof *induce* the neural ectoderm to thicken as the **neural plate**. The gastrula is transformed into the **neurula** with formation of the neural plate.

Obtain a slide containing transverse sections of a neurula at the neural plate stage. Select a section closely resembling Plate 1, Figs. 4, 5 and identify the **neural plate**. The roof of the **archenteron** at the neurula stage is formed by *endoderm*. Between the gastrula and neurula stages, endoderm migrated upward over the inner surface of the mesoderm that previously formed the archenteron roof. Note that the dorsal mesoderm is now organized into a midline rod of cells, the **notochord**, flanked by two bands of cells, the **segmental plate mesoderm**. This latter mesoderm is the source of the **somites**. The segmental plate mesoderm gradually merges laterally with the **lateral plate mesoderm**. The **coelom** forms within the latter mesoderm.

Obtain a slide containing transverse sections of a neurula at the neural fold stage and select a section closely resembling Plate 2, Figs. 1, 2. Identify the paired **neural folds**, which have formed at the lateral margins of the neural plate, and the **neural groove**. The **notochord, segmental plate mesoderm**, and **lateral plate mesoderm** are more clearly defined at this stage, and the *endoderm* of the roof of the **archenteron** exists as a more distinct layer. During subsequent development the neural folds will fuse in the dorsal midline to close the neural groove and thus establish the **neural tube**. **Neural crest cells** will *later* form from the roof of the neural tube and give rise to a multitude of structures, including **pigment cells** (see Exercise 4).

EXERCISE 1 Spawning of Eggs and Observations of Living Embryos (Amphibian Embryos)

Materials

Etheridge and Richter's *Xenopus laevis: Rearing and Breeding the African Clawed Frog*. 1978. Nasco, 901 Janesville Ave., Fort Atkinson, WI 53538. Phone: (414) 563-2446.
Mature male and female *Xenopus* frogs
Covered holding tanks (see Etheridge and Richter's booklet)
Nasco frog brittle
Chorionic gonadotropin
Rubber gloves
Sterile 5-ml syringes
Sterile 30-gauge needles
Sterile distilled water
Paper towels
100% Steinberg solution (distilled water, sodium chloride, potassium chloride, calcium nitrate, magnesium sulfate, TRIZMA hydrochloride, TRIZMA base)
Dejellying solution (DL-Dithiothreitol)
HEPES buffer
Sodium hydroxide pellets

Petri dishes
Pasteur pipettes
Wide-mouth pipettes
Pipette bulbs
Safety glasses
Stereomicroscopes (dissecting microscopes)

Observation of the development of living frog eggs is an exciting adventure for both student and professional embryologists. Methods for spawning eggs of *Xenopus laevis,* the African clawed frog, will be summarized in this exercise. Details on the rearing and breeding of *Xenopus* can be obtained in Etheridge and Richter's superb, inexpensive booklet. The course instructor should obtain and read the booklet thoroughly before this exercise is attempted. It is recommended that several copies of the booklet be kept on hand for student use, especially during the staging of embryos according to the criteria of Nieuwkoop and Faber (1956; *Normal Table of Xenopus laevis.* Amsterdam: North Holland Publishing Co.), which are reproduced in the booklet.

Store *Xenopus* frogs at room temperature in *covered* holding tanks (see Etheridge and Richter's booklet). Fasten the cover or weight it to prevent frogs from escaping but be sure to allow air exchange to occur. Each tank should contain a minimum of 2 inches of water. Feed frogs Nasco frog brittle according to the schedule given in the booklet. Select a pair of mature frogs for breeding. The adult female is much larger than the male and will have **cloacal valves**; the mature male has "**nuptial pads**" on its forearms (see Figs. 2–4 in Etheridge and Richter's booklet).

Ovulation will be induced by injecting a solution of **chorionic gonadotropin** (Sigma Chemical Co., St. Louis, MO; stock no. CG-5). Gonadotropin is teratogenic, so *wear gloves and handle with care.* Each vial of gonadotropin contains 5,000 international units (IU). Use a sterile syringe to add 5 ml of sterile distilled water to each vial. Females will be injected with 1.5 ml of solution (1,500 units) and males with 1 ml (1,000 units). Injection will be made into the **dorsal lymph sac** with a 30-gauge needle attached to a 5-ml syringe. Wrap each frog in a paper towel to immobilize it (see Fig. 8 in Etheridge and Richter's booklet), and inject the dorsal lymph sac (see Figs. 9, 10 in Etheridge and Richter's booklet). Place 1 or 2 pairs of injected frogs into a breeding tank (see Fig. 5 in Etheridge and Richter's booklet). Add 15 l distilled water, 1.5 l 100% Steinberg solution at pH 7.4 (to make a 5-l stock solution, take 5 l of distilled water and add 17 g sodium chloride, 0.25 g potassium chloride, 0.40 g calcium nitrate, 1.02 g magnesium sulfate, 3.3 g TRIZMA hydrochloride, and 0.48 g TRIZMA base; the latter two components can be obtained from Sigma), and 1.3 g TRIZMA base to the tank. In our tanks, this gives the optimal water level of 3–4 inches above the false bottom.

Store the breeding tanks, if possible, in an undisturbed cool room (20°C) in the dark. Frogs must not be disturbed during mating or fertilized eggs will not be obtained. If frogs are injected at 5 P.M. early cleavage stages will be obtained under these conditions by morning. Dejelly eggs to facilitate observation. To do this, first prepare a stock solution of 6.5 g DL-Dithiothreitol (DTT) (Sigma, no. D-0632) in 100 ml distilled water. Also prepare a buffer stock solution of 28.8 g HEPES (Sigma, H3375) in 200 ml distilled water. Adjust its pH to 8.9 with sodium hydroxide pellets. Mix 4 ml of the DTT stock solution with 20 ml of the buffer stock solution and add distilled water to make 200 ml of dejellying solution. Dejelly eggs by removing them from the breeding tank with a wide-mouth pipette (the blunt end of a Pasteur pipette works well; carefully break off the tip, protecting your hands and eyes, and add a bulb to the pointed end). Place them in a petri dish containing dejellying solution for a *maximum* of 4 minutes (longer exposures result in abnormal development). Remove the dejellying solution and wash the eggs 3× with 100% Steinberg solution. After washing, place the eggs in 70% Steinberg solution (dilute some of the 100% Steinberg stock solution with distilled water to obtain this concentration) and gradually dilute the Steinberg solution to 20% over the next hour. Remove nondeveloping eggs from the dish and reduce the density of the eggs to about 1 egg/ml solution. Use the Nieuwkoop and Faber (1956) staging criteria (Figs. 11–13 in Etheridge and Richter's booklet) to stage your embryos. Examine embryos and tadpoles over several days (that is, at 1-to-2 day intervals) but especially during the first 24 hours after spawning (that is, at 1- to 2-hour intervals when possible). Fertilized eggs tend to rest on their vegetal poles with animal poles directed upward. Egg pigmentation is generally distributed more heavily in the *animal-ventral* quadrant, although this is variable. Therefore, as you look at the embryo, you will see the animal hemisphere divided into *dorsal* (lightly pigmented) and *ventral* (heavily pigmented) quadrants. Use the space below to sketch the stages you observe, as well as the times at which they appear.

EXERCISE 2 Mapping of Morphogenetic Movements (Amphibian Embryos)

Materials

Materials from Exercise 1
Dejellied *Xenopus* blastulae
20% Steinberg solution
Modeling clay
Pencils
Nile blue sulfate agar staining slides (agar, sterile distilled water, sterile glass slides, paper
    tissues, aluminum foil, glass pans, medium-sized forceps, 70% ethanol, sterile paper
    towels, scalpel blades)
Watchmaker's forceps

In this exercise **morphogenetic movements** will be mapped, using vital dyes, as the embryo passes from blastula to gastrula stages. Obtain dejellied and washed blastula -stage*Xenopus* embryos using the procedures described in Exercise 1. Place blastulae in a petri dish filled with 20% Steinberg solution and containing modeling clay on its bottom. Use a pencil tip to poke small wells in the clay and then pipette a single blastula into each well. Immobilizing eggs within the wells aids in subsequent staining. Blastulae will be vital stained through their **vitelline membrane** with chips of agar impregnated with Nile blue sulfate. First, make some agar staining slides. To do this, prepare a 1% solution of agar in sterile distilled water (heat the solution while stirring until the agar is dissolved). Have on hand some ordinary microscope *glass* slides, which have been washed with 70% ethanol, dried with tissues, and sterilized by autoclaving or heating. Pour a thin agar layer onto one side of each glass slide. Allow the slides to dry overnight (cover them with a canopy made from aluminum foil to prevent dust from accumulating on them). Soak the slides for one week in a *glass* pan (covered with aluminum foil) containing a 1% solution of Nile blue sulfate in sterile distilled water. Do not stack slides on top of one another or incomplete dye impregnation will occur. Finally, remove each slide from the pan with forceps, wash it with sterile distilled water, allow it to dry, and wrap it in a sterile (autoclaved) paper towel for storage. To stain embryos, unwrap a slide and place a drop of sterile distilled water on the coated side of the agar slide. Remove a *tiny* chip of agar from the moistened area using a scalpel blade (the chip should be as small as possible, preferably only slightly larger than the tip of the blade). Transfer the chip with a pair of watchmaker's forceps and lay it on the desired region of the surface of the blastula. Staining should occur within a minute or two. Remove the chip with a gentle stream of fluid generated with a pipette.

Use the space below (and on the following page) to sketch blastulae and the initial positions of the dye marks. Examine embryos periodically over the next several hours and resketch them at each interval, noting the changing positions of the marks. Pay particular attention to the shapes of marks placed in close vicinity to the forming **blastopore**.

16   CHAPTER 2

EXERCISE 3 Exogastrulation (Amphibian Embryos)

Materials

Materials from Exercises 1 and 2
Dejellied *Xenopus* blastulae
100% Steinberg solution
20% Steinberg solution
Watchmaker's forceps
Nile blue sulfate agar staining slides

Morphogenetic movements during gastrulation result in changes in the original positions of cells composing the blastula and give rise to the germ layers: ectoderm on the outside of the embryo, forming the surface epithelium; endoderm on the inside, forming the archenteron; and mesoderm filling the space between ectoderm and endoderm. Cells are brought into new positions by this process, allowing them to undergo tissue interactions (inductions) and form new structures (such as the neural plate). Normal morphogenetic movements will be inhibited in this exercise, preventing cells from involuting over the lips of the blastopore and forming the archenteron (that is, **exogastrulation** will occur). Instead, cells will remain on the surface to form an epithelial vesicle. We will cause exogastrulation by allowing blastulae to develop in 100% Steinberg solution, a hypertonic salt solution.

Obtain dejellied and washed blastula-stage *Xenopus* embryos using the procedures described in Exercise 1. Place eggs in a petri dish containing 100% Steinberg solution and maintain them in this solution during the course of the experiment. Remove the vitelline membrane covering each blastula by using two pairs of fine-tipped watchmaker's forceps, one in each hand. Use one pair to poke and grasp the membrane and the other to grasp and tear it. This can be difficult to do without injuring the blastula, so it requires practice.

Use the space below (and on the following page) to sketch blastulae at the beginning of the experiment. Observe embryos periodically over the next several hours and sketch them at each interval. Compare morphogenetic movements in embryos undergoing exogastrulation with those of control embryos (developing in 20% Steinberg solution with or without an intact vitelline membrane) by staining them with chips of agar impregnated with Nile blue sulfate (see Exercise 2). What differences can you detect?

EXERCISE 4 Neural Crest Ablation
(Amphibian Embryos)

Materials

Materials from Exercises 1–3
Dejellied *Xenopus* late gastrulae
100% Steinberg solution
20% Steinberg solution
Watchmaker's forceps
Cactus needles (magnifying glasses, cactus spines, medium-sized forceps, wooden sticks,
    nail polish)
70% ethanol

A neural fold will be extirpated in this exercise, thereby eliminating a patch of **neural crest cells** on one side of the embryo. *Xenopus* embryos contain **pigment cells** in their **epidermis**. Neural crest cells are the source of this pigment (do not confuse crest-derived pigment *cells* with egg pigment *granules*; the latter are deposited in the egg by the ovary during oogenesis, whereas the former migrate from the roof of the neural tube during late neurulation and invade the epidermis). This fact will be confirmed by deleting neural crest cells and noting the absence of pigmentation in a portion of the embryo.

Obtain dejellied and washed late gastrulae using the procedures described in Exercise 1. Let embryos develop in 20% Steinberg solution until neurula stages are obtained. Then place them in 100% Steinberg solution, to facilitate healing during microsurgery. Remove vitelline membranes, by using 2 pairs (one in each hand) of fine-tipped watchmaker's forceps, as described in Exercise 3. Use care to avoid damaging the embryo. Cactus needles will be used to extirpate a portion of one of the elevated neural folds. To make cactus needles, simply obtain a few cactus plants from a local florist (examine their needles carefully with a magnifying glass prior to purchase, and select several plants with needles of various sizes), pluck the desired needles from the plant with forceps, and mount the needles onto wooden sticks with nail polish. Sterilize needles by dipping them into 70% ethanol followed by sterile water. Make two transverse cuts through a neural fold some distance apart (as you repeat the experiments on other embryos, vary the craniocaudal level and side of the embryo at which you extirpate and also the distance between the two transverse cuts). Connect these two cuts with a horizontal incision and remove the neural fold. Determine the depth at which you make the horizontal cut by examining Plate 2, Fig. 1. Allow embryos to remain in 100% Steinberg solution for 30 minutes, and then transfer them to 70% and eventually to 20% Steinberg solution, as described in Exercise 1.

Use the space provided below (and on the following page) to sketch the appearances of neurulae at the time of surgery. Observe embryos periodically over the next few days and sketch their morphogenesis, especially during early tadpole stages. Pay particular attention to patterns of pigmentation on the operated side.

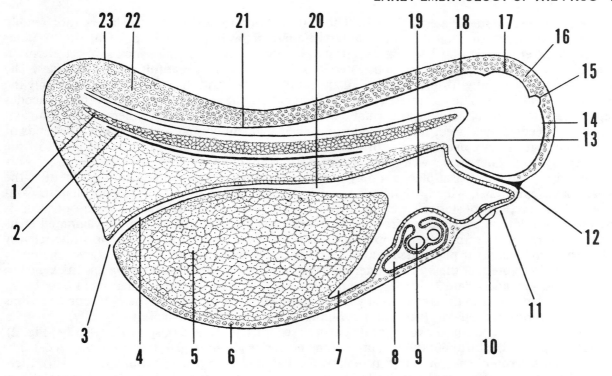

Fig. F. Schematic drawing of a midsagittal section of a 4-mm frog embryo.

1. Notochord
2. Subnotochordal rod
3. Anus
4. Hindgut
5. Yolk-filled endodermal cells
6. Lateral plate mesoderm
7. Liver rudiment
8. Pericardial cavity
9. Heart (ventricle)
10. Oral membrane
11. Stomodeum
12. Rudiment of the anterior pituitary gland
13. Infundibulum
14. Prosencephalon
15. Pineal gland
16. Head mesenchyme
17. Mesencephalon
18. Rhombencephalon
19. Pharynx
20. Midgut
21. Spinal cord
22. Neural crest cells
23. Dorsal fin

F. 4-MM FROG EMBRYOS

1. Introduction.

Aids: Figs. Aa, F; A–V#1; B, Fig. 268; M, Figs. 103, 104.

Fig. Aa shows the general shape of the body at this stage, and Fig. F shows the structures visible in a midsagittal section. Familiarize yourself with the spatial relationships of these structures before examining serial transverse sections.

2. Serial transverse sections.

Aids: Plates 2–4; A–V#1; B, Figs. 269–275; M, Figs. 108–114.

Position your slide on the microscope stage so that, when viewed through the microscope, each section is oriented as in Plate 2, Fig. 3. *Do not place microscope stage clips (if present) on slides to hold them in place as this could fragment sections.* Examine slides in anteroposterior sequence, unless directed otherwise (see Introduction).

a. Ectodermal derivatives. The first few sections cut through the tip of the head. Identify the large **prosencephalon** (future **telencephalon** and **diencephalon** of the brain), which is enclosed by

skin (surface) ectoderm (Plate 2, Fig. 3). The skin ectoderm consists of two layers (not readily distinguishable from one another): the **outer ectodermal layer** is heavily pigmented; the **inner ectodermal layer** contains far less pigment. Try to identify a region of thickened skin ectoderm on each side ventral to the prosencephalon. These thickenings are the **nasal (olfactory) placodes**. The nasal placodes eventually form the linings of the **nasal cavities**, and they are derived from only the *inner* ectodermal layer. The increased density of pigment granules at the periphery of these placodes is characteristic of invaginating ectodermal derivatives. Presumably, the peripheral ends of invaginating cells become narrowed, thus concentrating their pigment content, whereas the inner ends of the cells enlarge. **Young neurons** *later* originate from these placodes and produce the **axons** of the **olfactory (I) cranial nerves**, as well as the **dendrites** that function as **olfactory receptors** (receptors for the sense of smell). Nasal placodes may not have yet developed in some embryos. Identify the **pineal gland (epiphysis)**, which originated as a dorsal evagination from the prosencephalon. Continue to trace sections posteriorly and identify the **optic cups** (Plate 2, Fig. 4). Each optic cup is derived from a lateral evagination from the prosencephalon, which secondarily invaginated at its blind end, forming a double-layered optic cup. The thickened layer of the optic cup is the **sensory retina**; the thin layer is the **pigmented retina**. The optic cups are connected to the prosencephalon by the **optic stalks**. Note that the *inner* ectodermal layer adjacent to the sensory retina has thickened to form the **lens placode** (Plate 3, Fig. 1). The *outer* pigmented layer of the ectoderm will *later* be induced by the lens to form the transparent **corneal epithelium**. At the level of the optic cups, sections cut across the prosencephalon (ventrally) continuous with the **mesencephalon** (dorsally).

The brain constricts into two separate parts as sections are traced posteriorly (Plate 3, Fig. 2). The ventral part is the **infundibulum**, source of the **posterior pituitary gland (neurohypophysis)**. The dorsal part is the **rhombencephalon** (future **metencephalon** and **myelencephalon** of the brain). Identify a solid ectodermal rod at about this level, just ventral to the infundibulum. This is the **rudiment of the anterior pituitary gland**. Reverse direction and trace sections *anteriorly*. The rudiment of the anterior pituitary gland is continuous with an ectodermal invagination, the **stomodeum**, from which it originated as an outgrowth. (See Plate 3, Fig. 1; Plate 2, Fig. 4 for the location of the stomodeum. The rudiment of the anterior pituitary gland and the stomodeum are continuous at a section level between those illustrated by Plate 2, Figs. 4, 3). Reverse direction and trace sections *posteriorly*. Identify prominent ectodermal thickenings (Plate 3, Fig. 1), the **adhesive glands (ventral suckers)** to either side of the stomodeum and extending through many sections.

Return to the level where the infundibulum first appears (Plate 3, Fig. 2) and trace sections posteriorly. As the optic cups fade from view, identify an accumulation of ectodermal cells (**neural crest cells**) just above each of them. These are the **semilunar ganglia** of the **trigeminal (V) cranial nerves** (Plate 3, Fig. 2). (*Later* cells derived from a thickening of the *inner* ectodermal layer, on each side, an **epibranchial placode**, will also contribute to these ganglia.) Continue to trace sections posteriorly and identify the paired **auditory vesicles** lying ventrolateral to the rhombencephalon (Plate 3, Fig. 3). These vesicles originated from thickenings of the *inner* ectodermal layer, which subsequently invaginated. The auditory vesicles later differentiate into the **inner ears**.

Continue to trace sections posteriorly and note that the neural tube gradually narrows, indicating the level of the **spinal cord** (Plate 4, Fig. 1). Examine the spinal cord with high magnification. Note its characteristic thin **roof** and **floor plates** and its thick lateral walls. At about this level, identify pigmented or nonpigmented cells lying dorsal to the spinal cord and beneath the skin ectoderm; these are **neural crest cells** (Plate 4, Fig. 1). As you approach the final sections in your set, identify the **dorsal fin** above the spinal cord (Plate 4, Figs. 2–5). The loose cells forming its core are **neural crest cells**, which *induce* formation of this structure. Note that the body narrows progressively at caudal levels; identify the **ventral fin** at the caudal end of the body (Plate 4, Fig. 5). Identify the **proctodeum**, a ventral invagination of skin ectoderm, a few sections *anterior* to the ventral fin (Plate 4, Fig. 4).

b. Endodermal derivatives. Return to the level of the nasal placodes (Plate 2, Fig. 3) and trace sections posteriorly. Identify a small cavity lying beneath the prosencephalon (Plate 3, Fig. 1). This is the cranial end of the **foregut**; its walls are formed from endoderm. The **stomodeum** has invaginated toward the foregut, and the stomodeal *ectoderm* and the foregut *endoderm* are in contact as the **oral membrane**. This membrane *later* ruptures to form the **mouth opening**. The outer part of the mouth is therefore lined by stomodeal ectoderm, and the inner part by foregut endoderm.

The foregut expands as the **pharynx** as sections are traced posteriorly (Plate 3, Fig. 3). (In a few embryos the lateral walls of the pharynx may contact the skin ectoderm, which invaginates slightly to meet them. Such localized pharyngeal expansions are the **pharyngeal pouches**.) Continue tracing sections posteriorly. The foregut narrows and then forms a prominent ventral evagination, the **liver rudiment** (Plate 3, Fig. 4). The level of the foregut that is continuous ventrally with the liver rudiment is the **duodenum**. The liver rudiment separates from the duodenum and then fades out a few sections more posteriorly. The remaining portion of the gut is the **midgut** (Plate 4, Figs. 1, 2). It contains a small cavity bounded dorsally by a thin layer of endodermal cells and ventrally by a large mass of yolk-filled endodermal cells. Continue to trace sections posteriorly following the midgut. It gradually moves ventrally and enlarges somewhat as the **hindgut** (Plate 4, Fig. 3). (In some embryos the *endoderm* of the hindgut fuses with the *ectoderm* of the proctodeum in more posterior sections to form the **cloacal membrane**. The cloacal membrane ultimately ruptures to form the **anus**.)

c. Mesodermal derivatives. Return to the level where the infundibulum first appears (Plate 3, Fig. 2) and trace sections posteriorly. Identify a group of mesodermal cells, the **notochord**, lying beneath the rhombencephalon (Plate 3, Fig. 3). The vacuolated condition of the notochord is apparently responsible for its rigidity, allowing this structure to serve as a longitudinal supporting rod in young embryos. Quickly trace sections posteriorly, noting the changes that the notochord undergoes. It is smaller at caudal levels than at more cranial levels, and vacuolization is progressively reduced toward the caudal end (compare Plate 4, Figs. 1–5). The caudal end of the notochord is less developed at this stage because the notochord develops in craniocaudal sequence. In posterior sections identify the **somites** (Plate 4, Figs. 2, 3), paired blocks of mesoderm lying ventrolateral to the spinal cord. Also identify a small cluster of mesodermal cells lying beneath the notochord in caudal regions, the **subnotochordal rod (hypochord)** (Plate 4, Figs. 2–4). Its developmental significance is unknown.

Return to the level at which the liver rudiment is continuous with the duodenum (Plate 3, Fig. 4) and trace sections posteriorly. The mesoderm ventrolateral to the somites is usually in the form of more or less distinct epithelial vesicles (Plate 4, Fig. 1). The round vesicle on each side farthest from the spinal cord is the **pronephric duct**. Just above the latter, and often continuous with it, are the **pronephric tubules**. The pronephric duct and tubules on each side constitute the **pronephric kidney**, which is functional in amphibian larvae. The pronephric kidney when well formed causes the body to bulge laterad as the **pronephric ridge**.

The **lateral plate mesoderm** (often difficult to identify as a distinct area) lies ventral to each pronephric kidney, between the skin ectoderm and the endoderm. This mesoderm is in the process of splitting into an *outer* layer of **somatic mesoderm**, adjacent to the skin ectoderm, and an *inner* layer of **splanchnic mesoderm**, adjacent to the endoderm. If somatic and splanchnic mesoderm have formed, identify a space (or a series of small spaces) between them, the **coelom**.

Return to the level at which the foregut first appears (Plate 3, Fig. 1) and trace sections posteriorly. Identify the **bulbus cordis** region of the developing heart lying beneath the pharynx (Plate 3, Fig. 3). The heart enlarges as the **ventricle** in more posterior sections (Plate 3, Fig. 4). Note that the heart consists of an *inner* layer, the **endocardium**, surrounded by an *outer*, thicker layer, the **myocardium**. Both these layers are derived from *splanchnic* mesoderm. (*Splanchnic* mesoderm will *later* contribute to a third layer of the heart: its outermost covering.) Identify a thin layer of cells enclosing the heart, the **parietal pericardium**, derived from *somatic* mesoderm. The parietal pericardium is usually separated from the skin ectoderm by a shrinkage space. The space between the heart and the parietal pericardium is the **pericardial cavity**. The heart is suspended within the pericardial cavity by a dorsal bridge of *splanchnic* mesoderm, the **dorsal mesocardium**.

The major blood vessels are in early stages of formation at this time, and they are thus difficult to identify with certainty in most embryos. Two major blood vessels can sometimes be identified. The **first aortic arches** mainly lie ventrolateral to the pharynx (Plate 3, Fig. 3). (They will soon establish connections with the bulbus cordis via a pair of blood vessels that will lie ventral to the pharynx, the **ventral aortae**. These latter vessels can sometimes be identified at this stage.) The dorsal end of each first aortic arch is continuous with a blood vessel lying dorsolateral to the pharynx, the **dorsal aorta** (Plate 3, Fig. 3). The dorsal aortae extend caudad and fade out at about the level of the midgut (Plate 4, Fig. 1).

3. Summary of the contributions of the germ layers to structures present in the 4-mm frog embryo.

Ectoderm		
adhesive glands	nasal placodes	rhombencephalon
auditory vesicles	neural crest cells	rudiment of the anterior
corneal epithelium	optic cups	pituitary gland
dorsal fin	optic stalks	semilunar ganglia
infundibulum	pineal gland	stomodeum
lens placodes	proctodeum	spinal cord
mesencephalon	prosencephalon	ventral fin

Mesoderm	Endoderm	Ectoderm and Endoderm
bulbus cordis	duodenum	cloacal membrane
dorsal aortae	foregut	oral membrane
dorsal mesocardium	hindgut	
first aortic arches	liver rudiment	
notochord	midgut	
parietal pericardium	pharynx	
pronephric kidneys		
somites		
subnotochordal rod		
ventricle		

G. SCANNING ELECTRON MICROSCOPY

Aids: Plates 5, 6; L, Figs. 1.7, 8.2. (See Appendix II for a brief explanation of how the various images shown are produced; that is, images of intact specimens and slices.)

Examine scanning electron micrographs (Plates 5, 6) to help you visualize the shapes of developing frog eggs and embryos three dimensionally. Note at cleavage stages (Plate 5) the positions and orientations of **cleavage furrows** separating **blastomeres** and the differences in sizes of the **micromeres** and **macromeres**. Boundaries between blastomeres become less well defined as cleavage advances (compare Plate 5, Figs. 2, 6).

The lips of the blastopore form during gastrula stages (Plate 6, Fig. 1). First the **dorsal lip** forms, followed by the **lateral lips,** and finally the **ventral lip.** The **yolk plug** continues to occupy the **blastopore** throughout gastrulation.

The neural plate forms and rolls up into the **neural tube** between the gastrula stage and early embryo stage. Concomitant with formation of the neural tube, the embryo begins to elongate craniocaudally. This elongation is an obvious feature of developing frog embryos (Plate 6, Figs. 2, 3). The neural tube extends throughout the length of the embryo. It bulges laterad at its cranial end to form the developing **eyes** in conjunction with the overlying **skin ectoderm.** Note that the skin ectoderm in the embryos illustrated in Plate 6, Figs. 2, 3, is covered with **ciliary tufts.** These structures establish currents around the embryos as they beat, circulating fluids. Also, these structures function in primitive locomotory movements before swimming begins. In 4-mm embryos the skin ectoderm at the cranial end of the embryo has invaginated in the midline forming the **stomodeum.** Caudally, the skin ectoderm is attenuated, demarcating the **dorsal** and **ventral fins.**

Chapter 3

EARLY EMBRYOLOGY OF THE CHICK

The chick embryo has long been used for the study of early embryonic development because the stages desired can be readily obtained. Many of the developmental changes in the chick embryo are almost identical with those characteristic of other vertebrates, and particularly of mammals, whose young embryos are difficult to obtain in sufficient numbers in the stages needed for study. Consequently, the chick will be used extensively for the study of early stages of development. This is

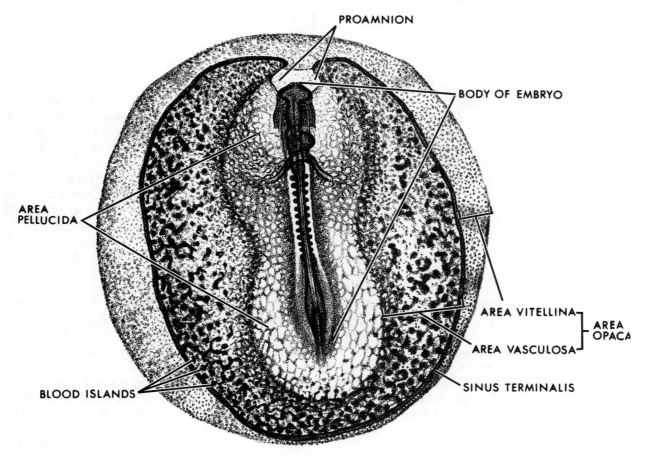

Fig. G. Drawing of a 33-hour chick embryo whole mount.

especially appropriate because many outstanding experimental embryologists (including Frank Lillie, Benjamin Willier, and Viktor Hamburger and their several students) chose the chick embryo as their model to analyze vertebrate development. The stages we will study are those that have been designated classically as 18-, 24-, 33-, 48-, and 72-hour embryos. Embryos within each classical stage vary somewhat in the degree of development attained and thus your embryos may be slightly different than those described and illustrated here. Descriptions have been sufficiently generalized to permit study of most embryos within each classical stage.

A. THE PART OF THE EGG TO BE STUDIED

From an embryological point of view, the bird's egg consists of a large spherical mass of **yolk** on which rests a small white disc of cytoplasm. If this disc has not initiated **cleavage** (that is, if it is unsegmented), it is called the **blastodisc**. If this disc has initiated cleavage (that is, it is segmented into two or more cells by the process of mitosis), it is called the **blastoderm**. All parts of the embryo and its membranes originate from the blastodisc.

Developmental stages can be examined in detail after the blastoderm is removed from the yolk and then either mounted flat on a slide so it can be studied as a whole mount or cut into serial sections and then mounted. (See Appendix I for a brief explanation of how whole mounts and serial sections of chick embryos are produced.) The center of the blastoderm is separated from the underlying yolk by a **subgerminal cavity**; the periphery is not. Furthermore, the periphery of the blastoderm contains cells laden with yolk, but yolk is absent in the cells of the central region. Thus, the central region of the blastoderm is more translucent than its periphery. The central region of the blastoderm is therefore named the **area pellucida**, and the peripheral region, the **area opaca**.

B. 33-HOUR CHICK EMBRYOS

1. Whole mounts.

Aids: Fig. G; Plate 7; A–V#1; A, Figs. 543, 544; B, Fig. 286; H, Figs. 67–70; HU, Figs. 105–107; M, Figs. 170, 172, 173; P, Figs. 53, 55, 57, 64.

First examine your slide with the naked eye. Note the round to oval shape of the mounted specimen. The specimen is divisible into two main areas, the peripheral **area opaca** and the central **area pellucida** (Fig. G). The area opaca is further divided into the inner mottled **area vasculosa**, containing developing **blood islands**, and the outer **area vitellina**, a nonmottled area overgrowing the yolk. Try to identify the **sinus terminalis**, a circular blood vessel separating the area vasculosa from the area vitellina. This vessel may appear light or dark, depending on whether it contains blood cells. Most of the area vitellina is usually trimmed off from mounted specimens, so the sinus terminalis will probably be located just within the margin of the blastoderm. Running lengthwise within the area pellucida is a dark region, the **body** of the developing embryo. The darker and wider part of this region is the **head (cranial) end** of the embryo; the lighter part is the **tail (caudal) end.** Note a very clear area beneath and in front of the head; this area is called the **proamnion** (a misnomer because it is not the source of the amnion, an extraembryonic membrane that develops later). It is the only region of the blastoderm that still lacks **mesoderm**, the middle **germ layer.**

Position your slide on the microscope stage so that when viewed through the microscope the embryo is oriented as in Fig. G and Plate 7. Examine the slide under low magnification. First examine the **area vasculosa.** The **blood islands,** which give this area its mottled appearance, consist of irregularly shaped accumulations of mesodermal cells. The peripheral cells of each blood island form the **endothelium** constituting the walls of the blood vessels; central cells form **primitive blood cells.** Note that blood islands are most numerous lateral and caudal to the body of the embryo and that they are fusing together to form blood vessels. The primitive blood cells are therefore enclosed within these developing blood vessels, the **vitelline blood vessels,** which may open peripherally into the sinus terminalis and extend across the area pellucida toward the body of the embryo. Note that within the area pellucida blood vessels are clear (empty) channels containing no blood cells and that the vitelline vessels are all about the same size. Circulation of the blood begins slightly later, although the heart at this stage contracts weakly. Initiation of the heartbeat and onset of circulation begin long before the heart is supplied with nerve fibers.

Next examine the **head end** of the embryo. Focus up and down on the head with the coarse adjustment of your microscope. Different structures and lines will become apparent to you at different levels of focus. This means that in addition to *length* and *width,* the body of the embryo has considerable *depth*; therefore, you can focus only on a part of its thickness at one time.

Notice two dense, thick bands running parallel to each other throughout the middle region of the embryo (Plate 7, Figs. 1-3). Just lateral to these bands are paired blocks of mesoderm, the **somites,** separated by **intersomitic furrows.** These bands are the thick lateral walls of the **neural tube.** The neural tube is formed from the outermost **germ layer,** the **ectoderm.** The bands diverge in a bilaterally symmetrical fashion at the cranial end of the embryo where they constitute the lateral walls of the **brain.** Caudal to the brain these bands constitute the lateral walls of the **spinal cord.** Thus, most of the **central nervous system** (that is, brain and spinal cord) present at this stage exists as a *hollow ectodermal tube.* More caudally the bands diverge laterally as **neural folds.** The space between the neural folds is the **neural groove.** At the caudal end of the embryo the converging bands represent the **primitive ridges (folds),** which are the lateral margins of the primitive streak. The **primitive streak** is the site of **mesoderm** formation at this stage.

Turn your attention now to the brain region and note the two largest lateral expansions (that is, evaginations) of the neural tube; these are the **optic vesicles,** the earliest rudiments of the **eyes** (Plate 7, Fig. 3–5). The region of the brain from which these evaginate is the **diencephalon.** Note by carefully focusing that these vesicles are in close contact laterally with the overlying **skin (surface) ectoderm.** These regions of skin ectoderm are probably not thickened, but they will *later* thicken and transform into the **lenses** of the eyes. Experiments have shown that the optic vesicles stimulate (that is, *induce*) the ectoderm to form the lenses. Note a dark, shadowy mass lying in the midline between the optic vesicles. This is the **infundibulum,** which forms as an evagination from the floor of the diencephalon (Plate 7, Figs. 2, 4, 5). It will *later* form the **posterior pituitary gland (neurohypophysis).**

The level of the brain cranial to the diencephalon is the **telencephalon** (Plate 7, Fig. 4). It is poorly demarcated from the diencephalon at this stage, and the two are usually spoken of collectively as the **prosencephalon.** Focus down into the telencephalon and notice a white median notch or cleft, the remnant of the **cranial (anterior) neuropore.** Earlier, the cavity of the neural tube opened broadly to the outside through the cranial neuropore. At the 33-hour stage, the neural folds that originally flanked the cranial neuropore are approximated but not yet completely fused.

The division of the brain caudal to the diencephalon is the **mesencephalon,** and the next caudal expansion is the **metencephalon** (Plate 7, Fig. 2). The most caudal region of the brain is the **myelencephalon,** which is characterized by several smaller enlargements of the neural tube, the **neuromeres.** The metencephalon and myelencephalon are spoken of collectively as the **rhombencephalon.** Note that the space between the walls of the brain and the skin ectoderm is filled with loosely packed cells, the **head mesenchyme** (Plate 7, Figs. 4, 5).

Recall that the somites are located lateral to the neural tube throughout the middle region of the embryo. How many pairs are present in your embryo? The most cranial pair is incomplete (has no definite cranial boundaries). It lies just caudal to the last neuromere. All somites cranial to the *fifth* intersomitic furrow are later contained within the head of the chick. Thus, more than one-third of the embryonic body formed by this stage is future head. Note that lateral to each neural fold a band of tissue extends caudally from the last pair of somites. These two bands are the **segmental plates,** which will form additional somites in craniocaudal sequence (Plate 7, Fig. 1). By carefully focusing down through the neural tube, you will be able to identify a narrow mesodermal rod, the **notochord** (Plate 7, Figs. 2-5). This structure lies directly beneath the neural tube and neural groove, between the infundibulum and the cranial end of the primitive streak. The cranial tip of the notochord *induces* the infundibulum to form. Notice that the notochord is widest just cranial to the primitive streak.

Observe lines extending craniocaudally by carefully focusing just laterally to the mesencephalon and rhombencephalon. These lines represent the lateral boundaries of the **foregut** (see H, Fig. 69; HU, Figs. 105, 106; M, Fig. 172; P, Fig. 55). The cranial boundary of the foregut usually lies near the caudal boundaries of the optic vesicles, but it is often very difficult to see. The foregut is formed from the innermost **germ layer,** the **endoderm,** and resembles a finger of a glove:

closed cranially but open caudally. The opening is called the **cranial (anterior) intestinal portal** (Plate 7, Fig. 4) and can be seen more readily if slides are viewed from the ventral surface (Plate 7, Fig. 5). It lies beneath the myelencephalon, and its margin forms a distinct curvature with its concavity facing caudally.

Note that the cranial part of the head is sharply bounded and that it protrudes above the underlying blastoderm. The head is separated from the blastoderm by an ectoderm-lined space, the **subcephalic pocket.**

Focus down through the level of the rhombencephalon and observe the **heart,** usually bent somewhat toward the right (Plate 7, Fig. 4). It can be seen more readily from the ventral surface (Plate 7, Fig. 5). Two large veins, the **vitelline veins,** enter the heart from behind, immediately cranial to the cranial intestinal portal. The cranial ends of these veins are continuous with the **sinoatrial region** of the heart (*future* **sinus venosus** and **atrium**). The region of the heart that bulges slightly to the right (or the widest part of the heart, if bending has not yet occurred) is the **ventricle.** The heart narrows cranial to the ventricle, indicating the level of the **bulbus cordis.**

EXERCISE 5 Preparation of Graphical Reconstruction
(Avian Embryos)

Aid: Fig. H.

Materials

Fig. Hb or similar graph paper
Millimeter rulers
Colored pencils

It is recommended that you prepare a graphical reconstruction of *your* embryo to help you visualize relationships of parts of an embryo to one another in three dimensions. A sample is given in Fig. Ha. Examine your slides of serial transverse sections with the naked eye. Note that the sections are mounted in horizontal rows. Count and record the number of rows and the number of sections in each row. Add the number of sections in each row to determine the total number of sections.

On the sheet of graph paper provided (Fig. Hb: ruled with 1-cm squares), let each centimeter along the longest (horizontal) axis represent the thickness of *ten* sections. At the top of the paper, every 10 sections have been numbered off from left to right. Draw vertical dashed lines at the levels of the last section number in each row (determine millimeter markings with the aid of a millimeter ruler). Number the rows at the bottom of the paper. The paper has been subdivided into three areas by brackets at the left. The following labels have been placed at the right of the page within each subdivision. Under *ectodermal structures,* the first centimeter line from the bottom has been labeled *neural tube and groove,* and the third centimeter line *subcephalic pocket.* Under *mesodermal structures,* the first centimeter line has been labeled *notochord,* and the second centimeter line *head mesenchyme, somites, and segmental plates.* The space between the fifth and sixth centimeter lines has been labeled *heart and related vessels.* The ninth centimeter line has been labeled *right dorsal aorta.* Under *endodermal structures,* the second centimeter line has been labeled *foregut.* Instructions for plotting structures on the graph paper are given in brackets below.

2. Serial transverse sections.

Aids: Plates 8, 9; A-V#1; A, Fig. 544; B, Figs. 289–295; HU, Figs. 105, 106, 108; M, Figs. 172–182; P, Figs. 57, 60D, 63.

Position your slide on the microscope stage so that, when viewed through the microscope, each section is oriented as in Plate 8 (that is, with the dorsal surface at the top). *Do not place microscope stage clips (if present) on slides to hold them in place as this could fragment sections.*

Begin your slide study by examining sections in anteroposterior sequence (see Introduction) until you find a section resembling Plate 8, Fig. 1. This section cuts through the portion of the head containing the **diencephalon.** The **proamnion** lies beneath the head, separated from it by a space, the **subcephalic pocket.** The proamnion consists of two layers: upper **ectoderm,** lower **endoderm.** To

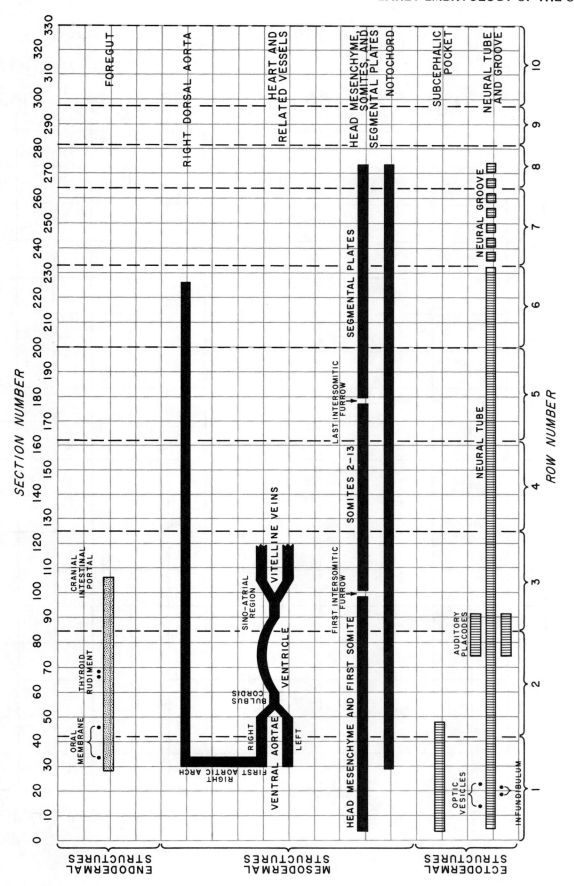

Fig. H. Graphical reconstruction of a 33-hour chick embryo, showing relationships of parts to one another along the craniocaudal axis. (Fig. Ha) sample reconstruction; (Fig. Hb) graph paper for use in Exercise 5.

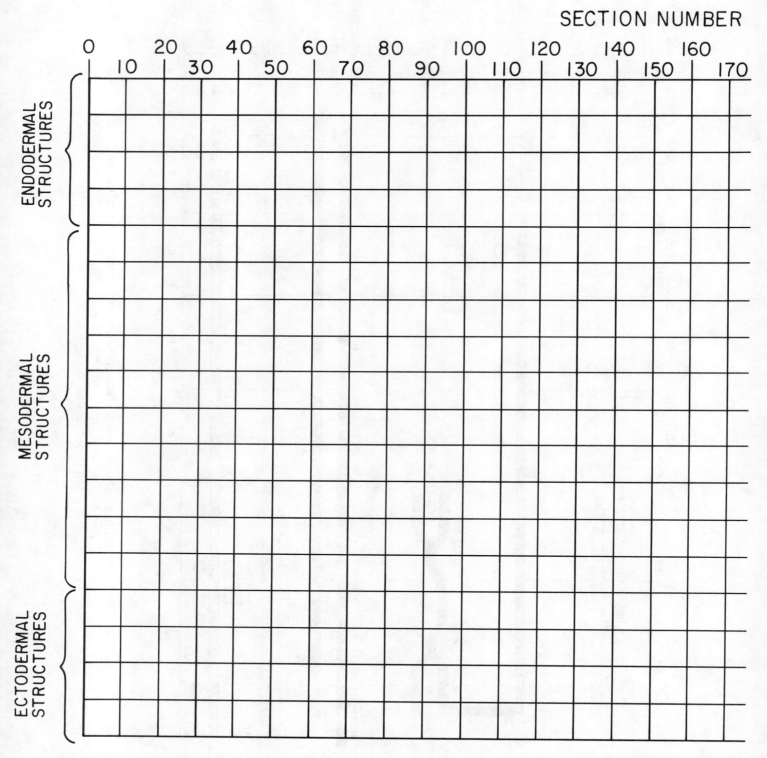

180   200   220   240   260   280   300
  190   210   230   250   270   290   310

FOREGUT

RIGHT DORSAL AORTA

HEART AND
RELATED VESSELS

HEAD MESENCHYME,
SOMITES,AND
SEGMENTAL PLATES
NOTOCHORD

SUBCEPHALIC
POCKET

NEURAL TUBE AND
GROOVE

either side of it are four cell layers. The dorsal two constitute the **somatopleure** (upper **ectoderm,** lower **somatic mesoderm**); the ventral two, the **splanchnopleure** (upper **splanchnic mesoderm,** lower **endoderm**). The space between somatic and splanchnic mesoderm is the **coelom.**

From this level trace sections *anteriorly* until the head disappears. Identify the proamnion, somatopleure, splanchnopleure, and coelom at this level. Then trace sections *posteriorly* and note the reappearance of the head. The first part of the brain seen is the **telencephalon.** [Record the first section through the neural tube on the *neural tube and groove* line of your graph.] It will usually seem divided into right and left halves by a narrow white slit, the remnant of the **cranial neuropore.**

Continue to trace sections posteriorly. The region of the brain to which the **optic vesicles** attach is the **diencephalon** (Plate 8, Fig. 1). Part of each optic vesicle may lie caudal to its connection to the diencephalon and thus appear in some sections as an isolated vesicle. [Record the craniocaudal extent of the optic vesicles by blue dots above the *neural tube and groove* line. Record these boundaries for one side only, if your embryo is not sectioned symmetrically.] As the optic vesicles begin to fade out, note an evagination from the floor of the diencephalon, the **infundibulum.** [Record the craniocaudal extent of the infundibulum by blue dots below the *neural tube and groove* line.] Identify the thin **skin ectoderm,** the outer layer of the head, and the **head mesenchyme** between the skin ectoderm and brain wall.

A few sections behind the infundibulum a small mass of cells appears beneath the neural tube, closely applied to its surface. This is the cranial tip of the **notochord.** [Record the first section through the notochord on the *notochord* line.] Continue to trace neural tube and notochord caudally, noting that the notochord becomes more distinct and separated from the neural tube. The level of the neural tube that is oval or pear shaped is the **mesencephalon** (Plate 8, Figs. 2, 3). It appears as the optic vesicles fade out, just caudal to the infundibulum. The neural tube usually becomes smaller in more posterior sections. In this general region the **metencephalon** can be identified as that portion of the neural tube that lies above the bulbus cordis region of the heart (Plate 8, Fig. 4). The caudal end of the **subcephalic pocket** can also be identified at about this level. [Record the craniocaudal extent of the subcephalic pocket by a blue bar on the appropriate line under *ectodermal structures.*] In more posterior sections the **myelencephalon** can be identified as that portion of the neural tube that lies above the ventricle and sinoatrial region (Plate 9, Figs. 1, 2). The skin ectoderm has thickened alongside part of the myelencephalon, forming the **auditory (otic) placodes,** the rudiments of the **inner ears.** [Record the craniocaudal extent of the auditory placodes by blue bars above and below the *neural tube and groove* line.] Formation of the auditory placodes is *induced* by the myelencephalon and adjacent head mesenchyme.

Focus on the dorsal surface of the myelencephalon just cranial to or just caudal to the auditory placodes. You may be able to identify a straggling line of cells wedged between the skin ectoderm and myelencephalon (HU, Fig. 108d; M, Fig. 178; P, Fig. 63D). (If you cannot identify these cells at the level of the myelencephalon, look more cranially at the level of the metencephalon or mesencephalon; Plate 8, Figs. 3, 4.) These are **neural crest cells,** which are derived from *ectoderm.* Both neural crest cells and mesoderm contribute to the **head mesenchyme.**

Note the change in shape of the neural tube as you continue caudally from the level of the myelencephalon, indicating that you have reached the level of the **spinal cord** (Plate 9, Fig. 3). The lateral walls of the spinal cord are much thicker than its dorsal and ventral walls. Recall that only the thick lateral walls of the neural tube can be readily seen in whole mounts. The dorsal wall is designated as the **roof plate,** the ventral as the **floor plate. Skin ectoderm** overlies the roof plate.

In more posterior sections, the neural tube may seem to contain no cavity. This is because the walls of certain levels of the spinal cord are normally in contact during this stage, occluding the lumen (the fact that the lumen of the spinal cord is occluded is usually not ascertainable in whole mounts). This occlusion confines **cerebrospinal fluid** to the brain region, aiding in the subsequent enlargement of the brain as fluid pressure increases (compare the size of the brain in 33-, 48-, and 72-hour embryos; Plates 7, 20, 30). The roof plate disappears as sections are traced posteriorly; this is the beginning of the **neural groove** (Plate 9, Fig. 4). [Record the craniocaudal extent of the neural tube by a blue bar on the *neural tube and groove* line.] The neural groove is flanked by the **neural folds.** Continue following the neural groove caudally and note the progressive enlargement and flattening of the notochord. The notochord then becomes indistinct, seeming to fuse with the floor of the neural groove. [Record the craniocaudal extent of the notochord by a red bar on the *notochord* line.] The neural folds are widely separated at this level (see Plate 7, Fig. 1). Slightly more caudally, a large mass of cells, which extends across the midline, gradually appears in place of the notochord. You are now near the caudal end of the neural groove in the region of the **primitive streak.** [Record the craniocaudal extent of the neural groove by a broken blue bar on the *neural tube and groove* line.] In more posterior sections, identify the smaller **primitive groove,** which is flanked by the **primitive ridges** (Plate 9, Fig. 5). The primitive ridges are directly continuous with the neural folds, so the transition between the two is gradual. The primitive ridges and groove disappear in more posterior sections, indicating that you are now caudal to the primitive streak.

Return in your sections to the level of the optic vesicles and again trace sections posteriorly. A small endoderm-lined cavity, the **foregut,** appears just beneath the neural tube near the caudal ends of the optic vesicles (Plate 8, Fig. 1). [Record the cranial boundary of the foregut on the *foregut* line.] In more posterior sections, the foregut widens and its endodermal floor contacts the ventral skin ectoderm of the head, forming the **oral membrane** (Plate 8, Fig. 2). If a wide space exists between the two layers, it is a shrinkage space caused by section preparation. These two layers will *later* rupture to establish the **mouth opening.** [Record the craniocaudal extent of the oral membrane by yellow dots above the *foregut* line.]

Examine the floor of the foregut as you continue to trace sections caudally. Identify a midline thickening, the **thyroid rudiment,** which usually appears as a shallow depression above the ventricle (Plate 9, Fig. 1). [Record the craniocaudal extent of the thyroid rudiment by yellow dots above the *foregut* line.] Continue to trace the foregut caudally and note the sudden disappearance of its floor; this is the region of the **cranial intestinal portal** (see HU, Fig. 108d). [Record the craniocaudal extent of the foregut by a yellow bar on the *foregut* line, and label the level of the cranial intestinal portal.] Note that in more posterior sections the embryo progressively flattens dorsoventrally and that endoderm forms its lower layer (Plate 9, Fig. 3). The endoderm becomes indistinguishable in the midline at the level of the primitive streak.

Return again to the level of the rhombencephalon and identify the loosely packed cells of the **head mesenchyme.** The mesoderm to either side of the neural tube just caudal to the auditory placodes forms compact masses, the **somites.** The first somite pair is difficult to identify because it has no distinct cranial boundaries. Two to three sections posteriorly, the first somite pair begins to fade out as sections cut through the first **intersomitic furrows.** [Record the approximate craniocaudal extent of the head mesenchyme and first somite pair by a red bar on the *head mesenchyme, somites, and segmental plates* line.] The second somite pair appears slightly more caudally and soon begins to fade out at the level of the second intersomitic furrows. Continue tracing the somites caudally and determine the approximate number of pairs present in your embryo. [Record the distance between the first and last intersomitic furrows by a red bar on the *head mesenchyme, somites, and segmental plates* line, and indicate how many somite pairs this bar represents.]

Examine in detail the structure of one of the best-formed somites under higher magnification. It is roughly triangular in transverse section and usually contains a small core of cells (Plate 9, Fig. 3). Note the close relationship of the somites and notochord to the neural tube. Experiments have shown that the characteristic shape of the neural tube (that is, its thick lateral walls and thin roof and floor plates) depends on this relationship. At this level it might be possible to observe **neural crest cells** lying between the neural tube, skin ectoderm, and somites.

Just lateral to each somite is a slender area of mesodermal cells, the **nephrotome (intermediate mesoderm).** The nephrotome on each side produces a solid mass of cells called the **pronephric cord** (Plate 9, Fig. 3). The cords constitute the paired rudimentary **pronephric kidneys.** (The pronephric cord on each side *later* separates from the underlying nephrotome and elongates to form a **mesonephric [pronephric] duct rudiment.**) The mesoderm lateral to the nephrotome is the **lateral plate.** It is divided into an upper layer of **somatic mesoderm** (adjacent to the ectoderm) and a lower layer of **splanchnic mesoderm** (adjacent to the endoderm). The space between the somatic and splanchnic mesoderm is the **coelom.** Note the presence of **vitelline blood vessels** in the splanchnic mesoderm.

Identify the **segmental plates** in sections posterior to the last pair of intersomitic furrows. As you trace them caudally, observe that they become continuous with the more lateral mesoderm (Plate 9, Fig. 4) and that they become indistinguishable more caudally at the level of the primitive streak. [Record the craniocaudal extent of the segmental plates by a red bar on the *head mesenchyme, somites, and segmental plates* line.]

There remains for consideration only the circulatory system, a mesodermal derivative (see A, Fig. 544; HU, Figs. 105, 106, 108b–e; M, Figs. 172, 173; P, Figs. 57, 60D, 63B–E). Return to the level of the diencephalon and again trace sections posteriorly. A white space should be visible on each side of the foregut at about the level where its cranial end appears. These spaces are the **first aortic arches** (Plate 8, Fig. 2). [Record the craniocaudal extent of the right first aortic arch by a red bar interconnecting the sixth and ninth centimeter lines under *mesodermal structures.*] Each is continuous with a small **ventral aorta,** lying below the foregut, and a larger **dorsal aorta,** lying above the foregut. The first aortic arch is often very small, so it may not be readily seen in your sections.

Trace sections posteriorly, watching all aortae. The two ventral aortae may be difficult to follow because they are just forming. Note that they merge with the **bulbus cordis** caudal to the oral membrane. [Record the craniocaudal extent of the ventral aortae by red bars on the fifth and sixth centimeter lines under *mesodermal structures.* Connect the right ventral aorta with the right first aortic arch.] The bulbus cordis lies in the midline and has a small diameter. It consists of an inner, very thin lining of **endocardium,** continuous with the endothelium of the ventral aortae, reinforced by an outer thick layer, the **myocardium.** The space between the endocardium and myocardium is filled with a cellular secretion called the **cardiac jelly** (usually not visible in conventional paraffin sections). (A third cellular layer, forming the outermost covering of the heart, will appear between the third and fourth days of development.) When sections are traced posteriorly, the heart usually seems to bend from the midline somewhat toward the *embryo's right,* the *apparent left* (Plate 9, Fig. 1). This is the region of the **ventricle.** Even if the ventricle has not yet bent to the right in your embryo, it can be readily identified because its endocardium and myocardium are widely separated. Note that the ventricle is suspended within the coelom by a bridge of mesoderm, the **dorsal mesocardium.** The portion of the coelom surrounding the heart is the **pericardial cavity.** The endocardium and myocardium are no longer widely separated in more posterior sections, and the heart lies in the midline. This is the beginning of the **sinoatrial region.** The sinoatrial region is incompletely formed caudally, consisting of two rudiments, one on either side of the cranial intestinal portal. As you continue tracing sections posteriorly, there is a gradual transition between the sinoatrial region and **vitelline veins.** The vitelline veins shift laterad and consist only of endothelium. [Record the approximate craniocaudal extents of the bulbus cordis, ventricle, sinoatrial region, and vitelline veins by red bars under *mesodermal structures.*]

Shift your attention to the dorsal aortae and trace them caudally. The dorsal aortae lie just below the nephrotomes and somites throughout most of their extent (Plate 9, Fig. 3). Their endothelium is so thin that it may not be visible in some sections. [Record the craniocaudal extent of the right dorsal aorta by a red bar on the *right dorsal aorta* line. Connect the right dorsal aorta with the right first aortic arch.]

3. Serial sagittal sections.

Aids: Plate 9, Fig. 6; A–V#1; A, Fig. 545; M, Fig. 171.

Careful study of serial sagittal sections can help you immeasurably to understand relationships among developing parts of early chick embryos. These sections are cut lengthwise in the dorsoventral plane. First examine your slide with the naked eye. Only the darkest sections are cut through the body of the embryo. Position your slide on the microscope stage so that when viewed through the microscope the neural tube is uppermost (Plate 9, Fig. 6). Trace sections until you find one closely resembling Plate 9, Fig. 6. Identify the various levels of the **neural tube** in midsagittal sections. Similarly identify the **neural groove** caudal to the neural tube. The **notochord** lies beneath the neural tube and groove, but only part of the notochord's length will be cut through in any one section. Determine the craniocaudal extent of the notochord. It merges caudally with the **primitive streak.** Its cranial end lies just caudal to the **infundibulum.** Identify the endoderm-lined **foregut,** the double-layered **oral membrane,** and the **cranial intestinal portal.** Note that the head is separated from the **proamnion** by the **subcephalic pocket.**

Beneath the foregut is the portion of the **coelom** containing the heart, the **pericardial cavity.** Identify the **bulbus cordis, ventricle,** and **sinoatrial region.** It may be necessary to trace sections to either side of the midline to identify these structures. By carefully tracing sections, you may also be able to identify the **dorsal aortae,** above the foregut, the **ventral aortae,** below the foregut, and the **first aortic arches.**

Note that as the **prosencephalon** fades out in sections to either side of the midline, the **optic vesicles** remain for several more sections. Also note that as the **myelencephalon** begins to fade out, the skin ectoderm overlying it thickens as the **auditory placodes.** Identify the **head mesenchyme, somites, intersomitic furrows,** and **segmental plates** in sections to either side of the neural tube.

4. Summary of the contributions of the germ layers to structures present in the 33-hour chick embryo.

Ectoderm	Mesoderm	Endoderm
auditory placodes	blood islands	foregut
infundibulum	blood vessels (endothelium)	thyroid rudiment
neural crest cells	dorsal mesocardium	
neural folds and groove	heart	**Ectoderm and Mesoderm**
neural tube	lateral plates	head mesenchyme
optic vesicles	nephrotomes	
	notochord	**Ectoderm and Endoderm**
	primitive blood cells	oral membrane
	pronephric cords	proamnion
	segmental plates and somites	

5. Scanning electron microscopy.

Aids: Plates 10–12; L, Fig. 10.3. (See Appendix II for a brief explanation on how the various images shown are produced; that is, images of intact specimens, slices, cryofractures, and sectioned blocks.)

Scanning electron microscopy of intact embryos gives a much different view than does light microscopy of whole mounts (compare Plate 7, Figs. 1–3 to Plate 10, Fig. 1). Because the embryo is covered by **skin ectoderm** and scanning electron microscopy reveals only surface features (that is, we cannot "see" through the ectoderm as we can in cleared and stained whole mounts examined with light microscopy), details of the shapes of the neural tube and somites are largely obscured. Identify the **auditory placodes** near the caudal end of the head. Where the neural tube had not yet formed (and hence is not covered by skin ectoderm), the **neural groove** and **neural folds** are readily visible (Plate 10, Figs. 1, 2). Less well defined is the **primitive streak,** consisting of the shallow **primitive groove** flanked by the paired **primitive ridges.** The most prominent feature of intact embryos at this stage occurs at their head end. The neural tube bulges bilaterad as the **optic vesicles** (Plate 10, Figs. 1, 3). The remnant of the **cranial neuropore** lies in the midline between the optic vesicles.

Transverse slices through the region of the **optic vesicles** reveal the **infundibulum,** the remnant of the **cranial neuropore** on the wall of the **telencephalon,** and the connections of the **optic vesicles** to the **diencephalon** (Plate 10, Fig. 4). A close spatial relationship exists between the elongated cells of each optic vesicle and the much shorter covering cells of the future **lens** ectoderm (Plate 10, Fig 5).

The **heart** is encountered in more caudal levels (Plate 11, Figs. 1–3). The **bulbus cordis** is present at the level of the **metencephalon** (Plate 11, Figs. 1, 2). Also present at this level are the **notochord** (not readily visible in Plate 11, Figs. 1, 2), **dorsal aortae,** and **foregut.** The space surrounding the heart is the **pericardial cavity** (lined with **somatic mesoderm** above and **splanchnic mesoderm** below), and the bulbus cordis is suspended in this cavity by the **dorsal mesocardium.**

The bulbus cordis is continuous caudally with the **ventricle** (Plate 11, Figs. 1, 2). (Note that the ventricle joins a third region of the heart more caudally, the **sinoatrial region;** Plate 11, Figs. 2, 3.) The two layers of the ventricle, the **endocardium** and **myocardium,** are widely separated by the **cardiac jelly** (Plate 11, Figs. 3, 4). Note that this extracellular material has a complex structure, consisting of numerous slender fibrils and tiny, spherical bodies. Many elegant investigations have concentrated on determining the chemical constituents of the cardiac jelly and their role in the morphogenesis of the heart.

The division of the brain at the level of the ventricle is the **myelencephalon** (Plate 11, Fig. 3). The **skin ectoderm** lateral to the myelencephalon has thickened (forming the **auditory placodes**) and (in the embryo shown in Plate 11, Fig. 3) invaginated, forming the **auditory vesicles.** Each auditory vesicle consists of a bowl-shaped depression in surface views of intact embryos (Plate 11, Fig. 5).

The **foregut** is present at the levels of the bulbus cordis and ventricle. The floor of the foregut is thickened and evaginated at the level of the ventricle, forming the **thyroid rudiment** (Plate 11, Fig. 3). More caudally, the **cranial intestinal portal** is present and, consequently, the gut has not yet formed. The embryo has a relatively simple organization in areas caudal to the foregut, consisting of three germ layers arranged in dorsoventral sequence (Plate 11, Fig. 6; Plate 12, Fig. 1). The outer (dorsal) surface of the embryo consists of **skin ectoderm.** The lower (ventral) surface consists of **endoderm.** The **mesoderm** occupies most of the area between these two layers, except in the central region occupied by the ectoderm-derived **spinal cord.** The mesoderm is subdivided into the midline **notochord** (ventral to the spinal cord), the **somites** (flanking the spinal cord), the ill-defined **nephrotome,** and the **lateral plate** (subdivided into an upper layer of **somatic mesoderm** and a lower layer of **splanchnic mesoderm**; the space between these two layers is the **coelom**). The **dorsal aortae** (also derived from mesoderm) lie beneath the nephrotomes and lateral portions of the somites.

A neural tube has not yet formed at more caudal levels. Depending on the exact level, a **neural groove** (flanked by **neural folds**) or a flat **neural plate** is present. The **notochord** occupies the midline, beneath the neural groove and neural plate. The remainder of the mesoderm at these levels consists of the **segmental plates** (Plate 12, Fig. 2), which merge laterally without distinct boundaries with mesoderm that will *later* form the **nephrotomes** and **lateral plates.**

A short **primitive streak** is present at the caudal end of the embryo (Plate 12, Fig. 3). Three well-defined germ layers are present lateral to the streak. Medially, cells are involuting through the streak to contribute to the mesodermal layer. A pair of poorly defined **primitive ridges** and a shallow **primitive groove** can be identified.

Micrographs of tissue blocks sectioned sagittally and then examined by scanning electron microscopy greatly aid beginning students in visualizing embryos in three dimensions. Plate 12, Fig. 4 shows such a micrograph of an embryo slightly more developed than most 33-hour embryos. Most of the major subdivisions of the brain are clearly visible (that is, the **diencephalon, mesencephalon, metencephalon,** and **myelencephalon**), as well as associated structures such as the **infundibulum** and left **optic vesicle.** Also visible are small sections of the **notochord** and associated mesoderm, **foregut, oral membrane, cranial intestinal portal, sinoatrial region,** and the ectoderm-lined **subcephalic pocket.**

C. STRUCTURE AND FUNCTION OF THE REPRODUCTIVE SYSTEM OF THE ADULT HEN

Aids: Fig. I; G, Chap. 11, Fig. 20; M, Figs. 144–146.

Adult hens possess a functional reproductive system (**ovary** and **oviduct**) only on the *left* side of the body. The fully developed ovary (Fig. I) consists of a mass of protruding **follicles.** It usually contains 5–6 larger follicles and many smaller ones. The smallest follicles are called **primary follicles.** The larger ones are rapidly **growing follicles,** the largest of which is about to rupture within an area called the **stigma.** The rupture of the follicle and the release of its contained **ovum** constitute **ovulation.** Each ovulation is apparently triggered by a sudden release of **luteinizing hormone (LH)** from the **anterior pituitary gland (adenohypophysis).** The ovary illustrated in Figure I also contains a **collapsed follicle** from which an ovum has just escaped (labeled: ovum after ovulation) through the ruptured stigma.

The fully developed oviduct is a highly differentiated organ and is subdivided into five distinct regions: **infundibulum, magnum, isthmus, shell gland,** and **vagina.** The first subdivision of the oviduct is the **infundibulum.** It is expanded at its opened end as a delicate, funnel-shaped structure with processes called **fimbria** along its margin. The **ovum** enters the opening of the infundibulum, the **ostium,** within 15 minutes after ovulation. The **outer vitelline membrane** is added to the ovum within the infundibulum, or perhaps within the next subdivision of the oviduct, the **magnum.** The ovum remains in the infundibulum for about 15 minutes before it is carried by peristalsis to the magnum.

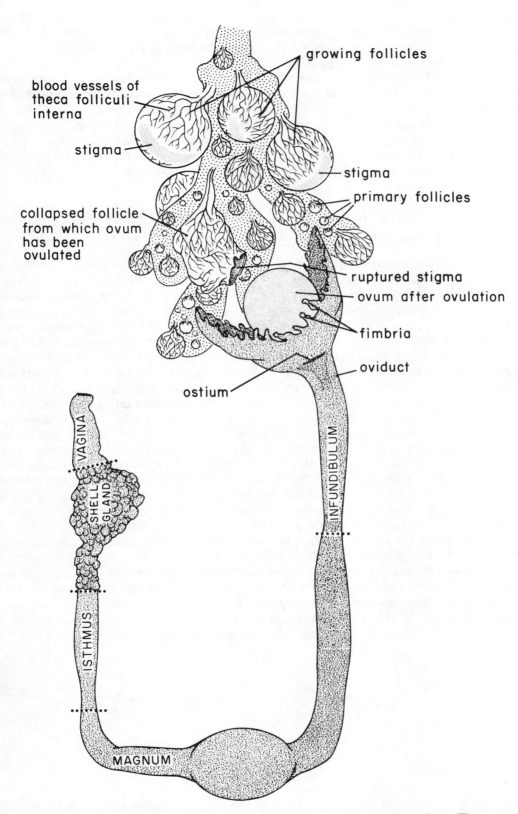

growing follicles

blood vessels of
theca folliculi
interna

stigma

collapsed follicle
from which ovum
has been
ovulated

stigma

primary follicles

ruptured stigma

ovum after ovulation

fimbria

oviduct

ostium

VAGINA

SHELL GLAND

INFUNDIBULUM

ISTHMUS

MAGNUM

Fig. I. Drawing of the functional reproductive system of the mature hen. The ovary is the lobulated structure at the top of the drawing; the subdivisions of the oviduct are illustrated below it. The magnum is greatly distended by the passage of an ovum.

There is no clear line of demarcation between the infundibulum and the longest subdivision of the oviduct, the **magnum.** Principally **albumen (egg white)** is added to the ovum in the magnum. Albumen is a mixture of proteins, most of which protect the embryo from infection. It takes about 3 hours for the ovum to traverse the magnum.

The next region of the oviduct, the **isthmus,** secretes the **inner** and **outer shell membranes.** The ovum remains within the isthmus for about 1 hour and is then carried to the **shell gland.** The major function of the shell gland is formation of the calcified **shell,** a process that requires about 20 hours. The ovum is retained in the shell gland during this period by a sphincter muscle that separates the shell gland from the last region of the oviduct, the **vagina.** During laying of the bird's egg, or **oviposition,** the sphincter muscle is relaxed and the egg is rapidly forced through the vagina to the outside by contractions of the shell gland and abdominal musculature.

D. OOGENESIS, FERTILIZATION, AND CLEAVAGE

Aids: Fig. J; BR, Figs. 9.19, 9.20; HV, Figs. 2–9; L, Fig. 8.4; M, Fig. 147.

Development of the **ovum (oogenesis)** begins in the *embryonic* left ovary with formation of small cells called **oogonia.** These cells rapidly increase in number by mitotic division. *Before* the embryo hatches, oogonia stop dividing mitotically and enlarge slightly to form **primary oocytes,** 2 mm in diameter. Each chromosome and its contained **DNA** are replicated early in the primary oocyte stage. Shortly *after* hatching, each primary oocyte becomes enclosed by a single layer of cells, called **follicle cells,** derived from the surface layer of the ovary. The composite structure, consisting of a primary oocyte enclosed by a layer of follicle cells, is called a **primary follicle.** These structures cause the surface of the ovary to bulge outward (Fig. I). Starting at puberty, and at intervals thereafter, a group of primary follicles begins to enlarge rapidly due to the accumulation of **yolk** by the primary oocytes. Yolk accumulation is principally stimulated by **follicle stimulating hormone (FSH)** from the **anterior pituitary gland.** Yolk components are synthesized by the hen's liver, transported to the blood vessels in the connective tissue surrounding the follicle, the **theca folliculi interna,** and then transported to the primary oocyte via the follicle cells. Each primary follicle increases in diameter from about 5 mm to 35 mm as a result of this accumulation of yolk. As the yolk accumulates, most of the cytoplasm of the oocyte is crowded off to one side as a small circular disc, the **blastodisc,** approximately 3.5 mm in diameter. The blastodisc contains the enlarged nucleus of the primary oocyte, the so-called **germinal vesicle.** Meanwhile, during the rapid growth phase, the **inner vitelline membrane** forms between the **plasmalemma** of the primary oocyte and the adjacent follicle cells.

The primary oocyte undergoes the **first meiotic division** shortly before ovulation occurs. The meiotic spindle involved in this division forms within the blastodisc, and as the division is completed a tiny **first polar body** is pinched off between the inner vitelline membrane and the large **secondary oocyte.** The latter contains most of the yolk plus the blastodisc. The spindle for the **second meiotic division** forms within the blastodisc soon after the first meiotic division occurs, and the second meiotic division proceeds to the metaphase stage and then stops. The ovum (although still a secondary oocyte arrested in the metaphase stage of the second meiotic division) is sufficiently mature to

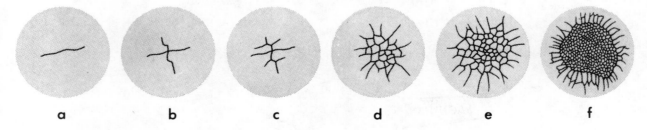

Fig. J. Drawings of early cleavage stages of the chick blastoderm removed from the yolk and viewed from the upper surface. (a) 2-cell stage showing first cleavage furrow; (b) 4-cell stage showing first and second cleavage furrows; (c) 8-cell stage showing two third-cleavage furrows in addition to the first and second; (d) approximate 32-cell stage; (e) and (f) progressively more advanced cleavage stages.

be fertilized at this point and is therefore ready for ovulation. One ovum will be ovulated daily over a period of 2 or more days, constituting a **clutch** of ova. Ovulation will then cease for at least 1 day, after which it will resume in a new clutch of ova.

Following ovulation the ovum enters the infundibulum of the oviduct, the site of **fertilization.** **Sperm** must penetrate the *inner* (and often the *outer*) vitelline membrane to reach the surface of the blastodisc. To do this they pass through large gaps, or pores, in the outer vitelline membrane and then digest pathways through the inner vitelline membrane. Fertilization can no longer occur after addition of albumen in the magnum. Recall that at ovulation the ovum is a secondary oocyte arrested in the metaphase stage of the second meiotic division. The second meiotic division is completed as a successful sperm contacts and penetrates the blastodisc, resulting in formation of a **second polar body** and a **mature ovum** containing the **female pronucleus.** The sperm nucleus enlarges to form the **male pronucleus** within the cytoplasm of the blastodisc, and the two pronuclei closely approach one another. The ovum remains as a secondary oocyte arrested in the metaphase stage of the second meiotic division if it is not fertilized, and the cytoplasmic cap on the yolk remains as the undeveloped blastodisc.

The blastodisc initiates **cleavage** (that is, it partially subdivides by mitosis into cells called **blastomeres**) following fertilization and is subsequently designated as the **blastoderm.** Cleavage occurs only within the cytoplasm (the yolk is not cleaved), and the **cleavage furrows** neither extend all the way to the periphery of the cytoplasm nor cut entirely through its thickness. Cleavage in the hen's ovum is therefore classified as **partial (meroblastic);** it is also classified as **discoidal** because it is restricted to the circular disc of cytoplasm.

Cleavage normally begins as the fertilized ovum enters the isthmus of the oviduct, approximately 3.5 hours after ovulation. The first cleavage furrow (Fig. Ja) extends across the central portion of the cytoplasm, partially separating it into two blastomeres. The second cleavage furrow forms at approximately right angles to the first and about 15 minutes later (Fig. Jb). The result is four partially separated blastomeres. The blastoderm usually undergoes the third cleavage, while the ovum is still within the isthmus (Fig. Jc). Two third-cleavage furrows form at approximately right angles to the second-cleavage furrow and parallel to the first, forming eight partially separated blastomeres. Later cleavages usually take place in the shell gland (Figs. Jd–Jf). The size and shape of the blastomeres become variable by the 32-cell stage (Fig. Jd). At this time it is possible to distinguish **central blastomeres,** which appear to be completely bounded in surface view, from **marginal blastomeres,** which still are incompletely separated from one another in surface view. The central blastomeres are separated from the yolk by a cavity, the **subgerminal cavity,** whereas the marginal blastomeres contact the yolk. More advanced cleavage stages (Figs. Je, Jf) possess increased numbers of smaller blastomeres, some formed by division of marginal blastomeres. The central portion of the blastoderm will probably be more than one cell thick by the stage illustrated by Fig. Jf. This is because cleavage furrows also form horizontally in this region, separating outer cells from inner cells.

E. FORMATION OF THE HYPOBLAST

Aid: Fig. K; S, Fig. 9.24.

While the developing ovum is still present in the shell gland, and after formation of the subgerminal cavity beneath the central cells, two distinct regions of the blastoderm can be readily distinguished in surface view: the lighter, central **area pellucida,** and the darker, peripheral **area opaca.** A lower layer of large, yolky cells forms beneath the area pellucida. This layer of cells is called the **hypoblast** (Fig. Ka). The surface layer of the area pellucida is called the **epiblast** following formation of the hypoblast.

The mechanism of hypoblast formation is unclear. However, observations and experiments suggest that cells separate from the area pellucida and move inward (that is, they **delaminate,** or **polyinvaginate**), forming the more central portion of the hypoblast. Other cells migrate centripetally, from the area opaca, to form the more peripheral area of the hypoblast. Hypoblast formation is initiated caudally and progressively occurs more cranially. The fertilized egg is usually laid during the stage of hypoblast formation. Further development of the egg requires incubation.

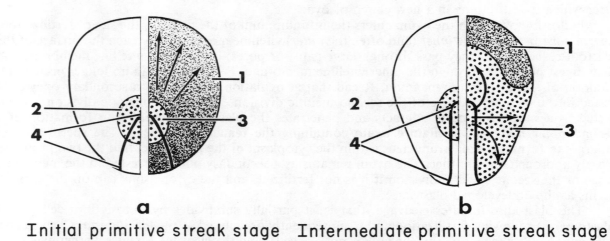

a
Initial primitive streak stage

b
Intermediate primitive streak stage

c
Definitive primitive streak stage

d
Head process stage

Fig. K. Schematic drawings of the area pellucida showing the formation of the ingressed endoderm and the displacement of the hypoblast. The epiblast is shown on
the left side of each diagram, but not on the right side. Arrows indicate the direction of displacement of the hypoblast in Fig. Ka and directions of migration of
the ingressed endodermal cells in Figs. Kb, Kc.

1. Hypoblast
2. Prospective endoderm
3. Endoderm
4. Primitive streak
5. Head process
6. Germ cell crescent

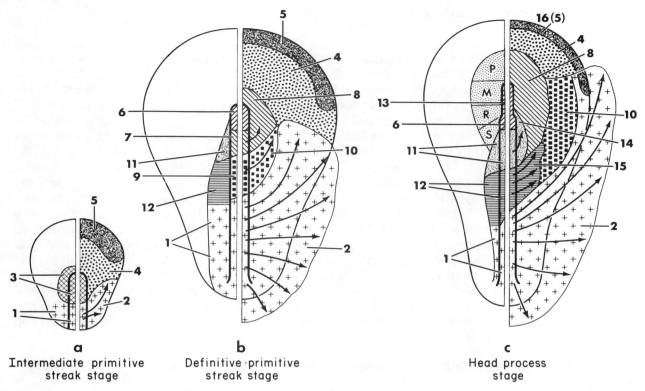

a
Intermediate primitive
streak stage

b
Definitive primitive
streak stage

c
Head process
stage

Fig. L. Schematic drawings of the area pellucida showing the formation of the subdivisions of the ingressed mesoderm. The epiblast is shown on the left side of each diagram, but not on the
right side. Arrows indicate the directions of migration of the ingressed mesodermal cells. The
boundaries of the primitive streak and head process are indicated by a heavy black line. P, M,
R, and S represent, respectively, prospective prosencephalon, mesencephalon,
rhombencephalon, and spinal cord of the left half of the neural plate.

1. Prospective extraembryonic
   mesoderm
2. Extraembryonic mesoderm
3. Prospective head mesenchyme,
   prospective notochord
4. Endoderm
5. Hypoblast

6. Prospective notochord
7. Prospective head mesenchyme
8. Head mesenchyme
9. Prospective heart mesoderm
10. Heart mesoderm
11. Prospective segmental plate
    mesoderm

12. Prospective lateral plate
    mesoderm
13. Head process
14. Segmental plate
    mesoderm
15. Lateral plate mesoderm
16. Germ cell crescent

F. GASTRULATION

Our understanding of events occurring during **gastrulation** (the process of germ-layer formation) has been clarified by experiments initially using vital dyes (see Exercise 8) and then **tritiated
thymidine** as a **cell marker.** Tritiated thymidine is incorporated specifically in **DNA,** thus radioac-
tively labeling cells. Specific sectors of the epiblast from labeled donor embryos are used to replace
corresponding sectors of unlabeled host embryos of the same stage. Movements of labeled cells can
then be followed precisely during gastrulation and their fates determined. Another technique has
been employed more recently to avoid the use of radioactivity. Sectors of *quail* epiblasts are
transplanted to *chick* epiblasts to form **chimeras** (that is, mixtures of different cell types) produced
from two species. Transplanted quail cells and their descendants can be distinguished from chick
cells in histological sections treated with the **Feulgen procedure** to stain **DNA.** Quail cells contain a
central mass of nucleolar-associated **heterochromatin**; in contrast, heterochromatin is finely dis-
persed in chick cells. Information obtained by the use of these techniques is used to construct **prospective fate maps.**

1. Location and migration of the prospective endoderm.

Aid: Fig. K.

Labeling experiments have clearly demonstrated that the **prospective endoderm** is located in an oval-shaped region of the epiblast of prestreak stages, around and within the cranial half of the initial **primitive streak** (Fig. Ka). The primitive streak is a midline thickening of the epiblast. At the initial primitive streak stage, prospective endoderm is migrating inward through the cranial half of the primitive streak. The inward migration of epiblast cells through the primitive streak is designated as **ingression.** The ingressed **endoderm** enters the **hypoblast** layer and begins to displace the hypoblast craniolaterally (Fig. Ka). Ingression of prospective endoderm and displacement of the hypoblast continue rapidly in the intermediate primitive streak stage (Fig. Kb). By the definitive primitive streak stage, the only prospective endoderm still in the epiblast is located in the cranial end of the primitive streak (Fig. Kc). The primitive streak has attained its maximal length at this stage, extending about two-thirds the length of the area pellucida. Elongation of the primitive streak is responsible for the change in outline of the area pellucida from circular (Fig. Ka) to pear-shaped (Fig. Kc). By the head process stage, the epiblast no longer contains any prospective endoderm because all of it has undergone ingression into the interior (Fig. Kd). The displaced hypoblast becomes condensed into a crescent-shaped area at the craniolateral margin of the area pellucida. This area is designated as the **germ cell crescent** because it contains the **primordial germ cells,** presumably of hypoblast origin. The primordial germ cells *later* undergo extensive migration and enter the embryonic gonads where they form **oogonia** in the female (see Chapter 3, Section D) and **spermatogonia** in the male.

2. Location and migration of the prospective mesoderm.

Aid: Fig. L.

By the intermediate primitive streak stage (Fig. La) ingression of the **prospective extraembryonic mesoderm,** through the caudal half of the primitive streak, and the craniolateral internal spreading of the ingressed **extraembryonic mesoderm** have begun. This first mesoderm to ingress is designated as extraembryonic because it does not contribute to the body of the embryo. Located around and within the cranial half of the intermediate primitive streak are the **prospective head mesenchyme** and **prospective notochord.** These subdivisions of **prospective embryonic mesoderm** have not yet started their ingression at this stage.

At the definitive primitive streak stage (Fig. Lb), ingression of the **prospective extraembryonic mesoderm** through the caudal half of the primitive streak continues, and the internal spreading of the ingressed **extraembryonic mesoderm** is now caudolateral as well as craniolateral. All the **prospective notochord** now occupies the cranial end of the primitive streak. **Prospective head mesenchyme** is undergoing ingression just caudal to the prospective notochord, and the ingressed **head mesenchyme** is spreading internally. Similarly, **prospective heart mesoderm** is ingressing just caudal to the prospective head mesenchyme, and the ingressed **heart mesoderm** is spreading internally. **Prospective segmental plate mesoderm** and **prospective lateral plate mesoderm** are located in the epiblast at this stage, just lateral to the cranial half of the primitive streak. These subdivisions of prospective embryonic mesoderm have not yet started their ingression.

At the head process stage (Fig. Lc), ingression of the **prospective extraembryonic mesoderm** and the internal spreading of the ingressed **extraembryonic mesoderm** are still under way. The **prospective head mesenchyme** and **prospective heart mesoderm** have now completed their ingression. The **prospective notochord** has already started ingressing through the cranial end of the primitive streak by this stage, forming the so-called **head process.** The head process is a mesodermal tongue of cells that subsequently forms the cranial part of the **notochord. Prospective segmental plate mesoderm** and **prospective lateral plate mesoderm** are ingressing just caudal to the prospective notochord, and the ingressed **segmental plate mesoderm** and **lateral plate mesoderm** are spreading internally.

3. Summary of epiblast ingression during gastrulation.

Initial Primitive Streak Stage
Prospective endoderm is ingressing through the cranial end of the primitive streak.

Intermediate Primitive Streak Stage

Prospective endoderm continues to ingress through the cranial end of the primitive streak.

Prospective extraembryonic mesoderm is ingressing through the caudal half of the primitive streak.

Definitive Primitive Streak Stage

Prospective endoderm continues to ingress through the cranial end of the primitive streak.

Prospective head mesenchyme and *prospective heart mesoderm* are ingressing through the cranial half of the primitive streak.

Prospective extraembryonic mesoderm continues to ingress through the caudal half of the primitive streak.

Head Process Stage

Ingression of *prospective endoderm, prospective head mesenchyme,* and *prospective heart mesoderm* is complete.

Prospective notochord, prospective segmental plate mesoderm, and *prospective lateral plate mesoderm* are ingressing through the cranial half of the primitive streak.

Prospective extraembryonic mesoderm continues to ingress through the caudal half of the primitive streak.

4. Location and changes of the prospective ectoderm.

Aid: Fig. L.

The region of the epiblast that does not undergo ingression remains on the surface as the **ectoderm.** The prospective ectoderm expands, as ingression of prospective endoderm and mesoderm occurs, spreading toward the primitive streak (that is, it undergoes **epiboly**) to replace those areas of the epiblast that have ingressed. At the head process stage (Fig. Lc), the ectoderm overlying the head mesenchyme, head process, and segmental plate mesoderm has thickened, forming the **neural plate,** the major rudiment of the central nervous system. Neural plate formation is induced principally by the mesoderm lying beneath it. The approximate locations of the **prospective prosencephalon, mesencephalon, rhombencephalon,** and **spinal cord** are indicated in Fig. Lc. Note that mesoderm has not yet spread at this stage into the cranial portion of the area pellucida. This area lacking mesoderm is called the **proamnion;** its chief characteristic is that it consists of only ectoderm and endoderm.

5. Location of epiblast areas prior to gastrulation.

Aid: Fig. M.

Cell-marking experiments have demonstrated the fates of different areas of the epiblast during gastrulation. A **prospective fate map** is a schematic representation of the location of these areas prior to the onset of gastrulation. Note that prospective extraembryonic mesoderm is positioned at the level of formation of the caudal half of the primitive streak, through which it later ingresses (Fig. M). All remaining subdivisions of prospective mesoderm and prospective endoderm are positioned at the level of formation of the cranial half of the primitive streak, through which they later ingress. Prospective ectoderm is located peripheral to the regions of the epiblast that undergo ingression.

G. 18-HOUR CHICK EMBRYOS

1. Whole mounts.

Aids: Fig. N; Plate 13; A–V#1; M, Figs. 151, 154; S, Fig. 9.25.

A diagrammatic surface and cross-sectional view of the cranial half of the blastoderm and definitive primitive streak is illustrated by Fig. N. The cranial end of the primitive streak is thick-

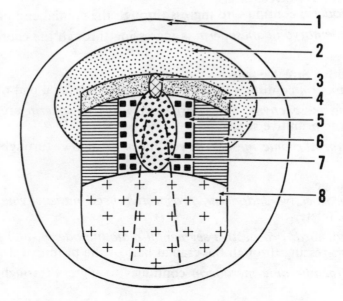

Fig. M. Prospective fate map of the chick epiblast. The approximate site of primitive streak formation is indicated by dashed lines.

1. Prospective ectoderm
2. Prospective neural plate
3. Prospective head mesenchyme, prospective notochord
4. Prospective segmental plate mesoderm
5. Prospective heart mesoderm
6. Prospective lateral plate mesoderm
7. Prospective endoderm
8. Prospective extraembryonic mesoderm

ened, constituting the **primitive knot (Hensen's node).** It partially surrounds a depression, the **primitive pit,** which is continuous caudally with the **primitive groove.** The **primitive ridges** lie lateral to the primitive groove. Note that cells of the **epiblast** are tightly apposed to one another, forming an epithelium. The outer ends of the epiblast cells become narrowed within the primitive groove, and the inner ends widen, forming the so-called **bottle (flask) cells. Filopodia** form at the broad inner ends of the bottle cells as the narrow outer connections to neighboring epiblast cells are lost. The ingressed cells then migrate away from the primitive streak, apparently through the action of their filopodia. The ingressed mesoderm consists of loosely packed, irregularly shaped cells (that is, mesenchyme) rather than an epithelium.

Examine whole mounts of embryos resembling Plate 13, Figs. 1–3. Identify all parts of the **primitive streak** and the **head process** when present. Although not visible in whole mounts, an ectodermal thickening, the **neural plate,** overlies the head process and adjacent ingressed mesoderm. Identify the **area pellucida** and **area opaca.**

Examine whole mounts of embryos resembling Plate 13, Fig. 4. Note the distinct curved line just cranial to the tip of the head process. This line is the beginning of the **head fold of the body,** a ventrad directed fold of ectoderm and endoderm that establishes the cranial boundary of the head. It very quickly seems to undercut the head, forming two cavities: the ectoderm-lined **subcephalic pocket** and the endoderm-lined **foregut.**

2. Scanning electron microscopy.

Aids: Plates 14, 15.

Dorsal views of intact embryos viewed with scanning electron microscopy reveal the subtle changes that occur in morphology during development from the definitive primitive streak stage to

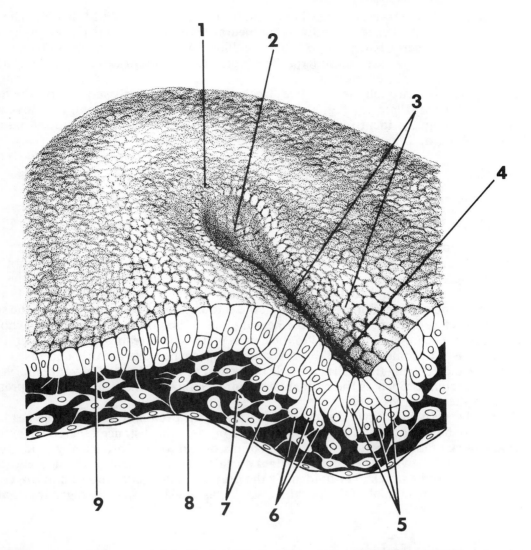

Fig. N. Drawing of the cranial half of a blastoderm at the definitive primitive streak stage. The blastoderm has been cut transversely.

1. Primitive knot
2. Primitive pit
3. Primitive ridges
4. Primitive groove
5. Ingressing prospective
   mesodermal cells

6. Bottle cells
7. Filopodia
8. Endodermal cell
9. Epiblast cell

the head process stage, and, finally, to the early head-fold stage (Plate 14, Figs. 1–3). At the definitive primitive streak stage (Plate 14, Fig. 1), the **primitive streak** occupies the caudal two-thirds of the embryo, and the **primitive knot, pit, groove,** and **ridges** can be identified. Cellular debris fills the primitive pit and cranial half of the primitive groove. At the head-process stage (Plate 14, Fig. 2), the position of the **head process** beneath the **neural plate** is indicated by a shallow trough. Finally, at the early head-fold stage (Plate 14, Fig. 3), the boundaries of the neural plate and the beginning of the **head fold of the body** can be recognized.

Slices through the blastoderm at the early head-fold stage show the simple structure of the area of the embryo cranial to the primitive streak (Plate 14, Figs. 4, 5). The early **head fold of the body** is indicated in midsagittal slices by a shallow depression that is beginning to undercut the cranial end of the **neural plate** (Plate 14, Fig. 4). The head fold consists of only two germ layers (an outer layer of **skin ectoderm** and an inner layer of ingressed **endoderm**), but just caudal to the head fold, three layers are present. These layers can best be seen in transverse slices (Plate 14, Fig. 5). The outer layer of the blastoderm is thickened medially as the **neural plate**, but remains thin laterally as the **skin ectoderm**. The mesoderm is organized into a midline **head process**, which is flanked by loosely organized cells of the ingressed **mesoderm**. The ingressed **endoderm** forms a single, flattened layer of cells beneath the ingressed mesoderm.

Transverse slices through the primitive streak at any of these early stages show the morphology of the **primitive knot** (Plate 15, Fig. 1), **primitive pit** (Plate 15, Fig. 2), and **primitive groove** and **ridges** (Plate 15, Fig. 3). Identify these structures as well as the **epiblast**, ingressed **mesoderm**, ingressed **endoderm**, and **ingressing prospective mesodermal cells**.

H. 24-HOUR CHICK EMBRYOS

1. Whole mounts.

Aids: Plate 16; A–V#1; A, Fig. 528; HU, Figs. 103, 104; M, Figs. 159, 160; P, Fig. 47.

Several major advances have occurred by this stage. The head process has transformed into an epithelial cord constituting the cranial part of the **notochord**. The remainder of the notochord, extending the length of the embryo, has formed from continual ingression of prospective notochord cells through the cranial end of the primitive streak. Four to six pairs of **somites** typically have developed from the **segmental plates**. Although the ectoderm overlying the region of the somites and segmental plates has thickened to form the **neural plate**, it cannot be readily seen in whole mounts. Distinct **neural folds** are present cranial to the neural plate. They are located at the lateral margins of the **neural groove**. In some embryos they may have approached one another and fused, closing the neural groove and forming the **neural tube**. If the neural tube has formed in your embryo, note that its cranial end remains open as the **cranial neuropore**. Similarly, the neural tube (if present) opens caudally into the neural groove.

The head usually juts forward some distance above the **proamnion**, so that the head fold of the body seems to have undercut the head over a considerable distance, thereby lengthening the **subcephalic pocket** and **foregut**. The lateral margins of the foregut are usually quite distinct. The foregut opens caudally via the **cranial intestinal portal**. The caudal end of the notochord is continuous with the **primitive streak**. Try to identify the **primitive knot, pit, groove**, and **ridges**. Note that the embryo is forming cranial to the primitive streak, as the latter steadily regresses (that is, moves caudad) and shortens.

2. Serial transverse sections.

Aids: Plate 17; A–V#1; BR, Fig. 12.39; HU, Fig. 102; HV, Fig. 2–28; L, Fig. 9.16; M, Figs. 162–167; P, Figs. 51, 59, 60.

Position your slide on the microscope stage so that, when viewed through the microscope, each section is oriented as in Plate 17, Figs. 1–4. Quickly trace through your sections until you find one closely resembling Plate 17, Fig. 4. At this level the **notochord** and **segmental plates** lie beneath the **neural plate**. The ectoderm that has thickened to form the neural plate is designated the **neural ectoderm**. It can be readily distinguished from the much thinner, adjacent **skin ectoderm**. In most embryos the neural plate is *not* a flat layer of cells. Typically it is sharply bent in the midline, where it overlies the notochord (Plate 17, Fig. 4). Begin tracing sections *anteriorly* and observe that the regions of continuity between the neural and skin ectoderm begin to fold, forming the **neural folds**. Each fold thus consists of an inner layer of neural ectoderm and an outer layer of skin ectoderm (Plate 17, Fig. 3). Concomitant with formation and elevation of the neural folds, the **neural groove** forms as a space lined with neural ectoderm. Continue tracing sections *anteriorly*. In some embryos the neural folds will approach one another and fuse, forming the **neural tube** (Plate 17, Fig. 2). As the neural tube is traced craniad in these embryos, note the appearance of the **cranial neuropore**. Fusion of neural folds has not yet occurred in other embryos.

Locate a section cut through the cranial end of the head and trace sections *posteriorly*. Identify the two-layered **proamnion** and the **subcephalic pocket**. The two layers of the proamnion sometimes are widely separated. A mass of cells appears beneath the neural ectoderm in more posterior sections. This mass is the endodermal cranial wall of the **foregut**. The foregut cavity appears as sections are traced posteriorly, and the foregut widens rapidly. Note the sparsity of **head mesenchyme** at these levels. Identify the **oral membrane**, if present, and the **notochord** between the foregut endoderm and neural ectoderm. At about this level note that mesoderm is wedged between ectoderm and endoderm on each side of the proamnion. This mesoderm is split into somatic and splanchnic layers that bound two enlarged portions of the **coelom** (Plate 17, Fig. 1). Also note at this level that two small portions of the coelom are located beneath the foregut within the body of the embryo.

Locate the last sections through the subcephalic pocket. The skin ectoderm covering the lateral surfaces of the body now becomes continuous with the ectoderm of the somatopleure on either side. At the point of continuity between these two regions, a distinct notch is formed by the somatopleural component of the **lateral body folds** (Plate 17, Fig. 2). The lateral body folds consist of two components, somatopleure and splanchnopleure, and are direct continuations of the head fold of the body. Verify that these body folds are directly continuous by examining models, if available. The lateral body folds delimit the body from extraembryonic regions laterally. At about this level note that on each side the two portions of the coelom, the enlarged portion and the small portion, are continuous, forming a large coelomic space (Plate 17, Fig. 2). These large spaces project toward the midline as the **rudiments of the pericardial cavity**. They later fuse to form a single cavity surrounding the heart.

Identify the **cranial intestinal portal**, at about this level or in slightly more posterior sections, and note the distinct thickening of the splanchnic mesoderm on either side of the midline (Plate 17, Fig. 2). These thickenings are the **cardiac primordia**. Cells emerge medially from each cardiac primordium at a later stage and organize into an **endocardial tube**. These tubes fuse ventral to the foregut in craniocaudal sequence, due to the action of the splanchnopleural component of the **lateral body folds** (see Exercise 10), thus forming the lining of the heart, the **endocardium**. The remaining cells of each cardiac primordium form the **myocardium** (see P, Figs. 59, 60).

As you continue to trace sections posteriorly, note that the embryo flattens dorsoventrally and that the mesoderm adjacent to the neural ectoderm progressively increases in density as you approach the level of the first pair of **somites**. Try to identify the first **intersomitic furrows** and successive somites and furrows as you continue to trace sections posteriorly. Approximately how many pairs of somites does your embryo possess? Note that there is little, if any, distinction between the **nephrotome** and **lateral plate** on each side.

The **neural groove** becomes progressively shallower as you continue to trace sections posteriorly and the notochord widens, changing in shape from round to oval. Identify the **segmental plates** caudal to the somites. The **neural folds** disappear in more posterior sections and the **neural plate** can then be identified. As you continue caudally, the notochord gradually increases in size and becomes indistinct, seeming to fuse with the neural plate. You are now at the level of the **primitive knot**. You can usually identify the **primitive pit** slightly caudal to this level. It is continuous caudally with the **primitive groove**. There may be discontinuities in the primitive groove in some embryos.

3. Serial sagittal sections.

Aids: Plate 17, Figs. 5, 6; A–V#1; A, Fig. 529; P, Fig. 50E.

First examine your slide with the naked eye. Only the darkest sections are cut through the body of the embryo. Position your slide on the microscope stage so that when viewed through the microscope the neural tube is uppermost (Plate 17, Figs. 5, 6). Quickly trace sections until you first encounter the one showing the greatest number of **somites**. How many somite pairs are present? Identify the **head mesenchyme** and **segmental plate**. Try to identify the **rudiment of the pericardial cavity** in this section or in sections nearer to the midline.

Select a section resembling Plate 17, Fig. 5. Identify the **proamnion, subcephalic pocket, foregut, cranial intestinal portal**, and **oral membrane**, if present. Is a **neural tube** present in your embryo? If so, identify the **cranial neuropore**. Also identify the **neural groove**, and more caudally, the **neural plate**. The **notochord** lies directly beneath the neural ectoderm and can be identified in the midsagittal plane. Try to identify the **primitive knot, pit**, and **groove**.

4. Scanning electron microscopy.

Aids: Plates 18, 19; L, Fig. 10.1.

Formation of the **neural tube** can be readily examined by scanning electron microscopy of the dorsal aspects of intact embryos (Plate 18, Figs. 1–3). The cranial end of the **neural plate** and the embryonic body are delineated by the **head fold of the body.** The lateral aspects of the neural plate become delineated from the **skin ectoderm** by the formation of the **neural folds.** The neural tube of the **mesencephalon** region is just about to form (Plate 18, Fig. 2), or has just formed (Plate 18, Fig. 3), in 24-hour embryos. After formation of the mesencephalon, the neural tube opens cranially as the **cranial neuropore** (Plate 18, Fig. 3; Plate 19, Fig. 1) and caudally into the **neural groove** (Plate 18, Fig. 3).

Note the presence of the **primitive streak** at the caudal end of the embryo. Identify the **primitive pit, groove,** and **ridges.**

Midsagittal slices reveal the action of the **head fold of the body** in formation of the endoderm-lined **foregut** and the ectoderm-lined **subcephalic pocket** (Plate 18, Fig. 4). The foregut opens caudally as the **cranial intestinal portal.**

Transverse cryofractures through 24-hour embryos reveal the major developmental events occurring during this stage. In less-developed 24-hour embryos, a neural tube has not yet formed and a broad **neural groove** (flanked by **neural folds**) is present in future brain regions (Plate 19, Fig. 2). A short **foregut,** which opens caudally via the **cranial intestinal portal,** is present in these embryos. A short **neural tube** has formed at the **mesencephalon** level in more advanced embryos (Plate 19, Figs. 3, 4), but a **neural groove** is still present more caudally. In these embryos the **cranial intestinal portal** is located considerably more caudally than in less-developed embryos. Similarly, in advanced embryos the **subcephalic pocket** extends farther caudally than in less-developed embryos. At levels slightly caudal to the cranial intestinal portal, the **foregut** has not yet formed and the lateral body folds are present (Plate 19, Fig. 4).

Note that at all levels of the developing brain, most of the space between the **skin ectoderm** and **endoderm** is filled with loosely packed **head mesenchymal cells** (Plate 19, Figs. 2–4). At the level of the future spinal cord (Plate 19, Fig. 5), however, this space is filled with mesoderm that has subdivided into a midline **notochord, somites,** ill-defined **nephrotomes,** and solid **lateral plates** (that is, lateral plates not yet split into **somatic** and **splanchnic mesoderm**).

I. SUMMARY OF DEVELOPMENT OF THE YOUNG CHICK EMBRYO

The embryo develops in craniocaudal sequence from germ layers established during gastrulation. Early developmental events following gastrulation can be summarized as follows:

1. Regional specialization of the mesoderm.

The ingressed mesoderm quickly becomes specialized. The mesoderm in the midline of the embryo forms a compact rod of cells, the notochord. Cranially, the rest of the mesoderm remains loosely packed as part of the head mesenchyme. More caudally, the mesoderm lateral to the notochord forms three distinct zones. The mesoderm immediately adjacent to each side of the notochord forms a thick band of cells, the segmental plate, which subsequently subdivides to form a row of somites. The mesoderm lateral to each row of somites forms a thin band of cells, the nephrotome. The lateromost mesoderm forms a thick plate of cells, the lateral plate, which splits into somatic and splanchnic layers bounding the coelom.

2. Formation of the neural tube.

The first indication of the formation of the central nervous system is the appearance of an ectodermal thickening, the neural plate. The neural folds form at the lateral margins of the neural plate. Each fold consists of an inner layer of neural ectoderm and an outer layer of skin ectoderm. As the neural folds form and elevate, a distinct neural groove forms. The neural folds progressively approach each other and fuse to form the neural tube. After fusion of the neural folds occurs, neural crest cells form and begin their migration, contributing to the head mesenchyme.

3. Formation and consequences of the body folds.

Aids: A–V#3; HV, Fig. 2–24; L, Figs. 10.5, 10.6; S, Fig. 11.61.

At first there is no indication as to how much of the blastoderm is destined to be *embryonic* and how much is *extraembryonic*. The first boundary of the embryo to become visible is the cranial boundary, which arises in the following way. Just cranial to the neural plate the ectoderm and endoderm of the proamnion begin to fold, forming the head fold of the body. The neural plate is rapidly expanding forward, and as it does so the head fold of the body seems to undercut the neural plate. To make this transformation clear, take two sheets of paper and superimpose them, considering the upper one the ectoderm, the lower one the endoderm. Hold the top edges of the papers firmly against a desk with your left hand; with your right hand grasp the bottom edges with your thumb beneath the sheets, and your other fingers above and pointing toward the top of the sheets. Then lift your right hand slightly above the desk and move it toward the top of the sheets. Both sheets of paper will elevate and project forward. This movement creates an internal bay in the endoderm, the foregut, and an external bay in the ectoderm, the subcephalic pocket. These bays are turned in opposite directions, the internal one opening into the subgerminal cavity caudally via the cranial intestinal portal, and the external one opening cranially onto the surface of the blastoderm. Simultaneously the cranial boundary of the head is created.

The lateral boundaries of the embryo are formed by the action of the lateral body folds, which are direct continuations of the head fold of the body. The lateral body folds differ from the head fold of the body in that they consist of somatopleure and splanchnopleure. The somatopleural component of these folds is involved in lengthening the subcephalic pocket. The splanchnopleural component is involved in lengthening the foregut and in swinging together the bilateral heart rudiments beneath the lengthening foregut. In addition, the splanchnopleural component brings together the paired rudiments of the pericardial cavity.

EXERCISE 6 Observations of Living Embryos (Avian Embryos at 18–33 Hours)

Materials

Fertile chicken eggs (incubated 18–25, 26–29, and 33–49 hours)
38 °C incubators
Finger bowls
Saline (NaCl, distilled water)
Microscope illuminators or high-intensity lamps
Stereomicroscopes (dissecting microscopes)
1% solution of neutral red in saline
1% solution of Nile blue sulfate in saline
0.05% solution of Nile blue sulfate in saline
Carbon/melted agar mixture (animal charcoal powder, mortar and pestle, agar,
    saline, hot plate, stirring rods)
5-ml disposable syringes
18-gauge needles

Obtain fertile chicken eggs incubated at 38 °C for 18–25, 26–29, and 33–49 hours. These eggs should contain, respectively, typical 18-, 24-, and 33-hour embryos. Carefully crack open the eggs against the side of a finger bowl half filled with warm saline (123 mM NaCl in distilled water). The crack in the shell should be held beneath the surface of the saline solution, and the two halves of the shell should be slowly pulled apart, releasing the egg contents into the solution. The side of the yolk containing the blastoderm should float to the upper surface of the bowl where the embryo can be readily observed. If not, use your fingertips to gently rotate the egg until the blastoderm is uppermost. Illuminate the blastoderm by placing an illuminator above and to the side of the blastoderm, so that light strikes its surface at about a 45° angle.

Two methods can be used to increase the contrast of the blastoderm relative to the yolk, aiding in the identification of embryonic structures. The simplest is to apply a drop of a 1% aqueous solution of vital stain (neural red or Nile blue sulfate) onto the vitelline membrane overlying the blastoderm. The second method requires injecting contrasting medium into the **subgerminal cavity**: a narrow cleft separating the area pellucida region of the blastoderm from the underlying yolk. Two solutions can be injected: a solution of 0.05% Nile blue sulfate in 123 mM saline, or a mixture of carbon and melted agar (grind animal charcoal powder with a mortar and pestle to a fine consistency; mix 3 g of the ground powder with 0.24 g agar and add 40 ml saline; heat the mixture almost to boiling while stirring; let the solution cool to 47° to 50°C and maintain it at this temperature to keep the agar melted; stir the mixture frequently). It is easier to inject a Nile blue sulfate solution than carbon/agar, but it quickly diffuses away and multiple injections are required if blastoderms are viewed over substantial periods. To inject the subgerminal cavity, take a 5-ml disposable syringe and fill it with one of the two solutions (work quickly if using the carbon/agar mixture, so that hardening does not occur). Attach an 18-gauge needle to the syringe, remove any air bubbles, insert the tip of the needle through the vitelline membranes slightly into the yolk just peripheral to the blastoderm, reorient the needle so that it lies within the yolk parallel to the surface of the blastoderm, and place the tip of the needle just beneath the center of the blastoderm. Slowly inject the solution and fill the subgerminal cavity.

Use the abridged Hamburger and Hamilton (1951) stage series appearing in Appendix III to stage your embryos. (Most of the illustrations shown in Appendix III were obtained from eggs injected subgerminally with carbon/agar and then photographed.) Draw the stages that you identify in the space below (and on the following page).

EXERCISE 7 Blastoderm Development in Culture
(Avian Embryos)

Materials

Materials from Exercise 6
Fertile chicken eggs (incubated 18–25, 26–29, and 33–49 hours)
Sterile paper towels
70% ethanol
Medium-sized scissors
Spoons
Blunt watchmaker's forceps
Fine-tipped watchmaker's forceps
Sterile pipettes
Sterile saline
Sterile finger bowls
Sterile petri dishes
Sterile beakers
Falcon, 35 x 10 mm, culture dishes
Thin albumen from fresh fertile eggs
Bacto-agar
Sterile saline (distilled water, NaCl)
Hot plate
Water bath
Plastic, covered food-storage container
Cotton
Safety glasses
Pasteur pipettes
Wide-mouth pipettes
Pipette bulbs
Razor blade knives (single-edge razor blades, two pairs of long-nose pliers, wooden han-
dles, nail polish)

Blastoderms will be cultured by modification of the method of Spratt (Spratt, N.T. Jr. [1947] Development *in vitro* of the early chick blastoderm explanted on yolk and albumen extract saline-agar substrate, *J. Exp. Zool.* 106:345–365). All procedures must be performed using sterile conditions. First clean your working area with paper towels soaked in 70% ethanol. Clean the bench top, dissecting microscopes, and all instruments (scissors, spoon, blunt and sharp watchmaker's forceps). Spread sterile (autoclaved) paper towels over the working area of the bench top. Have available sterile pipettes, saline (aqueous solution of 123 mM NaCl), and glassware (bowls, petri dishes, and beakers). Blastoderms will be cultured on an albumen/agar substrate in plastic culture dishes (Falcon, 35 x 10 mm).

Prepare the culture dishes by mixing together equal parts of *thin* albumen from fresh fertile eggs and a 0.6% solution of agar (Bacto-agar; Difco, Detroit, Michigan) in sterile 123 mM saline to produce a 0.3% agar concentration (the agar solution is first heated to boiling in a sterile beaker and then placed in a water bath at 47° to 50°C; the albumen also is placed in a sterile beaker in the same water bath and the temperatures of the two solutions are allowed to equilibrate before mixing). Maintain the mixture in a water bath at 47° to 50°C to keep the agar melted. Pour about 2.5 ml of the albumen/agar mixture into the bottom of each plastic dish. Cover each dish and refrigerate them in a humidified chamber until ready to use. (A plastic, covered food-storage container containing sterile paper towels soaked with sterile water makes an excellent, inexpensive chamber.)

Obtain typical 18-, 24-, and 33-hour embryos (18–25, 26–29, and 33–49 hours of incubation, respectively) as described in Appendix I (A. Whole Mounts), *but carry out all procedures under sterile conditions*. Begin by taking a piece of cotton moistened with 70% ethanol and wiping the shell of each egg (the cotton should be relatively dry, not soaking wet; *embryos will die if shells are soaked with ethanol*). Then crack open the shells and remove blastoderms as described in Appendix I, using sterile saline, glassware, and instruments. Transfer each blastoderm to a culture dish with a sterile wide-mouth pipette. (A Pasteur pipette makes an excellent wide-mouth pipette; see Exercise 1.) Use sterile forceps to position the blastoderm on the albumen/agar substrate, either dorsal side up or down, and to remove wrinkles. Remove most of the area opaca from the blastoderm so that only a narrow rim remains attached to the area pellucida. Fashion a small knife out of a single-edge razor blade to do this. Take a razor blade and two pairs of long-nose pliers; use one pair to hold the blade and the second to break off the smallest piece of edge possible. *Make sure you wear safety glasses when you do this, to protect your eyes from flying splinters.* Attach the piece of edge to a wooden handle using nail polish. Sterilize the blade prior to use by dipping it into 70% ethanol and then washing it in sterile saline to remove the ethanol, which is toxic to the embryo. Make sure that the blade is wet with sterile saline before it is touched to the blastoderm, to prevent the latter from sticking to the blade. Remove all the area opaca at the caudal end of the blastoderm (that is, cut into the area pellucida slightly); this facilitates embryo elongation. Use a fine-tipped pipette to remove excess saline from the dish, and cover each dish and return it to a humidified incubator at 38°C.

Use the space below (and on the following page) to sketch each blastoderm as it is set up in culture. Stage the embryo according to the criteria given in Appendix III. Carefully pass one of the tips of a fine-tipped watchmaker's forceps beneath the head of a typical 33-hour embryo. How far caudally (with respect to brain levels) can you place your forceps? What is the name of the space containing the forceps tip? Repeat this procedure with younger embryos. In such embryos, can you place the forceps tip as far as in older embryos? Why or why not?

Examine each blastoderm at convenient intervals over the next 24 hours and sketch them at each interval. Note if craniocaudal elongation of the embryo is inhibited. Also look for abnormal development of the neural tube. A high incidence of **neural tube defects** occurs in this culture system, especially if insufficient area opaca is removed.

EXERCISE 8 Mapping of Morphogenetic Movements
(Avian Embryos)

Materials

Materials from Exercises 6 and 7
Fertile chicken eggs (incubated 18–25 hours)
Spratt cultures
Powdered animal charcoal
Mortar and pestle
Cactus needles
Nile blue sulfate agar staining slides
Sterile saline
Sterile scalpel blades
Sterile watchmaker's forceps

Morphogenetic movements can be mapped in young blastoderms by applying marks to the surface of the blastoderm and then following their movements over time. Cells can be marked in a variety of ways. We will use two of the simplest: carbon particles and vital dyes. Collect typical 18-hour embryos (18–25 hours of incubation) using sterile conditions and set them up in modified Spratt cultures as described in Exercise 7. Blastoderms can be positioned either dorsal side up (to map morphogenetic movements in the epiblast) or ventral side up (to map morphogenetic movements in the endoderm).

Use powdered animal charcoal to mark blastoderms with carbon particles. Grind the powder to a fine consistency with a mortar and pestle. Use a fine needle to transfer a few of the particles to the surface of the blastoderm. Cactus needles work superbly for this purpose (see Exercise 4 for instructions for making cactus needles). Sterilize needles by dipping them into a beaker containing 70% ethanol and a second containing sterile saline; then allow them to dry. Stick the tip of a dried, sterile needle into the ground, powdered charcoal; a few particles will adhere to the tip. Gently touch the tip of the needle to the desired region on the surface of the blastoderm to deposit the particles.

Use agar impregnated with Nile blue sulfate to mark blastoderms with vital dyes (see Exercise 2 for instructions for making staining slides). Stain blastoderms by wetting a portion of an agar-coated staining slide (on the side containing the stained agar) with a drop of sterile saline, removing a small piece of agar with a sterile scalpel blade, picking up the piece with sterile forceps, and touching the *edge* of the agar to the blastoderm. Staining occurs within seconds.

Cover the cultures and reincubate them in humidified incubators at 38 °C. Remove the cultures at desired intervals over the next 24 hours to observe the displacement of the carbon particles or stain. Use the space below (and on the following page) to sketch the initial position of the marks and their new positions at each interval.

EXERCISE 9 Separation of Gastrulating and Neurulating Regions (Avian Embryos)

Materials

Materials from Exercises 6–8
Fertile chicken eggs (incubated 18–25 hours)
Spratt cultures
Cactus needles

Two major developmental processes are occurring simultaneously in young blastoderms: the cranial half of the blastoderm is undergoing neurulation, while the caudal half is undergoing gastrulation. Are these two processes causally related? That is, is regression of the **primitive knot** during gastrulation required for **neural plate** elongation and folding during neurulation? Or, alternatively, is neural plate elongation responsible for primitive knot regression? The purpose of this exercise is to do an experiment to answer these questions, as well as to determine whether Hensen's node is required for gastrulation to occur.

Collect typical 18-hour embryos (18–25 hours of incubation) using sterile conditions and set them up in modified Spratt cultures as described in Exercise 7. Position blastoderms *dorsal* side up. Some blastoderms will be left intact (except for the removal of most of their area opaca), to serve as controls; others will be completely transected. Transections will be done at two craniocaudal levels with cactus needles (see Exercise 4 for instructions for making needles): just cranial to the primitive knot and just caudal to the primitive knot. After transection, separate the two halves of the blastoderm with cactus needles so that the cut edges cannot heal together.

Cover the cultures and reincubate them in a humidified incubator at 38 °C. Examine cultures after an additional 24 hours of development. Use the space below (and on the following page) to sketch the initial appearance of the transected blastoderms and their appearance 24 hours later. Determine whether the cranial half neurulates after transection. If so, is the primitive knot required for this process to occur? Determine whether the caudal half gastrulates after transection. If so, is the primitive knot required for this process to occur? The portion of the neural plate that will eventually form the spinal cord lies alongside the cranial part of the primitive streak in 18-hour embryos (that is, the definitive primitive streak is partially flanked by neural plate, although this is not visible in whole mounts). Does this region form a neural tube after transection? If so, is the primitive knot required for this process to occur?

EXERCISE 10 Formation of a Double Heart
(Avian Embryos)

Materials

Materials from Exercises 6–9
Fertile chicken eggs (26–29 hours of incubation)
Spratt cultures
Cactus needles
Stopwatches

Recall that the heart develops from paired **cardiac primordia**, which are brought into apposition in the ventral midline by the action of the lateral body folds. This exercise will *demonstrate* the fact that paired rudiments contribute to the heart and that each rudiment is capable of developing into a miniature, beating heart.

Collect typical 24-hour embryos (26–29 hours of incubation) using sterile conditions and set them up in modified Spratt cultures as described in Exercise 7. Position blastoderms *ventral* side up. Some blastoderms will be left intact (except for the removal of most of their area opaca) to serve as controls; the others will be subjected to surgery. Surgery will be performed with cactus needles (see Exercise 4 for instructions for making needles). Cut the **splanchnopleure** in the *midline* of the embryo beginning at the **cranial intestinal portal** and extending craniad. As you cut through the floor of the foregut, make sure you do not cut beyond its cranial end.

Cover the cultures and reincubate them in a humidified incubator at 38 °C for an additional 48 hours. Examine cultures at about 24, 36, and 48 hours postsurgery. Use the space below (and on the following page) to sketch the initial appearance of the embryo and its appearance at each interval of observation. Do two beating hearts form? If so, do they beat in synchrony? Use a stopwatch to determine the heart rate (in beats/minute) of each beating heart. If paired beating hearts formed, do they have the same heart rate?

J. COMPARISON OF AMPHIBIAN AND AVIAN DEVELOPMENT

Aids: L, Fig. 1.8; G, Chap. 6, Fig. 16.

You have undoubtedly noticed several structural similarities between the 4-mm frog embryo and the 33-hour chick embryo during the course of your laboratory studies. This is because developmental events occur similarly among the various vertebrate classes. They certainly do not occur identically, as major differences exist among species. The purpose here is to emphasize two fundamental similarities between amphibian and avian development.

The first of these similarities concerns the structure of the **egg**. In both amphibians and birds, the egg consists of a large yolky mass covered by a **plasmalemma** and enclosed by a **vitelline membrane** (or by vitelline membranes). **Cleavage** subdivides the yolky mass into smaller units called **blastomeres**. The entire mass cleaves in amphibian embryos, whereas in avian embryos a cytoplasmic cap (the **blastodisc**) forms at one pole of the egg. It is only this disc that cleaves (to form the multicellular **blastoderm**). A space forms as cleavage progresses in both amphibian and avian embryos. In amphibian embryos, this space is completely surrounded by blastomeres and is called the **blastocoel** (see L, Fig. 1.8B). It allows cells to involute over the blastopore lips, where they move into the interior to form the **archenteron** and **mesoderm**. A similar space appears during avian development, but it is initially covered only dorsally by blastomeres. This similar space is the **subgerminal cavity**; it lies between the blastoderm and yolk. This space, like the blastocoel in amphibians, allows cells to move into the interior. As such cell movements occur, two layers can be identified: the dorsal, or outermost, **epiblast** and the ventral, or innermost, **hypoblast**. A space separates these two layers; it is appropriate to call this space the blastocoel, based on comparative embryology (see L, Fig. 1.8D). Why is this so? The blastocoel in amphibian eggs is displaced toward the **animal pole**. It "separates" the animal cap cells, which form **ectoderm, mesoderm,** and some **endoderm**, from **vegetal pole** cells, which form **endoderm**. Similarly, the space between the epiblast and hypoblast "separates," respectively, cells that form **ectoderm, mesoderm,** and **endoderm** from cells forming **extraembryonic endoderm**. Thus, although developing amphibian and avian embryos have a very different appearance, the fundamental events occurring during development are quite similar in the two organisms.

The second major similarity occurs in the general **body plan** of the embryo. Vertebrate embryos have a **tube-within-a-tube body plan**. That is, they consist of an outer ectodermal tube forming the **skin** and an inner endodermal tube forming the **gut** (see G, Chap. 6, Fig. 16). For example, compare Plate 4, Fig. 1 with Plate 9, Fig. 3. The tube-within-a-tube body plan is obvious in the frog embryo: there is an outer skin ectoderm and an inner gut (midgut). The mesoderm, subdivided into notochord, somites, nephrotome, and lateral plate, occupies the space between the inner and outer tubes, as does the neural tube (spinal cord), which originated from the outer ectodermal layer as an invagination. The tube-within-a-tube body plan is less obvious in avian embryos. This is because cleavage is restricted to the cytoplasmic cap at one pole of the yolky mass, rather than including all the mass as in amphibian embryos. Nevertheless, there is an outer **skin ectoderm** and an inner **gut** (in Plate 9, Fig. 3, the midgut lies beneath the endoderm, which forms its roof, and is open and continuous with the subgeminal cavity; the lateral body folds have not yet formed at this level). The mesoderm and its subdivisions, as well as the neural tube (spinal cord), occupy the space between the inner and outer layers. As a learning exercise, trace Plate 9, Fig. 3 in the space on the following page. Label the four layers at the left edge of the section with the following letters: skin ectoderm, *A*; somatic mesoderm, *B*; splanchnic mesoderm, *C*; and endoderm, *D*. Also label the four layers at the right edge of the section with the following letters: skin ectoderm, *a*; somatic mesoderm, *b*; splanchnic mesoderm, *c*; and endoderm, *d*. Sketch two or three stages in which the four layers on the left and right sides are extended toward the *ventral midline*, where they meet one another. Compare the final sketch to a sketch of Plate 4, Fig. 1; note the considerable similarity in the body plan of the two organisms.

K. 48-HOUR CHICK EMBRYOS

1. Whole mounts: injected and uninjected.

Aids: Fig. O; Plates 20, 21; A–V#1, #4; A, Figs. 469, 559; H, Fig. 98; HU, Figs. 110, 111; M, Figs. 183–186; P, Figs. 61, 74, 75, 78, 80, 103C–I, 104C–I, 105C–I.

First examine your uninjected whole-mount slide with the naked eye. Superimpose this slide on the 33-hour whole mount and note the increased size of the embryo. The entire diameter of the **blastoderm** is not seen because it was trimmed during preparation of the slides. Position your slide on the microscope stage so that, when viewed through the microscope, the embryo is oriented as in Plate 20; examine the slide under low magnification. You will note a change in the axis of the body at this stage. The cranial end of the body now lies on its *left* side (that is, it has undergone twisting, or **torsion**). In addition, the **prosencephalon** is bent toward the **rhombencephalon**, forming the **cranial (cephalic) flexure**, a sharp bend in the floor of the **mesencephalon**.

Examine the body of the embryo and note that it is more opaque than at the 33-hour stage, indicating its greater thickness. *Care must be taken not to focus the objective down into the elevated coverslip over these older embryos.* First examine the caudal half of the body and identify the thickened lateral walls of the **neural tube (spinal cord** level). Follow these two parallel lines forward until they curve toward the left and fade out. Then focus down slightly and you will see that, due to torsion, your view of the neural tube shifts from a dorsal view of the caudal half to a lateral view of the right side of the cranial half. Identify the following structures: **telencephalon** (the cranial neuropore is now completely closed); **diencephalon; infundibulum** (often difficult to identify); **optic cups** (formed by invagination of the optic vesicles); **lens vesicles** (formed by thickening and invagination of the ectoderm overlying the optic vesicles at the 33-hour stage); **optic fissures** (ventral gap in the optic cups; Plate 20, Fig. 2; A, Fig. 496); **mesencephalon** (rounded area at the apex of the embryo); **metencephalon; isthmus** (a prominent constriction of the neural tube between mesencephalon and metencephalon); **myelencephalon** (note its thin **roof plate**); **auditory vesicles**, or **otocysts** (formed by invagination of the auditory placodes); **notochord** (usually best seen beneath the mesencephalon and rhombencephalon); **foregut; cranial intestinal portal; heart; cranial liver rudiment** (an evagination of the floor of the foregut that extends toward the heart); **somites** (count the number of pairs present); and **segmental plates**.

Observe that the cranial half of the embryo seems to be veiled by some coverings that the caudal half lacks. The distinct curvature between covered and uncovered parts is the **boundary of**

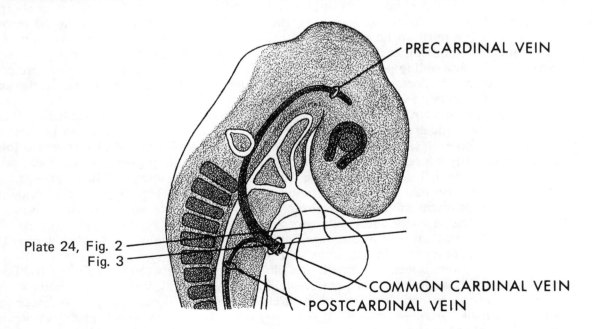

PRECARDINAL VEIN

Plate 24, Fig. 2
Fig. 3

COMMON CARDINAL VEIN
POSTCARDINAL VEIN

Fig. O. Drawing of the right side of the cranial half of a 48-hour chick embryo.

the amniotic folds. The amniotic folds arch over the head, as continuous **cranial (anterior)** and **lateral amniotic folds,** forming two **extraembryonic membranes:** the outer **chorion** and the inner **amnion.** These two membranes cannot be readily distinguished from one another in whole mounts.

Note that the boundaries of the body are now quite distinct in the cranial half, whereas caudally they are probably only slightly indicated. The **tail fold of the body** may have established the caudal boundary in some embryos. Following formation of the tail fold of the body, the caudal end of the embryo is separated from the underlying blastoderm by the **subcaudal pocket.** A curved line, with its concavity facing cranially, may be visible just cranial to the caudal boundary of the body (Plate 20, Fig. 1). This curvature is the beginning of the **caudal (posterior) intestinal portal.** The neural groove is no longer present in most embryos, and the neural tube merges caudally with a dark mass of cells, the **tail (end) bud,** which is derived from the cranial part of the primitive streak.

Observe three somewhat irregular white lines fanning out from the heart toward each auditory vesicle. The most cranial of these lines is the **first branchial groove,** the next one is the **second branchial groove,** and the last one is the **third branchial groove** (Plate 20, Figs. 1, 2). Cranial to the first groove is a darkly stained mass of cells, the **first branchial arch.** This arch is partially split into two processes by another white line, the **stomodeum** (not to be confused with the first branchial groove). The dark area just cranial to the stomodeum is the **maxillary process** of the first branchial arch. The dark area just caudal to the stomodeum is the **mandibular process** of the first branchial arch. Between the first and second grooves is the **second branchial arch,** and between the second and third grooves is the **third branchial arch.** *This series of structures causes no end of trouble in studying sections through this region, so their relationships should be mastered now.*

Examine the **heart** in uninjected embryos and in embryos whose circulatory system has been injected with india ink. (See P, Figs. 61, 103C-I, 104C-I, 105C-I to understand the changes that have occurred in the heart between the 33- and 48-hour stages.) At the cranial end of the heart, identify the **bulbus cordis,** which is continuous, without a distinct boundary, with the next region of the heart, the **ventricle.** Notice that the ventricle is U-shaped and that it extends craniad and to the left, underneath the bulbus cordis, to become continuous with a broad saccular region, the **atrium.** This is continuous, without a distinct boundary, with the **sinus venosus.** Observe that the heart consists of two layers: the inner **endocardium,** enclosing blood cells and india ink, and the outer **myocardium.**

Note, using injected embryos, that the bulbus cordis is also continuous with a very narrow region, the **aortic sac** (Plate 21, Fig. 2), which was formed by fusion of the paired ventral aortae. Continuous with the aortic sac are two or three pairs of blood vessels, the **aortic arches.** The **first aortic arch,** on each side of the body, runs through the mandibular process and then curves sharply around the stomodeum. Similarly, on each side, the **second aortic arch** runs through the second branchial arch, and the **third aortic arch,** if present, runs through the third branchial arch. The aortic arches are continuous on each side with a **dorsal aorta.** The paired dorsal aortae are fused more caudally as the **descending aorta** (Plate 21, Fig. 1). Numerous small blood vessels are continuous with the descending aorta dorsally; these are the **intersegmental arteries.** Paired **dorsal aortae** are again present caudal to the descending aorta.

Try to identify the **precardinal (cranial,** or **anterior, cardinal) vein** lying above each dorsal aorta in the region of the aortic arches (Fig. O; Plate 21, Fig. 2). This vessel is usually poorly injected. The precardinal vein on each side extends caudad from the **plexus of head blood vessels** and joins two other vessels (usually not readily visible): the **postcardinal (caudal,** or **posterior, cardinal) vein,** which extends further caudad, and the **common cardinal vein,** which joins the sinus venosus.

Identify the extensive plexus of **vitelline blood vessels** (Plate 21, Fig. 1). They are contained within the **yolk sac,** an **extraembryonic membrane** that overgrows the yolk. Identify the paired **vitelline arteries** continuous with the caudal dorsal aortae at approximately right angles. The vitelline arteries and dorsal aortae are continuous at about the 22nd somite level. Also identify the paired **vitelline veins** continuous with the sinus venosus.

The circulatory system is well developed, and blood circulates between the yolk sac and body of the embryo mainly in the following sequence: vitelline veins→sinus venosus→atrium→ventricle→bulbus cordis→aortic sac→aortic arches→cranial dorsal aortae→descending aorta→caudal dorsal aortae →vitelline arteries→plexus of vitelline blood vessels→vitelline veins. Some of the blood in the cranial dorsal aortae supplies the plexus of head blood vessels via small branches. The precardinal veins drain this plexus, returning blood to the sinus venosus via the common cardinal veins. Some of the blood in the descending aorta enters the intersegmental arteries. This blood is returned to the heart in the following sequence: postcardinal veins→common cardinal veins→sinus venosus.

EXERCISE 11 Observations of Living Embryos
(Avian Embryos at 48 Hours)

Materials

Materials from Exercises 6–10
Fertile chicken eggs (50–56 hours of incubation)
1% solution of neutral red
1% solution of Nile blue sulfate
Carbon/melted agar mixture

Obtain fertile chicken eggs incubated at 38°C for approximately 50–56 hours. These eggs should contain typical 48-hour embryos. Carefully crack open the eggs against the side of a finger bowl half filled with warm saline solution, as described in Exercise 6. Observe particularly the circulation of blood—especially its passage through the heart. If you watch the living heart, you can discern the relationships of its parts much better than if you examine only whole mounts of *fixed* embryos. Note the jerkiness of the circulation in the arteries and the smoother flow of blood in the veins. Observe as many as possible of the structures you previously identified in whole mounts. To make identification of most structures easier, apply a drop of a 1% aqueous solution of vital stain or inject eggs subblastodermically with Nile blue sulfate or carbon/agar (see Exercise 6). Use the space below to sketch the vitelline vessels and heart; add arrows to your sketch to indicate the directions of blood flow.

2. Serial transverse sections.

Aids: Figs. O–Q; Plates 22–26; A–V#1, #5; A, Figs. 561–574; B, Figs. 298–303; G, Chap. 6, Fig. 17; HU, Figs. 113–117; M, Figs. 188–202; P, Fig. 76.

Position your slide on the microscope stage so that, when viewed through the microscope, each section is oriented as in Plate 22. Begin tracing sections in anteroposterior sequence under low magnification. The first brain sections are probably cut through the **mesencephalon**, due to the cranial flexure. These first sections will actually be frontal (that is, cut lengthwise in the right-left plane), rather than transverse. Note the oval shape of the mesencephalon sections as you continue caudally. Sections then begin to lengthen, and a constriction appears in the brain. Sections at this level not only cut across the mesencephalon, but also the **metencephalon** and **myelencephalon** (Plate 22, Fig. 1). The constricted region between metencephalon and mesencephalon is the **isthmus**. The myelencephalon can be readily identified by its thin **roof plate**. The brain separates into two parts as you continue to trace sections posteriorly (Plate 22, Fig. 2). The upper part is the myelencephalon (or possibly the metencephalon and myelencephalon; the boundary between these two structures is indistinct); the lower part is now the **diencephalon**. A dark accumulation of cells appears on each side of the body at about this level, the **semilunar ganglia** of the **trigeminal (V) cranial nerves**. These ganglia originate from ectodermal **neural crest cells**, as well as from a thickening of the lateral skin ectoderm on each side. These ectodermal thickenings are called **epibranchial placodes**; they usually cannot be identified.

The **notochord** appears shortly after the brain separates into two parts. It is usually cut frontally, due to the cranial flexure, and it quickly separates into two parts, one beneath each brain section. The portion of the notochord beneath the diencephalon disappears as you continue to follow sections posteriorly (Plate 22, Fig. 3). Note an accumulation of cells on each side of the myelencephalon at about this level; these are the **acousticofacialis ganglia** of the **facial (VII)** and **auditory (VIII) cranial nerves**. The acoustic part of these ganglia originates from the ectodermal **auditory placodes** present earlier. The facialis part originates from both **neural crest cells** and from a second pair of epibranchial placodes (see Plate 23, Fig. 1). These **epibranchial placodes** may not be readily visible in your embryo. Note the close relationship between the **auditory vesicles** and the acoustico-facialis ganglia (Plate 22, Fig. 4; Plate 23, Fig. 1).

Return to the level where the portion of the notochord beneath the diencephalon disappears and trace sections posteriorly. Observe that the diencephalon becomes more and more elongated; the narrow end of the diencephalon that projects toward the myelencephalon is the **infundibulum** (Plate 22, Fig. 4; Plate 23, Fig. 1). The **optic cups** appear at about this level. They are not connected to the diencephalon in the first sections encountered. The **lens vesicles** appear in more posterior sections and are nestled within the double-layered optic cups (Plate 23, Figs. 1, 2). The layer of each optic cup that is next to the lens vesicle is thickened as the **sensory retina**; the much thinner layer is the **pigmented retina**. The space between these two layers, the **opticoel**, is continuous with the cavity of the diencephalon. A small accumulation of cells appears above each auditory vesicle at about this level; these are the **superior ganglia** of the **glossopharyngeal (IX) cranial nerves** (Plate 23, Figs. 1, 2). These ganglia originate from **neural crest cells**.

As you continue to trace sections posteriorly, the optic cups become continuous with the diencephalon via the **optic stalks** (Plate 23, Fig. 4). The **telencephalon** appears in more posterior sections. Note that the skin ectoderm lateral to the telencephalon is thickened as the **nasal (olfactory) placodes** (Plate 24, Fig. 1). The nasal placodes are induced to form by the adjacent regions of the telencephalon. They form the lining of the **nasal cavities**. The telencephalon disappears a few sections more posteriorly.

Return to the level of the auditory vesicles (Plate 22, Fig. 4; Plate 23, Fig. 1) and trace sections posteriorly. The transition from myelencephalon to **spinal cord** is so gradual that the boundary between the two is indistinguishable. Find a section closely resembling Plate 25, Fig. 4 and examine the spinal cord carefully. Identify the **roof** and **floor plates**. Try to identify **neural crest cells**. Continue to trace sections posteriorly. The caudal end of the neural tube often contains multiple cavities. In sections slightly posterior to this level, the notochord seems to fuse to the floor of the neural tube, and a solid mass of cells then appears in the midline. This mass is the **tail bud**. The caudal portion of the neural tube is formed by cavitation (hollowing out) of a portion of the tail bud, resulting in formation of multiple cavities that subsequently fuse, forming a single cavity.

Return to the level where the brain separates into two parts (Plate 22, Fig. 2) and trace sections posteriorly, noting that the **foregut** soon appears. It rapidly becomes somewhat triangular in shape (Plate 22, Fig. 4). Sections now cut through the **pharynx** and **first pharyngeal pouches**. The first pharyngeal pouches project laterad from the pharynx to contact the adjacent regions of the skin ectoderm, which they induce to invaginate, forming the **first branchial grooves**. The double-layered membranes formed by the endoderm of the pouches and the ectoderm of the grooves are the **first closing plates**.

Return to the first section through the foregut (Plate 22, Fig. 3) and again trace sections posteriorly. A small vesicle soon appears between the infundibulum and foregut (Plate 22, Fig. 4). This is **Rathke's pouch**, the rudiment of the **anterior pituitary gland**. Recall that the posterior pituitary gland is formed from the infundibulum. Note the close relationship between the infundibulum and Rathke's pouch. Rathke's pouch opens in more posterior sections into a transverse, slitlike space, the **stomodeum** (Plate 23, Fig. 1), which is lined by ectoderm. Rathke's pouch develops as an outgrowth from the stomodeum, perhaps due to induction by the infundibulum. The stomodeum lies between two rounded masses next to the foregut, the **mandibular processes** of the first branchial arches, and two rounded, or slightly flattened, masses on either side of Rathke's pouch, the **maxillary processes** of the first branchial arches. Note that the stomodeum dips between the two mandibular processes and is separated from the foregut only by a thin membrane of ectoderm and endoderm, the **oral membrane** (Plate 23, Fig. 1). This membrane will *later* rupture, forming the **mouth opening**. The outer part of the mouth is therefore derived from ectoderm of the stomodeum, and the inner part from foregut endoderm. Examine models, if available, to fully understand and visualize these relationships.

Continue tracing sections posteriorly. The pharynx becomes somewhat rounded and then suddenly expands laterad at the level of the **second pharyngeal pouches** (Plate 23, Fig. 4). Identify the **second branchial grooves**, and the **second closing plates**. The considerable depression in the floor of the pharynx at this level is the **thyroid rudiment**. Continue tracing sections posteriorly and identify the very broad **third pharyngeal pouches**, the **third closing plates**, and the **third branchial grooves**, if formed (Plate 24, Fig. 1).

Sections posterior to the third pharyngeal pouches cut through the portion of the **foregut** caudal to the pharynx. The foregut endoderm at this level is surrounded by splanchnic mesoderm (Plate 24, Fig. 2). In more posterior sections, the ventrolateral portions of the foregut may be slightly evaginated. These evaginations are the beginnings of the **lung buds** (Plate 24, Fig. 3). The paired portions of the coelom lateral to the developing lung buds and continuous with the **pericardial cavity** are the **pleural cavities**. The pleural and pericardial cavities are separate, caudal to this level (Plate 24, Fig. 4).

Notice a small mass of cells ventral to the foregut at about this level; this is the **cranial liver rudiment**. Continue caudally, noting that the cranial liver rudiment becomes continuous with the foregut (Plate 25, Fig. 1). This region of the foregut is the **duodenum**. Your embryo may also contain a **caudal liver rudiment**. If so, it will appear as a branch (or as branches) of the ventral part of the cranial liver rudiment. The paired portions of the coelom lateral to the duodenum are the **rudiments of the peritoneal cavity**. These paired rudiments continue caudally for many sections and *later* fuse, forming a single **peritoneal cavity** surrounding the gut. The **cranial intestinal portal** is encountered almost immediately as sections are traced posteriorly from the level of the duodenum. More caudally, the embryo progressively flattens dorsoventrally, and endoderm forms its lower layer (Plate 25, Fig. 4). An endoderm-lined cavity, the **allantois rudiment**, may appear in more posterior sections beneath the tail bud (Plate 26, Fig. 2). The exact mechanism by which this rudiment forms is unknown. It will *later* greatly enlarge and become covered externally with splanchnic mesoderm, forming the **allantois**, one of the **extraembryonic membranes**. In slightly more *anterior* sections, the floor of the allantois rudiment disappears; this is the region of the **caudal intestinal portal** (Plate 26, Fig. 1). Thus the allantois rudiment opens into the **subgerminal cavity**.

Return to the level of the first somite pair (Plate 24, Fig. 1) and trace sections posteriorly. The structure of the cranial **somites** is now quite different from that of the 33-hour stage. Examine them closely (Plate 24, Figs. 2, 3). Each somite is now subdivided into three parts: **dermatome** (a plate of darkly stained cells lying just beneath the skin ectoderm—source of some of the **dermis**); **myotome** (a plate of lightly stained cells lying just medial to the dermatome—source of some of the **skeletal muscles**); **sclerotome** (a diffuse mass of mesenchymal cells lying between myotome, neural tube, notochord, and dorsal aorta or descending aorta—source of the **vertebral column** and **ribs**). The manner of formation of these somite subdivisions can be studied by comparing the most caudal somites, in which the subdivision is just beginning, with more cranial somites.

Identify the **segmental plates** caudal to the last somite pair and note that their caudal ends are continuous with the **tail bud**. The tail bud is a mass of mesenchymal cells located at the caudal end of the embryo. It contributes cells to the neural tube, segmental plates, and mesenchyme of the tail. The notochord of the tail is *not* derived from the tail bud. Instead, the notochord extends into the developing tail from more cranial regions.

Return to the level of the cranial liver rudiment (Plate 24, Fig. 4) and trace sections posteriorly. Lateral to the descending aorta or dorsal aortae, identify the paired **mesonephric duct rudiments** (Plate 25, Figs. 2–4). They were initially solid longitudinal structures derived from the pronephric cords, but they have extended caudad and are now undergoing cavitation in most embryos. Medial to the mesonephric duct rudiments, identify the usually solid **mesonephric tubule rudiments**. The latter are induced to form from the **nephrotome** by the mesonephric duct rudiments. The mesonephric tubule rudiments undergo cavitation to form the **mesonephric tubules** of the paired **mesonephric kidneys**.

Return to the first section through the foregut (Plate 22, Fig. 3). A large blood vessel, the dorsal aorta, is cut frontally on each side of the foregut. Trace sections posteriorly and note that two vessels appear in the place of each **dorsal aorta** (Plate 22, Fig. 4). The one that lies above the first pharyngeal pouch is still the dorsal aorta; the one that lies beneath the first pouch is the **first aortic arch** (see Plate 21, Fig. 2). Note, as sections are traced further posteriorly, that the first aortic arches become located within the mandibular processes (Plate 23, Figs. 1, 2). Continue to trace sections posteriorly until the first aortic arches approach one another and become continuous with the **aortic sac**. Continue tracing the aortic sac caudally. Note a vessel extending downward from each dorsal aorta, just caudal to the first pharyngeal pouches. These vessels are the **second aortic arches** (Plate 23, Figs. 2–4). Their ventral ends become continuous with the aortic sac a few sections more posteriorly. The second aortic arches are contained within the second branchial arches. Continue tracing sections posteriorly. Just caudal to the second pharyngeal pouches, another pair of downward extensions from the dorsal aortae may be seen; these are the **third aortic arches**, which are usually just developing. The ventral ends of these vessels become continuous with the aortic sac more caudally. The third aortic arches are contained within the third branchial arches (Plate 24, Fig. 1).

Follow the aortic sac caudally, noting the appearance of **endocardium** clearly separated from **myocardium**, indicating the beginning of the **bulbus cordis** of the heart (Plate 24, Fig. 1). Identify the **ventricle** and **atrium** in more posterior sections (Plate 24, Fig. 2). Recall that these regions lie *beneath* the bulbus cordis in surface view. Notice that the endocardium of the atrium is in close contact with the myocardium, whereas these two layers are widely separated in the ventricle and bulbus cordis. The two dorsal aortae have fused at about this level, forming the **descending aorta**. In more posterior sections, a portion of the heart is attached to the foregut by the **dorsal mesocardium** (Plate 24, Fig. 3). This portion is the **sinus venosus**. The bulbus cordis and ventricle become continuous at about this level. Slightly more caudally, the sinus venosus is continuous with a blood vessel on each side; these vessels are the **common cardinal veins** (Plate 24, Fig. 4).

Continue caudally and note that the sinus venosus seems to divide into two vessels, one on each side of the cranial liver rudiment (Plate 25, Fig. 1). These two vessels are the **vitelline veins**. Trace the vitelline veins caudally, noting that they shift laterad within the splanchnic mesoderm. Shift your attention to the descending aorta and trace it caudally. Identify small blood vessels continuous with the descending aorta dorsally; these are the **intersegmental arteries** (see Plate 25, Fig. 1). Note that the descending aorta has not yet formed at more caudal levels, and paired **dorsal aortae** are again present. Continue to trace the dorsal aortae caudally. They become continuous with the **vitelline arteries**, which extend laterad within the splanchnic mesoderm (Plate 25, Fig. 4).

Return to the section where the common cardinal veins are continuous with the sinus venosus (Plate 24, Fig. 4). Each common cardinal vein is contained within a bridge of mesoderm connecting the lateral body wall to the sinus venosus. Trace sections *anteriorly*, observing that the lateral body walls separate from the heart (Plate 24, Fig. 3). Note a vessel located within the lateral body wall on each side near the heart at this level. These vessels are located progressively more dorsally within the lateral body walls in more *anterior* sections. They are still the **common cardinal veins** near the heart (Plate 24, Fig. 3), but they are the **precardinal veins** at a level approximately lateral to the foregut (Plate 24, Fig. 2). Thus, there is a gradual transition between these two vessels on each side, as sections are traced anteriorly from the level of the heart. Continue to trace sections *anteriorly*. The precardinal veins lie progressively more dorsally and come to lie ventrolateral to the myelencephalon (Plate 23, Fig. 2). They are cut frontally in more *anterior* sections, due to the cranial flexure (Plate 22, Fig. 2).

Return to a level similar to Plate 24, Fig. 1 and trace sections *posteriorly, carefully* observing the precardinal veins. They become located progressively more ventrally and suddenly, at about a level lateral to the foregut, each seems to separate into two vessels. The dorsomost vessel, usually very small, is the **postcardinal vein**; the ventromost vessel is the **common cardinal vein** (Plate 24, Fig. 3). See Fig. O. Continue to trace sections posteriorly and note again that the common cardinal veins become continuous with the sinus venosus. The postcardinal veins become located progressively more dorsally and eventually lie dorsal to the developing kidneys (Plate 25, Figs. 3, 4). Small blood vessels are continuous dorsally with the postcardinal veins in some embryos. These are the **intersegmental veins**.

Four **extraembryonic membranes** are in the process of formation (see G, Chap. 6, Fig. 17). Two originate from splanchnopleure, the **allantois** and **yolk sac**, and two from somatopleure, the **amnion** and **chorion**.

The development of the **allantois** is barely initiated. Only a small endoderm-lined cavity, the **allantois rudiment**, has formed (Plate 26, Fig. 2). Splanchnic mesoderm will later surround this endodermal lining to form the wall of the allantois. Consult Fig. P to help you understand the early changes involved in formation of the allantois rudiment and wall of the allantois, as well as their relationships to later changes involved in formation of the hindgut, cloaca, and tail gut. The allantois stores nitrogenous waste products when it is fully developed, and it will eventually fuse with the chorion to form the **chorioallantoic membrane**.

The **yolk sac** is formed from the splanchnopleure that overgrows the yolk. At cranial levels where **torsion** is complete, it lies between the amnion (covering the *left* side of the embryo) and the yolk (Fig. Qa; Plate 22, Fig. 2; Plate 23, Fig. 4). At these levels the yolk sac has been separated from the embryo by the action of the splanchnopleural component of the **lateral body folds**. More caudally, the yolk sac has not yet been separated from the developing gut (Plate 25, Fig. 2). Further caudally, **torsion** has not yet occurred, and the ventral surface of the embryo as well as the yolk sac lie above the yolk (Fig. Qc; Plate 25, Fig. 3). Notice the numerous **vitelline blood vessels** within the splanchnic mesoderm of the yolk sac. The endodermal cells of the yolk sac digest the yolk, the products of this digestion enter the plexus of vitelline blood vessels, and these products are transported to the developing embryo via the vitelline veins.

The **amnion** and **chorion** are formed simultaneously by elevation and fusion of amniotic folds. Select a section resembling Fig. Qc and Plate 25, Fig. 3, showing the **lateral amniotic folds**. Note that the amniotic folds consist of somatopleure and are continuous with the lateral body walls. The outer wall of each fold consists of *ectoderm on the outside*, with an adjacent layer of *somatic mesoderm on the inside*, and forms the **chorion**. The inner wall of each fold consists of *somatic mesoderm on the outside* and *ectoderm on the inside* and forms the **amnion**. The somatic mesoderm-lined cavity within each fold is the **extraembryonic coelom**; it is continuous with the **intraembryonic coelom** (that is, the pericardial, peritoneal, and pleural cavities). The extra- and intraembryonic coeloms become separated due to the action of the somatopleural component of the **lateral body folds**. The cavity developing between the amnion and embryo is the ectoderm-lined *amniotic cavity*. Trace sections *anteriorly* and observe the region of fusion of the amniotic folds (Fig. Qb). In more anterior sections the outer chorion is separate from the inner amnion. The amniotic cavity is later filled with **amniotic fluid**. The embryo then floats freely (Fig. Qa) within this protective fluid. The extraembryonic coelom later contains the enlarging allantois. Fusion occurs wherever the splanchnic mesoderm of the allantois contacts the somatic mesoderm of the chorion, forming the **chorioallantoic membrane**. The latter lies immediately beneath the inner shell membrane and functions in respiration and absorption of calcium from the shell.

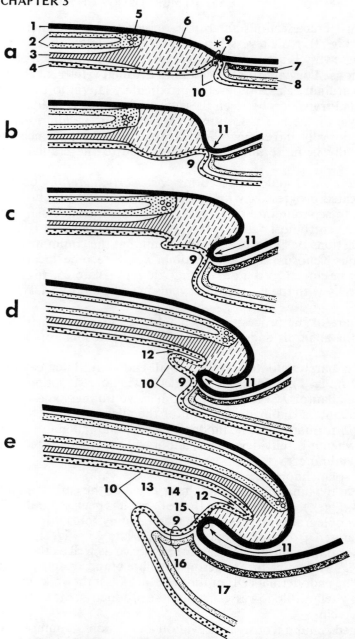

1. Ectoderm
2. Neural tube
3. Notochord
4. Endoderm
5. Area cavitating to form neural tube
6. Tail bud
7. Somatic mesoderm
8. Splanchnic mesoderm
9. Allantois rudiment
10. Caudal intestinal portal
11. Tail fold of the body
12. Tail gut
13. Hindgut
14. Cloaca
15. Cloacal membrane
16. Wall of allantois
17. Extraembryonic coelom

Fig. P. Schematic drawings of midsagittal sections of the caudal ends of chick embryos between 48 (Fig. Pa) and 72 (Fig. Pe) hours of incubation. The tail fold of the body changes the positions and orientations of the endodermal allantois rudiment and the caudal intestinal portal so that at 48 hours (Figs. Pa, Pb) the caudal intestinal portal opens cranioventrally, whereas at intermediate stages (Figs. Pc, Pd) and at 72 hours (Fig. Pe) it opens cranially. The allantois rudiment receives an outer investment of splanchnic mesoderm as it changes orientation, whereupon it is renamed the allantois (Figs. Pd, Pe), and a distinct tail gut forms as an evagination of the endoderm (Figs. Pd, Pe). At 48 hours the caudal intestinal portal is the opening of the allantois rudiment into the subgerminal cavity (Fig. Pa). However, at 72 hours the caudal intestinal portal is the opening of the endodermal hindgut (formed by the tail fold of the body) into the subgerminal cavity (Fig. Pe); the allantois then opens dorsally into a portion of the hindgut called the cloaca. Note that the endodermal floor of the cloaca contacts the skin ectoderm caudal to the allantois (Fig. Pe); this area of contact is the cloacal membrane. Although this membrane is generally not named prior to formation of the cloaca at the 72-hour stage, note that it actually forms at the 48-hour stage (Fig. Pa, asterisk), where the endodermal allantois rudiment contacts the overlying skin ectoderm.

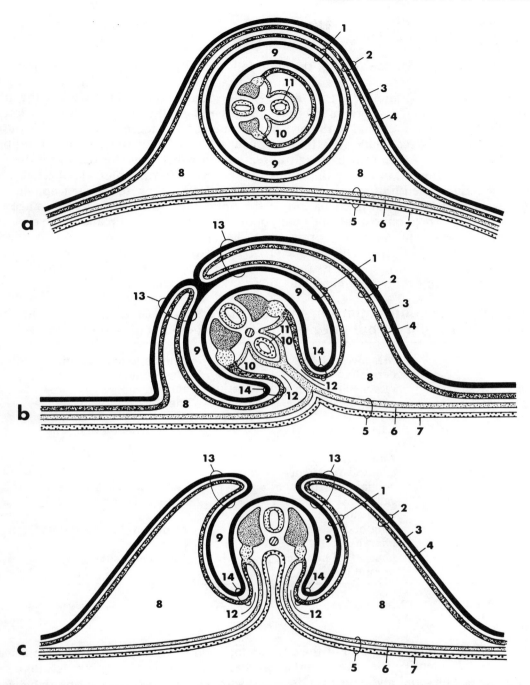

Fig. Q. Schematic drawings of transverse sections of 48-hour chick embryos showing the formation of the amnion, chorion, and yolk sac. Fig. Qa is more cranial than Fig. Qb, which in turn is more cranial than Fig. Qc. Torsion of the embryo occurs as the lateral amniotic folds elevate and fuse.

1. Amnion
2. Chorion
3. Ectoderm
4. Somatic mesoderm
5. Yolk sac
6. Splanchnic mesoderm
7. Endoderm
8. Extraembryonic coelom

9. Amniotic cavity
10. Intraembryonic coelom
11. Gut endoderm
12. Continuity between intra- and extraembryonic coeloms
13. Lateral amniotic fold
14. Lateral body fold

3. Serial sagittal sections.

Aids: Plate 26, Figs. 3, 4; A–V#1; M, Fig. 187.

Only about the cranial one-third of the embryo is actually cut sagittally; the remaining caudal regions are cut frontally. Try to find a section that is approximately a midsagittal section through the **brain** and **notochord** (Plate 26, Fig. 3). Identify all regions of the brain, including the **infundibulum**. Also identify the **pharynx, oral membrane**, and **preoral gut (Seessel's pouch)**. The latter is that part of the foregut that lies cranial to the oral membrane; it later degenerates. Identify the ectodermal **stomodeum** and its evagination, **Rathke's pouch,** which extends toward the infundibulum.

Now focus your attention on parasagittal sections in which you can recognize the following structures (Plate 26, Fig. 4): **optic cup** (including the **sensory retina** and **pigmented retina**), **lens vesicle,** and **optic fissure.** Identify the **optic stalk** connecting the optic cup to the **diencephalon.** The optic fissure is formed by ventral invagination of the optic cups and stalks. At this stage the optic fissure is probably formed only in the optic cup, or at most in the optic cup and in the part of the optic stalk immediately adjacent to the optic cup. The optic fissure is important in development because **optic nerve fibers** from the retina grow back to their proper connections within the diencephalon through the wall of the fissure. Moreover, the cavity of the fissure provides a pathway for blood vessels to enter the optic cup. This fissure will later close.

4. Summary of the contributions of the germ layers to structures present in the 48-hour chick embryo, but not present in the 33-hour chick embryo.

Ectoderm	**Mesoderm**	**Ectoderm and Somatic Mesoderm**
auditory vesicles	dermatomes	
branchial grooves	mesonephric duct rudiments	amnion
cranial ganglia:	mesonephric tubule rudiments	chorion
V. semilunar	myotomes	
VII.-VIII. acoustico-facialis	sclerotomes	**Endoderm and Splanchnic Mesoderm**
IX. superior	**Endoderm**	yolk sac
epibranchial placodes	allantois rudiment	
lens vesicles	cranial liver rudiment	**Ectoderm and Endoderm**
nasal placodes	caudal liver rudiment	closing plates
optic cups	duodenum	
optic stalks	lung buds	**Ectoderm, Mesoderm, and Endoderm**
Rathke's pouch	pharynx	branchial arches
stomodeum	pharyngeal pouches	
	preoral gut	

5. Scanning electron microscopy.

Aids: Plates 27–29.

A scanning electron micrograph of the developing brain from a block sectioned transversely is shown in Plate 27. Identify the **myelencephalon, diencephalon, infundibulum, Rathke's pouch, optic cups** (with **sensory** and **pigmented retinas**), and **lens vesicles**. Note the continuity between each lens vesicle and the adjacent **skin ectoderm.** The **acousticofacialis ganglia** lie ventrolateral to the floor of the myelencephalon, just dorsolateral to the **precardinal veins.** Also identify the **pharynx, first pharyngeal pouch, first closing plate, first branchial groove, dorsal aortae, first aortic arches, first and second branchial arches** (first arches are not split at this level into maxillary and mandibular processes), and **notochord.** Three extraembryonic membranes can be identified: the **chorion, amnion,** and **yolk sac.** Note the locations of the **amniotic cavity** and **extraembryonic coelom.**

Two representative transverse views of the spinal cord examined by scanning electron microscopy are shown in Plate 28, Figs. 1, 2. Near the level of the mid-portion of the spinal cord, identify the **skin ectoderm, spinal cord** (note that its lumen is partially occluded), **notochord, dorsal aortae, coelom, endoderm,** and **lateral body folds**. Note the **amniotic folds** (continuous **cranial** and **lateral amniotic folds**). These folds are seen in cross section at the top right of Plate 28, Fig. 1. Also note the **yolk sac, amnion,** and **amniotic cavity.** The slice shown in Plate 28, Fig. 1 passes through the level of a pair of **intersomitic furrows.** Therefore, the subdivisions of the somites are not recognizable. Instead, endothelial cells forming **intersegmental arteries,** and possibly **veins,** can be identified (note on the right side the continuity of an intersegmental artery and a dorsal aorta). Also identify **neural crest cells** leaving the roof of the spinal cord at this level. Identify near the caudal end of the spinal cord (Plate 28, Fig. 2) the **skin ectoderm, spinal cord, notochord, dorsal aortae, coelom, somites** (not yet subdivided at this level into dermatome, myotome, and sclerotome), **endoderm, allantois rudiment,** and **somatopleure** and **splanchnopleure** of the **lateral plate.**

A scanning electron micrograph of the cut surface of a block sectioned parasagittally is shown in Plate 29 (compare Plate 29 with Plate 26, Fig. 3; the section shown in Plate 26, Fig. 3 was cut mid-sagittally). Identify the **telencephalon, diencephalon, optic stalk, infundibulum, mesencephalon, metencephalon, myelencephalon, dorsal aorta, pharynx, first aortic arch, mandibular process,** and **ventricle.**

Exercise 12 Chemical Dissection of Organ Rudiments (Avian Embryos)

Materials

Materials from Exercises 6–11
Fertile chicken eggs (33–49 and 50–56 hours of incubation)
EDTA/trypsin solution (ethylenediaminetetraacetic acid, trypsin, glycine, sodium hydroxide, HCL)
Glass microscope slides

We will use chemical dissection in this exercise to demonstrate the structure of axial and paraxial organ rudiments (that is, the **neural tube, notochord,** and **somites**).

Collect typical 33- to 48-hour embryos (33–49 and 50–56 hours of incubation, respectively), as described in Appendix I, and place them in petri dishes (one per dish). Remove excess saline and flatten each blastoderm onto the surface of the dish. Cover each blastoderm with a large drop of EDTA/trypsin solution (0.4% ethylenediaminetetraacetic acid [Fisher Scientific Co., New Jersey] and 0.5% trypsin [Difco laboratories "1:250" trypsin] in an aqueous solution of 1 M glycine; to get the EDTA to dissolve, add 10 N NaOH dropwise to the glycine solution until the EDTA dissolves; then adjust the pH to 7 with 2 N HCL. After 10-15 minutes, place the tips of a partially closed pair of blunt watchmaker's forceps on either side of the midline of the blastoderm, just lateral to the somites, and allow the tips to gently spread apart. This tears the blastoderm and separates organ rudiments. Examine isolated somites and segments of the neural tube and notochord under high magnification. To do this, pipette individual rudiments in a drop of saline to ordinary glass microscope slides or depression slides (if available). Use the space below (and on the following page) to sketch the structures of the isolated rudiments. Compare the structures of cranial and caudal somites (in embryos at about Stage 15). Also note differences in the structures of each rudiment at early (Stage 10) and late (Stage 15) stages.

L. 72-HOUR CHICK EMBRYOS

1. Whole mounts: injected and uninjected.

Aids: Plates 30–32; A–V#1; A, Figs. 575, 577; HU Fig. 130; M, Figs. 203–207.

First examine your uninjected whole-mount slide with the naked eye. Superimpose this slide on the 48-hour uninjected whole-mount slide and note the changes that have occurred in the shape of the embryo. In addition to the **cranial flexure**, two other flexures are probably well developed. These are the **cervical flexure**, at the level of the first several somites (Plate 30, Fig. 1), and the **tail flexure**, at the caudal end of the embryo (Plate 30, Fig. 2). Note that the embryo is sharply bounded and that it lies on its *left* side throughout a considerable part of its length. This means that it has undergone (or is undergoing) **torsion** along most of its length. A saclike structure, the **allantois** (Plate 30, Figs. 2, 3), is somewhat encircled by the **tail**. Paired **wing** and **leg buds** can be identified, but they are not sharply bounded (Plate 30, Figs. 1, 2). Determine the approximate somite levels of the limb buds. The entire embryo is usually covered by **amnion** and **chorion**, although the oval or circular boundary of the continuous **cranial, lateral,** and **caudal (posterior) amniotic folds** still may be visible (Plate 30, Fig. 1).

Examine your slide under low power and identify the following structures: **telencephalon** (with its lateral oval-shaped expansions, the **cerebral hemispheres**); **nasal pits** (formed by invagination of the nasal placodes); **diencephalon; pineal gland** or **epiphysis** (a small dorsal evagination of the diencephalon); **optic cups; optic fissures; lens vesicle; infundibulum; Rathke's pouch** (examine it under high power and note its close relationship to the infundibulum; Plate 31); **mesencephalon; metencephalon; isthmus; myelencephalon** (note its thin **roof plate**); **auditory vesicles; endolymphatic ducts** (formed by evagination of the dorsal part of the auditory vesicles); **spinal cord; cranial intestinal portal;** and **caudal intestinal portal,** if visible.

Identify the **acousticofacialis ganglia** just cranial to the auditory vesicles (Plate 30, Fig. 2). They lie above the **second branchial arches.** The facialis part of these ganglia is the source of the **sensory nerve fibers** of the **facial nerves,** which innervate the *second* branchial arches. Identify the **semilunar ganglia** lying above the **first branchial arches** (Plate 30, Fig. 2). These ganglia are the source of **sensory nerve fibers** of the **trigeminal nerves,** which innervate the *first* branchial arches.

Observe that the first branchial arches are partially split by the **stomodeum** into **maxillary processes** (which will form the lateral portions of the **upper jaw** and most of the **cheeks**) and **mandibular processes** (which will form the **lower jaw**). The maxillary processes may partially overlap the mandibular processes in some embryos. Identify the **first branchial grooves,** just caudal to the mandibular processes; the **second branchial grooves,** between the **second** and **third branchial arches;** and the **third branchial grooves.**

In favorably injected embryos the **precardinal, postcardinal,** and **common cardinal veins,** as well as the **intersegmental veins** (continuous with the postcardinal veins dorsally) can be identified. The common cardinal veins return blood to the **sinus venosus.** Identify the following structures (see Plate 30, Figs. 1–3; Plate 32, Figs. 1, 2): **atrium; ventricle; bulbus cordis; aortic sac; first, second, third,** and possibly **fourth aortic arches** (the first aortic arches are degenerating and may be reduced in diameter); **dorsal aortae; internal carotid arteries** (cranial extensions of the dorsal aortae); **descending aorta;** and **intersegmental arteries.** Also identify the **vitelline arteries,** which are continuous with the dorsal aortae at approximately the 22nd somite level, and **vitelline veins.** The latter are fused near the level of the heart to form a single vessel, the **ductus venosus,** which is continuous with the sinus venosus. Try to identify the ductus venosus.

EXERCISE 13 Observations of Living Embryos
(Avian Embryos at 72 Hours)

Materials

Materials from Exercises 6–12
Fertile chicken eggs (72 hours of incubation)

Obtain fertile eggs incubated at 38 °C for approximately 72 hours. These eggs should contain typical 72-hour embryos. Open and examine these eggs exactly as described in Exercises 6 and 11.

Use the space below to sketch the vitelline vessels and heart; add arrows to your sketch to indicate the directions of blood flow.

2. Serial transverse sections.

Aids: Fig. P; Plates 32–38; A–V#1; A, Figs. 578–588; HU, Figs. 131–136b; M, Figs. 211–223.

Position your slide on the microscope stage so that, when viewed through the microscope, each section is oriented as in Plate 32, Fig. 3. Trace sections in anteroposterior sequence, unless otherwise specified. The first brain sections are probably cut through the **myelencephalon** (and possibly through the **metencephalon** as well), due to the **cervical flexure**. A variable amount of tissue may appear to be lying freely within the cavity of the myelencephalon. This tissue is the thin **roof plate** of the myelencephalon and the adjacent **skin ectoderm**. Continue tracing sections posteriorly. **Endo-lymphatic ducts** soon appear alongside the walls of the myelencephalon. These become continuous with the **auditory vesicles** a few sections more posteriorly. At about this level, sections begin to cut across a small, rounded region lying beneath the metencephalon. This region is the **mesencephalon**; it is continuous with the metencephalon in more posterior sections (Plate 32, Fig. 3). Note the segmental enlargements of the walls of the rhombencephalon; these are the **neuromeres**.

As sections are traced posteriorly from about the level at which the auditory vesicles are first identified, two groups of nerve fibers seem to emerge from neuromeres cranial to each auditory vesicle. They quickly become continuous with two prominent ganglia on each side (Plate 32, Fig. 3). The ganglia lying against the cranial wall of the auditory vesicles are the **acousticofacialis ganglia** (future **acoustic** and **geniculate ganglia**). The other very large ganglia are the **semilunar ganglia**. At about this level note, on the caudal side of each auditory vesicle, a poorly circumscribed, very small, rounded accumulation of cells, the **superior ganglia**. The neural tube separates into two parts in slightly more posterior sections. The upper part is either the myelencephalon or the **spinal cord**; the lower part is principally the mesencephalon.

As you continue tracing sections posteriorly, the superior ganglia are continuous, without a distinct boundary, with **sensory nerve fibers** of the **glossopharyngeal (IX) nerves** (Plate 33, Fig. 1). Similarly, the acousticofacialis ganglia are directly continuous with the **sensory nerve fibers** of the **facial (VII) nerves**. The facial nerves can be traced into the **second branchial arches**, where they merge on each side with a distinct **epibranchial placode**. These placodes contribute cells to the acousticofacialis ganglia and are the source of the geniculate ganglia. Trace the glossopharyngeal nerves into the **third branchial arches**, where each similarly merges, on each side, with an **epibranchial placode** (Plate 33, Fig. 3). These placodes are the source of the **petrosal ganglia** of the glossopharyngeal nerves. *If you trace the facial and glossopharyngeal nerves into their respective branchial arches, correct identification of these arches becomes relatively simple.* At about the level where each glossopharyngeal nerve merges with an epibranchial placode, try to identify an accumulation of **neural crest cells** on each side, the **jugular ganglion** of the **vagus (X) cranial nerve** (Plate 33, Fig. 3). The jugular ganglia fade out within the **fourth branchial arches**.

Return to sections through the semilunar ganglia (Plate 32, Fig. 3) and note that each one seems to subdivide caudally into three branches, the branches of the **trigeminal (V) nerve** (Plate 33, Fig. 1). The medial branch is the **maxillary branch**; the lateral branch closest to the mesencephalon is the **ophthalmic branch**; the lateral branch above the ophthalmic is the **mandibular branch**. These branches are contained within the region of the **first branchial arches** and fade out caudally.

Shift your attention to the mesencephalon and follow it posteriorly in your sections (cranially within the embryo). Nerve fibers **(axons)** seem to emerge from the floor of the mesencephalon to either side of the midline. These will probably *not* be cut symmetrically. The accumulations of **neural ectodermal cells** from which these nerve fibers arise lie within the floor of the mesencephalon. Each accumulation is designated as a **motor nucleus. Motor nerve fibers** grow out from the motor nuclei toward areas they will later innervate; collectively these nerve fibers constitute the **oculomotor (III) cranial nerves.** These nerves will innervate four pairs of extrinsic eye muscles, which develop *later.*

The following events occur in the establishment of *sensory* portions of cranial nerves. (1) Cranial ganglia, consisting of **cell bodies** of **young sensory neurons,** are formed adjacent to the brain from accumulations of ectodermal neural crest cells and/or cells derived from ectodermal placodes. (2) Sensory nerve fibers grow out from these ganglia and into the brain wall. These fibers are **axons;** they will eventually transmit nerve impulses *away from* their cell bodies. (3) Other sensory nerve fibers grow out from these ganglia toward the areas to be innervated. We will refer to these fibers as **dendrites** because they will eventually transmit nerve impulses *toward* their cell bodies.

The following events occur in the establishment of *motor* portions of cranial nerves. (1) Motor nuclei, consisting of **cell bodies** of **young motor neurons,** are formed within the ventral part of the wall of the brain from accumulations of neural ectodermal cells. (2) Motor nerve fibers, **axons,** grow out from these nuclei, leaving the wall of the brain and extending toward the areas to be innervated. (3) Other motor nerve fibers, **dendrites,** grow out from these nuclei but remain within the brain wall.

The following chart summarizes the development of cranial nerves through the 72-hour stage.

Cranial Nerves	Cranial Ganglia Present	Origin of Cranial Ganglia or Motor Nuclei	Type of Nerve Fibers Present	Regions Innervated
oculomotor	_____	neural ectoderm	motor	four pairs of extrinsic eye muscles
trigeminal	semilunar	neural crest cells and epibranchial placodes	sensory (*later* also motor)	first branchial arches
facial	acousticofacialis (*later* geniculate)	neural crest cells and epibranchial placodes	sensory (*later* also motor)	second branchial arches
auditory (nerves not yet formed)	acousticofacialis (*later* acoustic)	auditory placodes	(*later* sensory)	inner ears
glossopharyngeal	superior	neural crest cells	sensory (*later* also motor)	third branchial arches
vagus (nerves not yet formed)	jugular	neural crest cells	(*later* sensory and motor)	fourth branchial arches

The **infundibulum** appears in sections posterior to the oculomotor nerves, marking the beginning of the **diencephalon.** Identify the **optic cups** and the **optic fissures** (Plate 35, Fig. 2). The **lens vesicle** is now completely closed. It is separated from the overlying **skin ectoderm,** which *later* forms the **corneal epithelium** (Plate 35, Fig. 1). The lens vesicle is beginning to differentiate into two regions: the outer, thin **lens epithelium** and the inner, thick **lens fibers.**

Continue to trace sections posteriorly until sections cut through both the diencephalon and **telencephalon** (Plate 36, Figs. 2, 3). The telencephalon is expanded laterally as the **cerebral hemispheres.** Identify the **nasal pits** and **pineal gland** at about this level (Plate 36, Fig. 3). Continue tracing sections posteriorly, noting the disappearance of the diencephalon and telencephalon.

Quickly follow the **spinal cord** throughout its length. **Neural crest cells** are now aggregated alongside its most cranial levels, forming the paired **spinal ganglia.** Segmentation of these ganglia corresponds to segmentation of the **somites,** which are the much more prominent and elongated structures lateral to each ganglion. Spinal ganglia are located beneath the **myotome** in the middle of the craniocaudal extent of each somite. **Spinal nerves** will form *later.* Examine the most caudal tip of the spinal cord, observing that the **notochord** is still distinguishable at this level. The spinal cord and notochord are usually cut frontally at this level due to the **tail flexure.**

Return to the most anterior section in which the notochord can be identified (Plate 33, Fig. 1). It is cut frontally at this level due to the **cervical flexure.** Trace sections posteriorly. Sections soon cut through the **first,** and possibly the **second, pharyngeal pouches,** which at first appear as isolated structures (Plate 33, Fig. 2). Both pairs of pouches become continuous with the **pharynx** as you continue to trace sections posteriorly (Plate 33, Fig. 3). (Remember to use the facial nerves as a landmark for identifying the second branchial arches. This will enable you to identify the first and second pharyngeal pouches with certainty.) Both the first and second pharyngeal pouches may open to the outside via the **first** and **second branchial clefts,** which arise by rupture of the corresponding **closing plates.** Identify the shallow **first** and **second branchial grooves.** The **third pharyngeal pouches** appear in more posterior sections and almost immediately become continuous with the pharynx (Plate 34, Fig. 1). Identify the **third closing plates** and the shallow **third branchial grooves.** Note that the first pharyngeal pouches fade out at about this level. In more posterior sections, identify the **fourth pharyngeal pouches, fourth closing plates, fourth branchial grooves** (very shallow), and **thyroid rudiment** (Plate 34, Figs. 2, 3).

Return to a section similar to Plate 34, Fig. 1 and identify the **preoral gut,** which is located just cranial to the pharynx. Also identify the **first branchial arches,** just lateral to the preoral gut. The **stomodeum** appears in slightly more posterior sections and separates the first branchial arches into **maxillary** and **mandibular processes.** At about this level, the cavity of the gut usually opens into the stomodeum via the **mouth opening** because the **oral membrane** has probably ruptured. Try to identify the mouth opening in your embryo. It will be seen in sections located between those illustrated by Plate 34, Figs. 1 and 2. Identify **Rathke's pouch** in slightly more posterior sections (Plate 34, Fig. 2); it quickly becomes continuous with the stomodeum (Plate 34, Fig. 3). Note the close relationship between Rathke's pouch and the **infundibulum.**

Continue tracing sections posteriorly and identify the **laryngotracheal groove,** which is continuous, without a distinct boundary, with the pharynx (Plate 35, Fig. 1). (The laryngotracheal groove is formed by elongation of the ventral portion of the foregut, at the level where lung bud formation was initiated earlier. See Plate 24, Fig. 3.) More posterior sections cut through the **lung buds,** which at this stage are bilateral expansions of the laryngotracheal groove (Plate 35, Fig. 3). Moreover, the laryngotracheal groove is beginning to constrict between the pharynx and lung buds. This constriction is complete in slightly more posterior sections, and paired lung buds lie beneath the **esophagus** (Plate 36, Fig. 1). Both the esophagus and lung buds are contained within a thick mesentery composed of splanchnic mesoderm. The portion of the mesentery dorsal to the esophagus is the **mesoesophagus;** the portion dorsal to the sinus venosus is the **dorsal mesocardium.** The coelomic cavities lateral to the lung buds are the **pleural cavities.**

Continue tracing sections posteriorly and note the disappearance of the lung buds. Two narrow coelomic cavities are located ventrolateral to the esophagus at about this level. These cavities are extensions of the pleural cavities (Plate 36, Fig. 2). They become continuous with the more lateral portions of the pleural cavities in slightly more posterior sections (Plate 36, Fig. 3). The diameter of the gut is usually slightly larger at about this level; this is the region of the **stomach.** The mesentery dorsal to the stomach is the **dorsal mesogaster;** the one ventral to it is the **hepatogastric (gastrohepatic) ligament (ventral mesogaster).** Although the stomach lies medial to the pleural cavities at this stage, it will *later* descend and be enclosed by the **peritoneal cavity.**

Identify the **cranial liver rudiment** in sections at about the level of the stomach (Plate 36, Fig. 3); it lies just above a large blood vessel, the **ductus venosus.** The cranial liver rudiment and gut become continuous in more posterior sections (Plate 37, Fig. 1). This level of the gut is the **duodenum.** The mesentery lying dorsal to the duodenum is the **mesoduodenum;** the one ventral to it is the **hepatoduodenal (duodenohepatic) ligament.** Identify the **caudal liver rudiment** lying beneath the ductus venosus at about this level. The close relationship between the ductus venosus and liver tissue is very important. *Later,* as the liver tissue grows, it invades the ductus venosus and subdivides this vessel into smaller channels, the **hepatic sinusoids.**

Continue tracing sections posteriorly and notice that the cranial liver rudiment lengthens dorsoventrally and becomes continuous with the caudal liver rudiment (Plate 37, Fig. 2). The cranial liver rudiment lies between two blood vessels at this level, the **vitelline veins.** The boundaries between the duodenum, cranial liver rudiment, and caudal liver rudiment are indistinct. Note a solid mass of cells continuous with the dorsal wall of the duodenum at this level; this is the **dorsal pancreatic rudiment**. Identify the **cranial intestinal portal** in more posterior sections (Plate 37, Fig. 3).

Trace sections posteriorly and identify the paired **wing buds** (Plate 38, Fig. 1), and further posteriorly, the paired **leg buds** (Plate 38, Figs. 2, 3). Both wing and leg buds consist of a core of somatic mesoderm covered by skin ectoderm, which is thickened laterally as the **apical ectodermal ridge**. Experiments suggest that this ridge is necessary for normal outgrowth and development of limb buds.

In sections through about the level of the leg buds, identify an endoderm-lined cavity, the **hindgut** (Plate 38, Fig. 2), which is formed by the combined action of the **tail fold of the body** and **lateral body folds**. A portion of the hindgut, the **cloaca**, is continuous ventrally with the **allantois** in more posterior sections (Plate 38, Fig. 3). The allantois is formed by expansion of the endodermal allantois rudiment, which has become surrounded by splanchnic mesoderm (Fig. P). Trace the cloaca and allantois caudally, noting the disappearance of the latter and the separation of the **tail** from the **amnion** by the ectoderm-lined **subcaudal pocket** (Plate 38, Fig. 4). The ventral endoderm of the cloaca usually contacts the ventral skin ectoderm at about this level, forming the double-layered **cloacal membrane**. Caudal to this membrane, sections usually cut through the much smaller **tail gut**, which will soon degenerate.

Return to a section similar to Plate 38, Fig. 2 and trace sections *anteriorly,* noting the disappearance of the floor of the **hindgut**. This is the level of the **caudal intestinal portal,** the opening of the hindgut into the **subgerminal cavity.** (Recall that, at 48 hours of incubation, the caudal intestinal portal was the opening of the allantois rudiment into the subgerminal cavity. Carefully study Fig. P so that you understand why this spatial relationship has changed by 72 hours of incubation.)

Return cranially to a level showing well-formed **somites** and identify **dermatome, myotome,** and **sclerotome** (Plate 38, Fig. 1). Trace sections *posteriorly* noting that tail somites are considerably less advanced in their differentiation. Identify the short **segmental plates** caudal to the somites; their caudal ends are continuous with the small **tail bud.**

Return to the level where the cranial liver rudiment connects to the duodenum (Plate 37, Fig. 1). A tiny duct can be seen on each side at about this level, dorsolateral to the mesoduodenum. These ducts are the **mesonephric ducts,** which formed by cavitation of the mesonephric duct rudiments. The cranial end of each mesonephric duct is undergoing degeneration. Trace sections posteriorly and observe that **mesonephric tubules** are forming from **mesonephric tubule rudiments,** medial to each mesonephric duct (Plate 38, Fig. 1). Some mesonephric tubules may have established connections with the mesonephric ducts. The mesonephric tubules collectively form the paired **mesonephric kidneys.** Continue tracing sections posteriorly. Observe that the mesonephric ducts have extended caudad beyond the developing mesonephric tubules (Plate 38, Figs. 2, 3), and that they either join the cloaca laterally or terminate near it. The mesonephric tubules become functional slightly later than the 72-hour stage and extract nitrogenous wastes from the blood. These wastes pass through the mesonephric tubules and ducts and then to the cloaca; they then enter the allantois, where they are stored.

Return to the section in which the notochord is cut frontally (Plate 33, Fig. 1) and trace sections posteriorly. Identify the paired **dorsal aortae** (Plate 33, Fig. 2). They are at first cut frontally due to the **cervical flexure.** Each dorsal aorta seems to be constricted into two parts at the level of the first pharyngeal pouches. The lower part is the **internal carotid artery,** the cranial extension of the dorsal aorta. Quickly trace sections posteriorly and observe that the internal carotid arteries fade out at about the level, of the diencephalon.

Return to a level similar to Plate 33, Fig. 2 and trace sections posteriorly. Observe that the **second aortic arches** extend from the dorsal aortae into the second branchial arches, and subsequently the **third aortic arches** extend into the third branchial arches (Plate 33, Fig. 3). If the **first aortic arches** are still present in your embryo, note that they extend from the internal carotid arteries into the first branchial arches. The small **fourth aortic arches** extend from the dorsal aortae into the fourth branchial arches in more posterior sections (Plate 34, Fig. 2). Note that the dorsal aortae have fused at about this level, forming the **descending aorta.**

Continue tracing sections posteriorly, observing the aortic arches. They approach one another in the region of the thyroid gland (Plate 34, Fig. 3) and soon unite with the **aortic sac** (see Plate 35, Fig. 1). In more posterior sections, identify the **bulbus cordis; atrium,** which lies to the *left* (apparent right) of the bulbus cordis; and **sinus venosus,** which lies in the midline (Plate 35, Fig. 3). The sinus venosus is continuous with the **common cardinal veins** in more posterior sections. Usually the *right* (apparent left) common cardinal vein is continuous with the sinus venosus more cranially than is the *left* common cardinal vein (Plate 36, Fig. 2). At about this level, sections begin to cut across a small portion of the **ventricle**, which is continuous with the atrium.

Continue to trace sections posteriorly and observe the gradual disappearance of the atrium and the progressive enlargement of the ventricle in its place (Plate 36, Fig. 3). Also note the gradual transition between sinus venosus and **ductus venosus**. More caudally, the bulbus cordis and ventricle become continuous, without a distinct boundary, and the ductus venosus seems to separate into two vessels, the **vitelline veins**, which extend laterad into the **yolk sac** (Plate 37). Trace sections posteriorly, noting the gradual disappearance of the ventricle.

Return to the level where the **descending aorta** first appears (Plate 34, Fig. 2) and trace sections posteriorly. Identify small blood vessels, the **intersegmental arteries**, continuous with the descending aorta dorsally (Plate 34, Fig. 2). Quickly trace sections posteriorly, until paired **dorsal aortae** again appear (usually between the levels of the wing and leg buds). The **vitelline arteries** are continuous with the dorsal aortae just caudal to this level. The vitelline arteries extend laterad into the **yolk sac**; at this level they lie beneath (ventral to) the **vitelline veins**. Continue tracing the dorsal aortae caudally and note that they become markedly reduced in diameter (Plate 38, Fig. 2). They lie just dorsal to the gut within the tail region (that is, caudal to the leg buds) and are designated as **caudal arteries.**

Return to the level where the *right* (apparent left) **common cardinal vein** is continuous with the **sinus venosus** (Plate 36, Fig. 2). The right common cardinal vein, as at the 48-hour stage, is contained within a bridge of mesoderm connecting the lateral body wall to the sinus venosus. Trace sections *anteriorly*, observing that the lateral body wall separates from the heart. Two vessels are usually located within the right lateral body wall at this level (Plate 36, Fig. 1). The lower vessel, nearest the sinus venosus, is still the common cardinal vein; the upper vessel, lateral to the descending aorta, is the **postcardinal vein**. These vessels approach one another and become continuous in more *anterior* sections (Plate 35, Figs. 2, 1). At this level these vessels are cut *frontally*. (In some embryos the common cardinal and postcardinal veins may be interconnected by smaller vessels at some levels and completely separated in more anterior sections. If this is the case in your embryo, trace sections anteriorly, until the common cardinal and postcardinal veins are broadly continuous.) Continue to trace sections *anteriorly*, noting the disappearance of the upper portion of this frontally cut vessel. The lower, persisting portion is now the **precardinal vein**. In more *anterior* sections, the precardinal vein first lies ventrolateral to the descending aorta (Plate 34, Fig. 3), then lateral to the dorsal aorta (Plate 33, Figs. 3, 2); finally it is cut frontally (Plate 32, Fig. 3). It disappears in more *anterior* sections.

Return to the level where the right postcardinal and common cardinal veins are broadly continuous (Plate 35, Fig. 1) and trace sections *posteriorly*. The postcardinal vein quickly separates from the common cardinal vein and lies lateral to the descending aorta (Plate 35, Fig. 3; Plate 36, Fig. 1; Plate 37, Fig. 1; Plate 38, Fig. 1). Try to identify small blood vessels continuous with the postcardinal vein dorsally; these vessels are the **intersegmental veins**. Note that the postcardinal vein lies above the developing mesonephric kidney (Plate 38, Fig. 1). Try to identify a small vessel lying beneath each mesonephric kidney; these vessels are the **subcardinal veins**. Trace the postcardinal vein caudally, until it disappears.

Try to identify and trace the precardinal, common cardinal, and postcardinal veins on the *left* side of the embryo. These vessels are usually more difficult to identify with certainty than on the right side.

3. Serial sagittal sections.

Aids: Plate 39; A–V#1; A, Fig. 576; HU, Fig. 137; M, Figs. 208–210.

Approximately the cranial half of the embryo is actually cut sagittally; the caudal half is cut frontally. As with the 48-hour stage, find a section that is approximately a midsagittal section through the **brain** and **notochord**. Identify all regions of the brain, including the **infundibulum** and **pineal gland**. Also identify the **pharynx, preoral gut, stomodeum, Rathke's pouch,** and **mouth opening**. The mouth opening has formed by rupture of the oral membrane. Following this rupture the cavities of the foregut and stomodeum are continuous. Try to identify as many other structures as time permits.

4. Summary of the contributions of the germ layers to structures present in the 72-hour chick embryo, but not present in the 48-hour embryo.

Ectoderm	Mesoderm	Ectoderm and Somatic Mesoderm
cerebral hemispheres	mesenteries:	leg buds
cranial ganglia:	dorsal mesogaster	wing buds
X. jugular	hepatoduodenal	
cranial nerves:	ligament	
III. oculomotor	hepatogastric	**Endoderm and Splanchnic**
V. mandibular, maxillary,	ligament	**Mesoderm**
and ophthalmic branches	mesoduodenum	allantois
of trigeminal	mesoesophagus	
VII. facial	mesonephric ducts	**Ectoderm and Endoderm**
IX. glossopharyngeal	mesonephric tubules	cloacal membrane
endolymphatic ducts		
lens epithelium	**Endoderm**	
lens fibers	cloaca	
nasal pits	dorsal pancreatic rudiment	
pineal gland	esophagus	
spinal ganglia	hindgut	
	laryngotracheal groove	
	stomach	
	tail gut	

5. Scanning electron microscopy.

Aid: Plate 40.

A scanning electron micrograph of the cut surface of a block sectioned midsagittally is shown in Plate 40. Identify the **cerebral hemisphere** of the **telencephalon; diencephalon; optic stalk; infundibulum; Rathke's pouch; mesencephalon; isthmus; metencephalon; myelencephalon; notochord; dorsal aorta; pharynx; mouth opening; stomodeum; amniotic cavity; amnion; mandibular process; thyroid rudiment; first, second, third,** and **fourth pharyngeal pouches; aortic sac; bulbus cordis; ventricle;** and **atrium.**

EXERCISE 14 Extraembryonic Membrane Development in Culture (Avian Embryos)

Materials

Materials from Exercises 6–13
Fertile chicken eggs (72–96 hours of incubation)
Sterile petri dishes (20 x 100 mm and 25 x 150 mm)
Sterile distilled water

A culture system will be used in this exercise to examine **extraembryonic membrane** formation. The system we will use was developed by Auerbach and coworkers (Auerbach, R., L. Kubai, D. Knighton and J. Folkman [1974]. A simple procedure for the long-term cultivation of chicken embryos. *Develop. Biol.* 41:391–394). Sterile conditions must be maintained for cultures to develop successfully. With this culture procedure, eggs can be cultured until embryos reach near-hatching stages. Obtain chicken eggs incubated for 72–96 hours. Begin by taking a piece of cotton moistened with 70% ethanol and wipe the shell of each egg. Carefully crack eggs into sterile petri dishes (20 x 100 mm). This procedure must be done without breaking the yolk. Practice the procedure until this is possible. If the egg is cracked properly, the blastoderm will lie uppermost and the yolk and albumen will flatten over the bottom of the petri dish. Cover each petri dish and place it into the bottom of a larger sterile petri dish (25 x 150 mm). Add some sterile distilled water to the larger dish and cover it with its lid. Place the entire culture in a humidified incubator at 38 °C. Observe cultures at daily intervals; discard those that fail to develop as soon as possible, to prevent contamination of the incubator. Observe particularly the development of the **extraembryonic membranes:** the **amnion, chorion, yolk sac, allantois,** and **chorioallantoic membrane.** Also observe changes in the circulatory pattern over time. Finally, observe the embryo through its membranes. Watch for movement of the embryo caused by contraction of the **amnion.** When do such contractions begin? Also try to determine when the embryo beings moving actively. Its first movements occur jerkily, but eventually coordinated movements develop. Try to determine when coordinated movements arise and describe their appearance. Focus on a particular active movement, such as a leg kick. Determine the number of kicks over a 15-minute observation period. Does this value change with increase in developmental age?

Chapter **4**

10-MM PIG EMBRYOS

A. WHOLE SPECIMENS

Aids: Fig. R; A, Fig. 598; M, Fig. 233; PA, Fig. 58.

The development of chick embryos becomes increasingly less typical of vertebrates in general and more avian in character beyond the 72-hour stage. Consequently, for more advanced development, it is advisable to examine mammalian embryos. Pig embryos are preferred and are the most available in the stages and quantities needed. The 10-mm pig embryo, which has been developing for 20–21 days of a total gestation period of approximately 4 months (usual range 110–116 days), contains the rudiments of essentially all adult structures. Therefore, examination of this stage is almost a study of adult anatomy in miniature.

Examine models or, preferably, *whole specimens* preserved in 70% alcohol. Whole preserved specimens are far superior to any model and to specimens embedded in plastic. If preserved specimens are used, your instructor should remove the amnion and carefully cut the umbilical cord parallel to and as close to the body wall as possible (if these structures are still present). The preserved embryo should be examined in a small dish containing sufficient 70% alcohol to cover it; observations should be made with a dissecting microscope. Manipulate your embryo very carefully, preferably with the enlarged rounded end of a small glass rod. Make every effort not to damage the embryo, so that it can be used repeatedly.

Note the general C-shape of the embryo (Fig. R). This shape is due to the **cranial** (level of **mesencephalon**), **cervical** (level of **myelencephalon**), and **tail flexures.** Because of these pronounced flexures, the most *cranial* regions of your serially transverse sectioned embryo will not be seen in the most *anterior* sections of your set of slides. Similarly, the most *caudal* regions of the embryo will not be found in the most *posterior* sections.

Identify the **head, trunk, tail, foreleg** and **hindleg buds, eyes** (note dark coloration due to **pigment granules** within the **pigmented retinas**), **nasal pits** (note the raised ridges bounding them, the **lateral** and **medial nasal processes**), and **somites.** Also identify the regions of the **prosencephalon, mesencephalon, metencephalon, myelencephalon** (note its thin **roof plate**), and **spinal cord.** The **stomodeum** partially subdivides the large **first branchial arch** on each side into **maxillary** and **mandibular processes.** The large **first branchial grooves** are immediately behind the mandibular processes, followed by the **second branchial arches,** and then by the **second branchial grooves.** The **third branchial arches** are partially hidden behind the second branchial arches and grooves. They are directly in front of the small, deep **cervical sinuses** (combined **third** and **fourth branchial grooves**).

The sites of three large developing organs can be seen within the relatively straight trunk. The most cranial organ, indicated by a large bulge, is the **heart.** The bulge immediately behind the heart, toward which the foreleg buds project, indicates the **liver.** The depression between the heart and

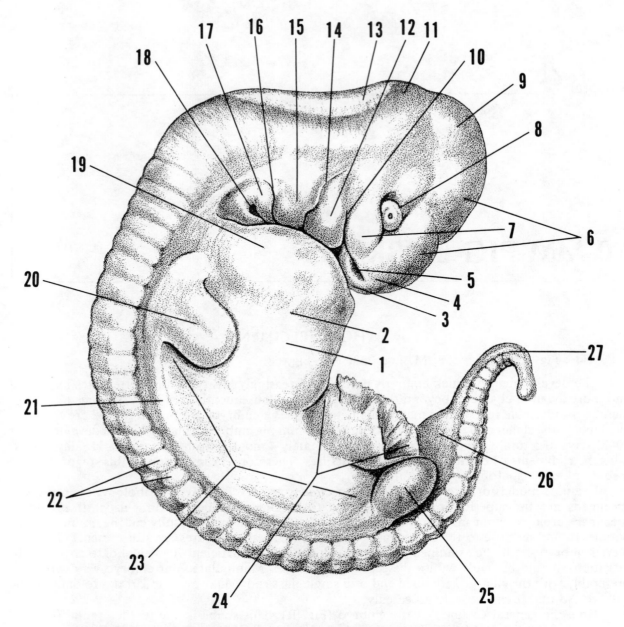

Fig. R. Drawing of the right side of a preserved 10-mm pig embryo.

1. Liver region
2. Location of developing septum transversum
3. Medial nasal process
4. Lateral nasal process
5. Nasal pit
6. Prosencephalon region
7. Maxillary process
8. Eye
9. Mesencephalon region
10. Stomodeum
11. Metencephalon region
12. Mandibular process
13. Myelencephalon roof plate region
14. First branchial groove
15. Second branchial arch
16. Second branchial groove
17. Third branchial arch
18. Cervical sinus
19. Heart region
20. Foreleg bud
21. Mammary ridge
22. Somites
23. Mesonephric kidney region
24. Umbilical cord
25. Hindleg bud
26. Genital eminence
27. Tail

liver bulges indicates the location of the developing **septum transversum** (source of part of the adult **diaphragm**). The very large bulges, one on each side, between foreleg and hindleg buds, indicate the **mesonephric kidneys.** Identify the **mammary ridges** (small ridges, one on each side, lying parallel to the ventral edges of the somites between foreleg and hindleg buds), which form the **mammary glands.** The trunk ends with a ventral swelling, the **genital eminence** (rudiment of the **external genitalia**), which lies between the hindleg buds and the tapering tail. Any part of the **umbilical cord** still attached to the body is located between the liver region and hindleg buds.

B. SERIAL TRANSVERSE SECTIONS

Aids: Plates 41–54; A–V#1; M, Figs. 240–271; PA, Figs. 61–63, 69–79.

Position your slide on the microscope stage so that, when viewed through the microscope, each section is oriented as in Plate 41. Examine sections in anteroposterior sequence under low magnification, unless directed otherwise. Because the amount of flexion encountered is quite variable and the plane of section is not always exactly the same from embryo to embryo, the order of appearance of structures in *your* specimen will not always coincide *exactly* with the sequence described here but should closely approximate it.

1. Nervous system.

Aids: Fig. S; A, Figs. 470, 471, 599, 600, 618–623; M, Fig. 235; PA, Figs. 59, 60, 92.

a. Brain. The first sections usually cut through the **myelencephalon,** but in some specimens the **metencephalon** appears first. The former is recognized by its thin **roof plate,** the latter by its thick walls. The myelencephalon and metencephalon are usually cut frontally when first encountered (Fig. S). This is also true of many other cranial structures. The thin roof plate of the myelencephalon together with an outer adjacent vascular layer, the **pia mater,** are the rudiments of the **choroid plexus.** (The pia mater is just developing and can be identified under high magnification as a thin layer of head mesenchymal cells just outside the brain wall. See Plate 41, Fig. 2.) The choroid plexus is formed by invagination of these rudiments into the cavity of the rhombencephalon, the **fourth ventricle,** and is the source of **cerebrospinal fluid** (that is, the fluid that fills the cavities of the brain and spinal cord). Continue tracing sections posteriorly and note that another section of the brain appears near the pointed apex of the metencephalon; this is the **mesencephalon.** The cavity of the mesencephalon, the **cerebral aqueduct,** soon becomes continuous with the fourth ventricle (Plate 41, Fig. 1). The constricted region between mesencephalon and metencephalon is the **isthmus.**

The rhombencephalon and mesencephalon are the sources of several major adult brain components. The **myelencephalon** forms the **medulla,** the **metencephalon** forms the **cerebellum** and **pons,** and the **mesencephalon** forms the **corpora quadrigemina (superior** and **inferior colliculi)** and the **cerebral peduncles.**

Observe under high magnification that the walls of all regions of the brain are subdivided into three mediolateral regions (Plate 41, Fig. 2). The innermost and darkest staining region (rich in nuclei) is the **ventricular zone;** the middle region containing fewer nuclei is the **intermediate (mantle) zone;** and the outer region, relatively free of nuclei and the lightest staining, is the **marginal zone,** consisting mainly of nerve fibers. The intermediate zone is formed by cells that migrate from the ventricular zone. Most of these migratory cells are **young neurons** at this stage. Some migratory cells may be **glioblasts (spongioblasts),** primitive nonnervous cells (that is, supporting cells) that remain within the wall of the brain.

Continue to trace sections posteriorly until the brain separates into two parts. The smaller oval-shaped (lower) section of the brain is still the mesencephalon; the larger (upper) section is still rhombencephalon (Plate 42, Figs. 1, 2). The neural tube is separated into three parts in more posterior sections (Plate 42, Fig. 3). The smaller (upper) section is either myelencephalon or **spinal cord** (the boundary between myelencephalon and spinal cord is indistinct), the middle section is still rhombencephalon, and the remaining section is still mesencephalon. The floor of the rhombencephalon fades out in more posterior sections (Plate 43, Fig. 3). The **infundibulum** appears at about this same level; it quickly becomes continuous with the **diencephalon,** which now occupies the position occupied by the mesencephalon in more anterior sections. The cavity of the diencephalon is the major part of the **third ventricle.**

Identify **Rathke's pouch** as you continue tracing sections posteriorly, a small flattened vesicle contacting the floor of the infundibulum (Plate 44, Figs. 2, 3). It quickly becomes continuous with the **stomodeum** in more posterior sections. The **eyes** can be identified at about this level. Quickly trace sections *anteriorly.* As the eyes fade out, identify dense masses of mesodermal cells, the **eye muscle rudiments,** lying lateral to Rathke's pouch (Plate 44, Figs. 2, 3). These rudiments will later form the extrinsic **eye muscles (inferior** and **superior oblique eye muscles; inferior, superior, medial [or internal]** and **lateral [or external] rectus eye muscles).** Return to the level of the eyes and identify the following components (Plate 45): **sensory** and **pigmented retinas, lens vesicles, optic stalks,** and **optic fissures.** Observe under high magnification that the pigmented retinas now contain **pigment granules.** Each lens vesicle is completely separated from, and covered externally by, **skin ectoderm,** the future **corneal epithelium.** (The adult **cornea** is derived from both skin ectoderm and **head mesenchyme** [neural crest].) Note that the head mesenchyme (neural crest and mesoderm) surround-

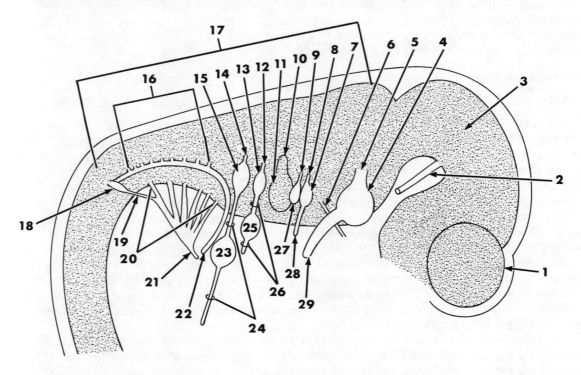

Fig. S. Schematic drawing of the cranial nerves and ganglia in the 10-mm pig embryo.

1. Cerebral hemisphere
2. Oculomotor nerve
3. Mesencephalon
4. Semilunar ganglion
5. Sensory root of the trigeminal nerve
6. Abducens nerve
7. Geniculate ganglion
8. Sensory root of the facial nerve
9. Auditory nerve
10. Endolymphatic duct
11. Auditory vesicle
12. Sensory root of the glossopharyngeal nerve
13. Superior ganglion
14. Sensory root of the vagus nerve
15. Jugular ganglion

16. Roots of the spinal accessory nerve
17. Rhombencephalon
18. Froriep's ganglion
19. Nerve fibers contributed by Froriep's ganglion to the hypoglossal nerve
20. Roots of the hypoglossal nerve
21. Hypoglossal nerve
22. Spinal accessory nerve
23. Nodose ganglion
24. Vagus nerve
25. Petrosal ganglion
26. Glossopharyngeal nerve
27. Acoustic ganglion
28. Facial nerve
29. Mandibular branch of the trigeminal nerve

ing each pigmented retina is condensed, initiating formation of the **choroid** (from both neural crest and mesoderm) and **sclera** (from neural crest) of the eye. Trace sections posteriorly and note that the lateral walls of the brain begin to bulge outward to form the **cerebral hemispheres** of the **telencephalon** and that the diencephalon fades out (Plate 46, Fig. 3; Plate 47, Fig. 1). The cavities of the cerebral hemispheres are the **lateral ventricles** (or **first** and **second ventricles**) and are broadly continuous with the cavity of the middle portion of the telencephalon (minor part of the **third ventricle**). The connections between the lateral and third ventricles later become greatly narrowed as the **interventricular foramina.** Continue tracing sections posteriorly and note that the two cerebral hemispheres separate from one another (Plate 48, Fig. 2). The portion of the telencephalon wall lying between the two cerebral hemispheres is the **lamina terminalis. Commissures** (transverse bundles of nerve fibers) will *later* form within the lamina terminalis to interconnect the cerebral hemispheres.

The prosencephalon is the source of several major adult brain components. The **diencephalon** forms the **thalamus, epithalamus, hypothalamus, pineal gland,** and **posterior pituitary gland** (derivative of the infundibulum); the **telencephalon** forms the **cerebrum, olfactory lobes,** and **corpora striata.**

b. Cranial nerves. The cranial nerves will be described in order, beginning with the first pair. Refer periodically to Fig. S to help you understand the three-dimensional structure of the cranial nerves and their relationships to the various subdivisions of the brain. Return to the most anterior section through the cerebral hemispheres (Plate 46, Fig. 3) and trace sections posteriorly. Identify the **nasal pits.** The cavity of each nasal pit is separated at first from the **amniotic cavity,** but these cavities become confluent in more posterior sections (Plate 47, Fig. 3). Many of the cells within the walls of the nasal pits are **young neurons.** Their **axons** are growing toward the cerebral hemispheres and may be identified in some specimens. These axons constitute on each side the **olfactory (I) cranial nerve** (a **sensory nerve**). **Dendrites** will develop *later* from the young neurons within each nasal pit and differentiate as **olfactory receptors** (receptors for the sense of smell). Identify elevated regions of head mesenchyme covered by skin ectoderm to either side of each nasal pit, the **lateral** and **medial nasal processes.** Each medial nasal process will eventually fuse laterally with a maxillary process and medially with the other medial nasal process to form the **upper jaw.** The lateral nasal processes eventually form the sides of the **nose.**

Return to the level of the optic fissures (Plate 45, Fig. 3) and examine the optic stalks and fissures under high magnification. Recall that within the region of each optic fissure the ventral lip of the optic cup is absent. Therefore the **marginal zone** of each sensory retina is continuous at this level, via the marginal zone of the optic stalk, with the marginal zone of the floor of the diencephalon.

Many of the cells within each sensory retina are **young neurons.** Some of these young neurons form **ganglion cells,** whose **axons** grow into the marginal zone of the sensory retina. These axons remain within the marginal zone and grow to the floor of the diencephalon, constituting the **optic (II) cranial nerves (sensory nerves).** The optic nerves cannot be identified at this stage. (Because the axons constituting each optic nerve remain within the marginal zone throughout their extent, the so-called optic nerves are not actually true nerves, but rather are **fiber tracts** located within derivatives of the diencephalon wall.)

Return to the level where the mesencephalon begins to separate from the metencephalon (Plate 42, Fig. 1) and trace sections posteriorly. Notice two slight thickenings of the floor of the mesencephalon, one on either side of the midline. Each thickening constitutes a **motor nucleus;** it is formed by an accumulation of **cell bodies** of **young neurons** within the **intermediate zone.** Identify **axons** growing out from these motor nuclei. These axons constitute on each side the **oculomotor (III) cranial nerve** (a **motor nerve**). Continue to trace sections posteriorly, noting that the oculomotor nerves terminate near the eye muscle rudiments. These nerves will later innervate four pairs of extrinsic **eye muscles (inferior oblique eye muscles; inferior, superior,** and **medial rectus eye muscles).**

The fourth cranial nerves, the **trochlear (IV) cranial nerves (motor nerves),** consist of **axons** that also grow out from **motor nuclei** developing within the floor of the mesencephalon. (The trochlear nerves grow dorsad within the wall of the brain, cross over to the opposite side, and emerge from the brain in the isthmus region.) These nerves and their motor nuclei cannot be identified at this stage. The trochlear nerves eventually innervate the **superior oblique eye muscles.**

Return again to the level where mesencephalon begins to separate from metencephalon (Plate 42, Fig. 1). As sections are traced posteriorly, **axons** appear at the broadest part of the rhombencephalon, continuous with the latter (Plate 42, Fig. 2). These axons constitute on each side the **sensory root** of the **trigeminal (V) cranial nerve** (a **sensory** and **motor,** that is, **mixed nerve**). These sensory roots are continuous with the large **semilunar ganglia** a few sections more posteriorly (Plate 42, Fig. 3). Continue to trace sections posteriorly. Each semilunar ganglion eventually gives rise to three branches of the **trigeminal nerve,** as in the 72-hour chick embryo: the **ophthalmic branch** (to eye region), **maxillary branch** (to maxillary process), and **mandibular branch** (to mandibular process). Usually only the mandibular branches can be readily identified in the 10-mm pig embryo (Plate 44, Fig. 1). The ophthalmic and maxillary branches are usually very small and are entirely sensory, consisting only of **dendrites.** The mandibular branches are eventually mixed but consist only of **dendrites** at this stage. (**Axons** later will grow out from a pair of **motor nuclei** within the floor of the rhombencephalon as the motor component of the mandibular branches.)

Return to the level where the neural tube is separated into three parts (Plate 42, Fig. 3) and trace sections posteriorly. Identify **axons** growing out on each side from the floor of the rhombencephalon as the latter begins to fade out (Plate 43, Fig. 2). These axons constitute the **abducens (VI) cranial nerves (motor nerves).** The abducens nerves are usually cut across frontally, are very small, and quickly disappear as sections are traced posteriorly. They will later innervate the **lateral rectus eye muscles.**

Return to a level similar to Plate 41, Fig. 1 and trace sections posteriorly. Note that a small vesicle soon appears on each side of the myelencephalon; these vesicles are the **endolymphatic ducts.** Identify the **auditory vesicles,** in slightly more posterior sections, which lie lateral to the endolymphatic ducts (Plate 41, Fig. 3). The dorsal portion of each auditory vesicle forms the **utriculus** of the **inner ear.** The endolymphatic duct and auditory vesicle on each side are continuous in more posterior sections (Plate 42, Fig. 2). The projection nearer the top of the section is the rudiment of the **posterior semicircular canal.** The projection nearer the bottom is the rudiment of the **anterior semicircular canal.** The rudiments of the anterior and posterior semicircular canals are attached to the dorsal portion of the auditory vesicle (that is, the future utriculus). (The rudiment of the **lateral semicircular canal** will form *later* from the utriculus portion of each auditory vesicle.) The rudiments of the anterior and posterior semicircular canals disappear in more posterior sections; this portion of each auditory vesicle is the future **sacculus** of the **inner ear** (Plate 42, Fig. 3). The utriculi, semicircular canals, and sacculi form receptors for maintaining equilibrium. The auditory vesicles narrow and fade out as sections are traced posteriorly. The ventral portion of each auditory vesicle becomes the **cochlea** of the **inner ear** (Plate 43, Fig. 2), which forms the receptor organ for sound (that is, the **spiral organ of Corti**).

The next two cranial nerves are closely associated with each other and with the auditory vesicles and will therefore be described together. Return to a level similar to Plate 42, Fig. 3 and note that two ganglia lie just below each future sacculus. The lowermost ganglion is the **geniculate ganglion** of the **facial (VII) cranial nerve** (a **mixed nerve**); the uppermost ganglion is the **acoustic ganglion** of the **auditory (VIII) cranial nerve** (a **sensory nerve**). At about this level, or in slightly more posterior sections, **axons** constituting the **sensory roots** of the **facial nerves** interconnect the geniculate ganglia and rhombencephalon (Plate 43, Fig. 1). (**Axons** constituting the **auditory nerves** similarly interconnect the acoustic ganglia and rhombencephalon, but they are difficult to identify with certainty because the auditory nerves are very short and closely applied to the sensory roots of the facial nerves.) Continue to trace sections posteriorly and identify the **facial nerves** extending from the geniculate ganglia into the *second* branchial arches (Plate 43, Fig. 2). The facial nerves consist only of **dendrites** at this stage. (**Axons** will later grow out from a pair of **motor nuclei** within the floor of the rhombencephalon as the motor component of the facial nerves.) Note that the acoustic ganglia and auditory vesicles fade out at about the same level (Plate 43, Fig. 2). (Each acoustic ganglion eventually subdivides into two parts [usually at later stages], the **vestibular** and **spiral [cochlear] ganglia. Dendrites** from **cell bodies** of **young neurons** within the **vestibular ganglia** terminate in equilibrium receptors in the semicircular canals, utriculi, and sacculi; **dendrites** from **cell bodies** of **young neurons** within the **spiral ganglia** terminate in the spiral organ of Corti within each cochlea.)

Return to the level at which the auditory vesicle and endolymphatic duct on each side become continuous (Plate 42, Fig. 1). Identify **axons** continuous with the wall of the myelencephalon just above each auditory vesicle. These axons constitute on each side the **sensory root** of the

glossopharyngeal (IX) cranial nerve (a **mixed nerve**). The **superior ganglia** of the **glossopharyngeal nerves** appear in slightly more posterior sections (Plate 42, Fig. 2). Continue tracing sections posteriorly. The dorsomost portions of the glossopharyngeal nerves soon appear in place of the superior ganglia (Plate 42, Fig. 3). Another pair of ganglia (much larger than the superior ganglia) appear in place of the glossopharyngeal nerves in more posterior sections (Plate 43, Fig. 2). These are the **petrosal ganglia** of the glossopharyngeal nerves. Finally, the ventromost portions of the **glossopharyngeal nerves** appear in place of the petrosal ganglia in slightly more posterior sections (Plate 44, Figs. 1, 2). Try to trace the ventromost portion of the glossopharyngeal nerves into the *third* branchial arches, where they terminate. **Cell bodies** of **young neurons** within the superior and petrosal ganglia form both **axons** and **dendrites.** The sensory roots of the glossopharyngeal nerves consist of **axons** formed by cell bodies of young neurons within both the superior and petrosal ganglia. The portion of the glossopharyngeal nerve that interconnects the superior and petrosal ganglia on each side (that is, the dorsomost portion) consists of **axons** formed by cell bodies of young neurons within the petrosal ganglion and **dendrites** formed by cell bodies of young neurons within the superior ganglion. The portion of the glossopharyngeal nerve that extends from the petrosal ganglion to the third branchial arch on each side (that is, the ventromost portion) consists of only **dendrites** formed by cell bodies of young neurons within both the superior and petrosal ganglia. (**Axons** constituting the motor component of the glossopharyngeal nerves will later grow out from a pair of **motor nuclei** within the floor of the myelencephalon.)

Return to a section similar to Plate 41, Fig. 1 and trace sections posteriorly. At about the level at which the endolymphatic ducts appear, identify **axons** continuous with the wall of the myelencephalon just caudal to the auditory vesicles (Plate 41, Fig. 3). These axons constitute on each side the **sensory root** of the **vagus (X) cranial nerve** (a **mixed nerve**).

The large **jugular ganglia** of the vagus nerves appear a few sections more posteriorly (Plate 42, Fig. 1). Note that the jugular ganglia lie just caudal to the superior ganglia. The jugular ganglia fade out in more posterior sections and the **vagus nerves** appear in their place (Plate 42, Fig. 3). (These portions of the vagus nerves consist of **dendrites** derived from **cell bodies** of **young neurons** within the jugular ganglia and axons derived from **cell bodies** of **young neurons** within a second pair of ganglia, the **nodose ganglia**.) Continue tracing sections posteriorly and observe that the vagus nerves fade out and that the **nodose ganglia** (derived from a pair of **epibranchial placodes**) appear in their place (Plate 44, Fig. 2). The nodose ganglia fade out in the area of the *fourth* branchial arches in more posterior sections. It is difficult to trace the **vagus nerves** caudal to this level. They have extended caudad in many embryos and lie ventrolateral to the esophagus (Plate 48, Fig. 2). At these caudal levels the vagus nerves consist mainly of **preganglionic axons** of the **parasympathetic division** of the **autonomic nervous system.** These axons grow out from **motor nuclei** (impossible to identify) developing within the floor of the myelencephalon. (The vagus nerves also contain **dendrites** formed by **cell bodies** of **young neurons** within both the jugular and nodose ganglia.)

Return to a level similar to Plate 41, Fig. 1 and trace sections posteriorly. Identify **axons** growing out from the myelencephalon (Plate 41, Fig. 2). These axons constitute on each side the **roots** of the **spinal accessory (XI) cranial nerve** (a **motor nerve**). A few sections more posteriorly, these roots merge together on each side and are cut frontally as the **spinal accessory nerve** (Plate 41, Fig. 3). Each spinal accessory nerve is cut across twice, a few sections more posteriorly (Plate 42, Fig. 1). The part of each spinal accessory nerve nearest the top of the section can be traced caudally where it eventually fades out adjacent to the spinal cord. Trace the lower part of each spinal accessory nerve caudally. It first lies adjacent to the jugular ganglion, then adjacent to the vagus nerve (Plate 42, Fig. 3), then adjacent to the nodose ganglion (Plate 44, Fig. 3); finally it fades out. The spinal accessory nerves eventually innervate mainly derivatives of the *fourth* branchial arches and certain **neck** and **shoulder** muscles (that is, the **sternocleidomastoid** and **trapezius muscles**).

Return to the level where the spinal accessory nerves are cut frontally (Plate 41, Fig. 3) and trace sections posteriorly. Identify several bundles of **axons** growing out from the myelencephalon (Plate 42, Fig. 2). These bundles constitute on each side the **roots** of the **hypoglossal (XII) cranial nerve** (a **motor nerve**). Trace these roots as far caudally as possible. It may be possible to observe in some embryos that the roots merge on each side and continue caudally as the **hypoglossal nerve.** The hypoglossal nerves eventually innervate the **tongue muscles.**

The chart on the following page summarizes the development of cranial nerves through the 10-mm stage.

Cranial Nerves	Cranial Ganglia	Origin of Cranial Ganglia	Type of Nerve Fibers Present	Regions Innervated
olfactory	_____	_____	sensory	lining of nasal cavities
optic (nerves cannot be identified)	_____	_____	sensory	retinas
oculomotor	_____	_____	motor	inferior oblique eye muscles; inferior, superior, and medial rectus eye muscles
trochlear (nerves cannot be identified)	_____	_____	motor	superior oblique eye muscles
trigeminal	semilunar	neural crest cells and epibranchial placodes	sensory (*later* also motor)	primarily derivatives of branchial arches
abducens	_____	_____	motor	lateral rectus eye muscles
facial	geniculate	neural crest cells and epibranchial placodes	sensory (*later* also motor)	primarily derivatives of second branchial arches
auditory	acoustic	auditory placodes	sensory	inner ears
glosso-pharyngeal	superior and petrosal	neural crest cells and epibranchial placodes, respectively	sensory (*later* also motor)	primarily derivatives of third branchial arches
vagus	jugular and nodose	neural crest cells and epibranchial placodes, respectively	sensory and motor	primarily derivatives of fourth branchial arches
spinal accessory	_____	_____	motor	primarily derivatives of fourth branchial arches and certain neck and shoulder muscles
hypoglossal	_____	_____	motor	tongue muscles

c. Spinal cord and spinal nerves. Return to the level where the spinal accessory nerves are cut frontally (Plate 41, Fig. 3) and trace sections posteriorly, watching the uppermost part of the neural tube in your sections. Observe a rather small, but prominent, ganglion on each side just caudal to the roots of the spinal accessory nerve; this is **Froriep's ganglion** (Plate 42, Fig. 2), which contributes nerve fibers to the hypoglossal nerve. The level of Froriep's ganglia is still the level of the myelencephalon, but the **spinal cord** gradually appears a few sections more posteriorly. At about this level, identify a pair of ganglia lying adjacent to the cranial end of the spinal cord, the most cranial **spinal ganglia.**

Quickly trace the spinal cord caudally and find one or more sections that show all the following structures (see Plate 51, Fig. 2; A, Figs. 470, 618–623): **dorsal root** (composed of **axons** entering the spinal cord, **spinal ganglion,** and **dendrites** entering the spinal ganglion), **ventral root** (composed of **axons** leaving the spinal cord), and **spinal nerve** with its three branches: the **dorsal ramus, ventral ramus,** and **visceral ramus (ramus communicans).** The visceral ramus extends ventromedially on each side toward an accumulation of **neural crest cells,** one of the **sympathetic chain ganglia** of the

autonomic nervous system. (The **sympathetic collateral** and **parasympathetic terminal ganglia** of the **autonomic nervous system** will form *later* from other accumulations of **neural crest cells.**)

Identify the following components of the spinal cord: **ventricular, intermediate,** and **marginal zones, alar plate** (dorsal half of spinal cord), **basal plate** (ventral half of spinal cord), **sulcus limitans** (slight depression on each side partially separating alar and basal plates), **roof** and **floor plates,** and **motor horns** (paired enlargements of the ventral part of the intermediate zone). Note the small diameter of the **notochord**; it is enclosed within a mass of sclerotome cells that will later form the **centrum** of each **vertebra.** Most of the notochord ultimately degenerates.

At the level of the foreleg buds, the ventral rami of adjacent spinal nerves are interconnected in complex ways to form the **brachial plexus** (Plate 49, Fig. 1). (A **lumbosacral plexus** will form *later* at the level of the hindleg buds.) Note that the **foreleg** and **hindleg buds** consist of an outer layer of ectoderm, part of which is thickened as the **apical ectodermal ridge,** and a core of somatic mesoderm. Note a small dorsolateral swelling on each side at section levels between the limb buds, the **mammary ridge** (Plate 49, Fig. 3).

Trace the spinal cord caudally until it is cut frontally due to the tail flexure (Plate 54, Fig. 3). Identify the **dermatome, myotome,** and **sclerotome** subdivisions of the **somites.** Note that each sclerotome has a dense *caudal* portion and a less dense *cranial* portion. Each **vertebra** is formed by the fusion of the caudal half of one sclerotome with the cranial half of the next caudal sclerotome. By examining sections anterior or posterior to this level, identify the **spinal ganglia** and the **ventral roots** of the **spinal nerves,** which leave the ventrolateral walls of the spinal cord.

2. Respiratory and digestive systems.

Aids: Fig. T; A, Figs. 601–604, 613; M, Fig. 235; PA, Figs. 60, 64.

Find the most anterior section showing a round **esophagus** (Plate 47, Fig. 2). The round **trachea** usually lies beneath the esophagus at this level. Trace sections posteriorly a considerable distance, watching both esophagus and trachea. Note a distinct asymmetrical evagination of the trachea toward the *right* (apparent left) side. This evagination is the **eparterial bronchus** (Plate 48, Fig. 2); it will form the upper lobe of the right **lung.** Continue tracing sections posteriorly and observe that a vesicle appears on each side of the trachea and quickly becomes continuous with the latter. These vesicles are the **lung buds.** The trachea fades out in more posterior sections and the lung buds continue caudally for a short distance (Plate 49, Fig. 1). (Each of the two lung buds bifurcates *later* to form two lobes of the lung. Therefore, in the adult the *right* lung contains three lobes, the *left* lung, only two.) Note at this level that the **pleural cavities** lie lateral to the lung buds and that they are continuous laterally with the **peritoneal cavity.** A thin layer of splanchnic mesoderm, the **visceral pleura,** lies just medial to each pleural cavity (examine this layer under high magnification). The **parietal pleura** has not yet formed at this level. The pleural cavities are isolated from all other portions of the coelom more *cranially,* and visceral and parietal pleura can be identified (Plate 48, Fig. 3).

Return to a level similar to Plate 49, Fig. 1 and trace sections posteriorly, noting that the esophagus shifts ventrad and the lung buds fade out (Plate 49, Fig. 2). Identify the **mesoesophagus.** The **stomach** appears in more posterior sections (Plate 49, Fig. 3). It has undergone a rotation around its longitudinal axis of approximately 45°, so its original *dorsal* surface lies to the *left* (apparent right) and its *ventral* surface lies to the *right* (apparent left). The original dorsal surface forms the **greater curvature** of the adult stomach; the original ventral surface forms the **lesser curvature.** Identify the **dorsal mesogaster,** which enlarges vastly as the adult **greater omentum.** (Mesenchymal cells will aggregate *later* within the dorsal mesogaster and form the **spleen.**) Also identify the mesentery connecting stomach and **liver,** the **hepatogastric ligament.** Note that the liver is subdivided into paired **dorsal** and **ventral lobes,** and that it consists of irregularly shaped cords of cells, the **hepatic cords**; the hepatic cords are separated by irregular vascular spaces, the **hepatic sinusoids.** The liver at this stage is functioning as a **hemopoietic organ** (that is, it is temporarily producing blood cells). Identify the **omental bursa,** a closed cavity to the *right* (apparent left) of the stomach.

Trace sections posteriorly, noting that the omental bursa opens into the **peritoneal cavity** via the **epiploic foramen** (Plate 50, Fig. 2). Lining the peritoneal cavity are the **visceral peritoneum** (a thin layer of splanchnic mesoderm on the surface of the abdominal organs) and the **parietal**

peritoneum (a thin layer of somatic mesoderm on the internal surface of the ventral and lateral body walls). Examine these layers under high magnification.

Return to the level of the stomach (Plate 49, Fig. 3) and trace sections posteriorly, noting that the stomach fades out and the **duodenum** appears in its place (Plate 50, Fig. 1). Sections at about this level also cut through the endodermal **hepatic duct**, located within the dorsal part of the liver. The mesentery connecting duodenum and liver is the **hepatoduodenal** ligament. (The hepatogastric and hepatoduodenal ligaments collectively constitute the adult **lesser omentum**.) The mesentery connecting the liver to the ventral body wall is the **falciform ligament**. In slightly more posterior sections, the hepatic duct constricts into an upper **common bile duct**, which quickly joins the duodenum, and a lower **cystic duct** (Plate 50, Fig. 2). The cystic duct gradually expands as the **gall bladder** in more posterior sections. The gall bladder may be bilobed or trilobed in some specimens. Continue to trace sections posteriorly until the liver disappears. Then reverse direction and trace sections *anteriorly*, noting the reappearance of the liver and finally the disappearance of its cranial end. Note that the cranial end of the liver terminates in a transverse partition, the **septum transversum** (Plate 49, Fig. 1).

Return to the level where the common bile duct joins the duodenum (Plate 50, Fig. 2) and trace sections posteriorly. As the common bile duct disappears, a small, darkly stained solid mass of cells, the **ventral pancreatic rudiment**, appears in its place (Plate 50, Fig. 3). The ventral pancreatic rudiment develops as an outgrowth from the common bile duct; its original connection to the common bile duct, the **ventral pancreatic duct (duct of Wirsung)**, is degenerating and probably cannot be identified. (In humans this connection usually persists.) Identify the **dorsal pancreatic rudiment** at about this same level. This rudiment develops as an outgrowth from the duodenum; its connection to the duodenum, the **dorsal pancreatic duct (duct of Santorini)**, persists in the adult pig to transport to the duodenum certain pancreatic secretions involved in digestion. (In humans this connection usually degenerates.) Dorsal and ventral pancreatic rudiments will fuse *later* to form the **pancreas**.

Trace sections posteriorly from the level at which the dorsal pancreatic duct connects to the duodenum (Plate 50, Fig. 3) and note that the duodenum lies dorsal to another region of the gut, which is contained within the lightly stained tissue of the **umbilical cord** (that is, the latter region of the gut is contained within **Wharton's jelly**, a mesodermal derivative). This latter region of the gut is the **cranial limb of the intestinal loop** (Plate 51, Fig. 1). The **intestinal loop** has herniated into the **extraembryonic coelom** of the umbilical cord, forming the temporary **umbilical hernia**. (The cranial limb of the intestinal loop later forms mainly the **jejunum** and most of the **ileum** of the adult **small intestine**.) The duodenum and cranial limb of the intestinal loop progressively approach one another and become continuous as sections are traced posteriorly. These regions of the gut are cut frontally at this level (Fig. T, level a; Plate 52, Fig. 1), and they quickly disappear as sections are traced posteriorly. Return to the level where the duodenum and cranial limb of the intestinal loop are cut frontally and trace sections *anteriorly*, observing the cranial limb of the intestinal loop. Note that it rotates somewhat toward the *right* (apparent left) to lie alongside another portion of the gut, the **caudal limb of the intestinal loop** (Plate 51, Fig. 3). (The caudal limb of the intestinal loop later forms principally the **ascending colon** and most of the **transverse colon** of the adult **large intestine**.) Trace sections *anteriorly* a considerable distance and try to observe the continuity of the two limbs at the apex of the intestinal loop (see Fig. T, level b; A, Figs. 601, 603). The **yolk sac** normally attaches to the intestinal loop at its apex. If the yolk sac is present in your specimen, it will first appear as a slight circular expansion of the gut tube as the apex of the intestinal loop is traced *anteriorly*. The yolk sac appears as a large, irregularly shaped vesicle in more *anterior* sections (Plate 49, Fig. 2). (Unfortunately, in some specimens the umbilical cord has been cut off so close to the body that the apex of the intestinal loop and the yolk sac are not present in sections.)

Return to the level of the apex of the intestinal loop, or as close to this level as possible, and trace sections *posteriorly*, observing the caudal limb of the intestinal loop. It rotates somewhat toward the *left* (apparent right) and is eventually suspended between the two large mesonephric kidneys by a long, thin mesentery (Plate 52, Fig. 3). Because this portion of the caudal limb of the intestinal loop will form part of the **colon** of the adult **large intestine**, this mesentery is part of the **mesocolon**. The caudal limb of the intestinal loop approaches another region of the gut as you continue to trace sections posteriorly. This latter region is the caudal part of the **colon** (Plate 53, Fig. 2); it quickly joins the caudal limb of the intestinal loop, and these two structures are cut frontally (Fig.

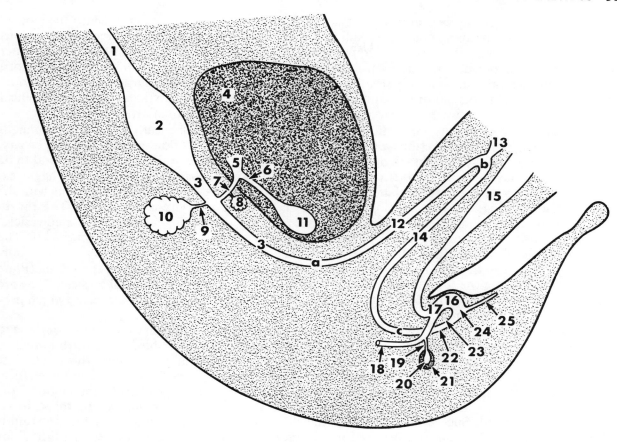

Fig. T. Schematic drawing of the digestive and urogenital systems in the 10-mm pig embryo. Letters a-c indicate gut levels described in text. The outer line indicates the boundaries of the caudal two-thirds of the embryo and of the umbilical cord.

1. Esophagus
2. Stomach
3. Duodenum
4. Liver
5. Hepatic duct
6. Cystic duct
7. Common bile duct
8. Ventral pancreatic rudiment
9. Dorsal pancreatic duct
10. Dorsal pancreatic rudiment
11. Gall bladder
12. Cranial limb of the intestinal loop
13. Yolk sac
14. Caudal limb of the intestinal loop
15. Allantois
16. Cloaca
17. Urogenital sinus
18. Mesonephric duct
19. Ureter
20. Renal pelvis
21. Nephrotome
22. Colon
23. Cloacal septum
24. Rectum
25. Tail gut

T, level c). They then quickly disappear as sections are traced posteriorly. Reverse direction and trace sections *anteriorly*, following the lower part of the gut in your sections (that is, the colon). Note that the gut becomes slightly elongated dorsoventrally, indicating the level of the **rectum.** The rectum then quickly joins a large cavity, the **cloaca** (Plate 52, Fig. 3). The cloaca is subdividing at this stage into a dorsal (lower) **rectum** and a ventral (upper) **urogenital sinus.** The mesodermal ingrowth that separates the cloaca into these two chambers is the **cloacal septum.**

Trace sections *anteriorly* while watching the cloaca, and note that, as it fades out, a solid cord of cells, the **cloacal membrane,** can be identified (Plate 52, Fig. 2). (This membrane appears different from the one seen in the 72-hour chick embryo because it is cut frontally rather than transversely.) Note that the cloacal membrane is contained within a large swelling, the **genital eminence.** A small degenerating **tail gut** can be identified at about this level in some specimens.

Trace sections *posteriorly* and try to observe that the tail gut opens cranially into the cloaca. Note that the cloaca becomes completely subdivided into the **urogenital sinus** and **rectum** as sections are traced posteriorly. The **colon** again appears in more posterior sections (note its rounded, rather than elongated, shape) and an endoderm-lined cavity, the **allantois**, emerges from the umbilical cord to join the urogenital sinus ventrally (Plate 53, Fig. 1). Reverse direction and trace sections *anteriorly*, following the allantois out into the umbilical cord (Plates 52, 51). Note that within the umbilical cord the allantois lies between two large arteries, the **umbilical (allantoic) arteries**.

Return to the most anterior section showing the round **trachea** beneath the round **esophagus** (Plate 47, Fig. 2) and trace sections *anteriorly*. The trachea elongates dorsoventrally as the **larynx**, which lies beneath the somewhat triangularly shaped esophagus. (The walls of the larynx tend to be in contact and may therefore be difficult to identify.) In more *anterior* sections, the esophagus expands, indicating the level of the **pharynx**, and the latter immediately becomes continuous with the larynx (Plate 46, Fig. 2). The opening of the larynx into the pharynx is the **glottis**. The **fourth pharyngeal pouches** can be identified at about this level. They usually first appear as isolated vesicles ventrolateral to the pharynx but then quickly join the pharynx as sections are traced *anteriorly*. The fourth pharyngeal pouches are the sources of the adult **superior parathyroid glands**. A small dorsolateral evagination of each fourth pharyngeal pouch can be identified in some specimens (Plate 46, Fig. 1). These are the rudimentary **fifth pharyngeal pouches (ultimobranchial bodies)**. They are later incorporated into the thyroid gland, where they give rise to **C (parafollicular) cells**, which produce the hormone **calcitonin**.

Note a broad *ectodermal* invagination on each side, lateral to the pharynx, as you continue to trace sections *anteriorly* (Plate 45, Fig. 2), the **cervical sinus** (combined **third** and **fourth branchial grooves**). The larynx usually opens broadly into the pharynx via the glottis at about this level. Note the prominent swellings on either side of the glottis, the **arytenoid swellings**. These will later form the **arytenoid cartilages** of the **larynx**. Identify the **thyroid gland**, lying beneath the floor of the pharynx at about this level. Its original connection to the floor of the pharynx, the **thyroglossal duct**, has degenerated. Such a ductless gland that drains its secretions only into the bloodstream is an **endocrine gland**. Continue to trace sections *anteriorly* and identify a midline swelling of the floor of the pharynx just cranial to the glottis. This swelling is the **epiglottis** (Plate 45, Fig. 1). It is derived from the third and fourth branchial arches.

Return again to the most posterior section through the glottis (Plate 46, Fig. 2) and trace sections *anteriorly*. Identify a pair of flattened vesicles lying just above (dorsal to) the third branchial arches, the **third pharyngeal pouches** (Plate 45, Fig. 3). The ventral portions of the two third-pharyngeal pouches (that is, the portions shown in Plate 45, Fig. 3) *later* fuse in the midline to form the **thymus gland**. The third pharyngeal pouches move dorsad and become continuous with the pharynx as sections are traced *anteriorly*. Identify the **third closing plates** at about this level. The dorsal portions of the third pharyngeal pouches (that is, the portions shown in Plate 45, Figs. 1, 2) form the **inferior parathyroid glands**. The rudiments of these glands can be seen in most embryos under high magnification as a thickening on each side just beneath the cavity of the third pharyngeal pouch (see A, Fig. 613). (Each entire third pharyngeal pouch, including the rudiments of the inferior parathyroid and thymus glands, later migrates caudal to the fourth and fifth pharyngeal pouches. Thus, in the adult the inferior parathyroid glands [derived from the third pharyngeal pouches] lie *caudal* to the superior parathyroid glands [derived from the fourth pharyngeal pouches].)

Continue to trace sections *anteriorly* and identify the **second pharyngeal pouches** (Plate 44, Figs. 3–1), the sources of the adult **palatine tonsils**. Also identify the **second branchial grooves** and **second closing plates**. The latter may be partially ruptured, forming the **second branchial clefts**. If so, the exact boundary between the second branchial groove and pharyngeal pouch on each side may be difficult to determine. Identify the **tongue rudiments** at about the level of the second pharyngeal pouches. They consist of a pair of **lateral lingual swellings**, a midline **tuberculum impar**, and a midline **copula** (Plate 44, Figs. 2, 3). The copula is derived from the second branchial arches; the lateral lingual swellings and tuberculum impar from the first branchial arches (although these three latter structures are now fused with the second branchial arches). Note that the tongue rudiments protrude into the pharynx.

Trace sections *anteriorly*. At about the level at which the tongue rudiments fade out, identify the **first branchial grooves, closing plates,** and **pharyngeal pouches** (Plate 44, Fig. 1; Plate 43, Fig. 3). The first branchial groove on each side forms the adult **external auditory meatus (external ear** canal). Each first closing plate, after mesodermal cells penetrate between its ectoderm and endoderm, forms a **tympanic membrane.** Note that each first pharyngeal pouch consists of two portions (Plate 44, Fig. 1). The upper portion in your sections connects to the pharynx and forms the adult **Eustacian (pharyngotympanic) tube;** the lower portion forms the **tympanic (middle ear) cavity.** The tympanic cavity on each side will eventually surround the **ear ossicles** (that is, the **malleus** and **incus** [derivatives of the first branchial arch] and the **stapes** [derivative of the second branchial arch]). Elevations will *later* form from the first and second branchial arches to either side of the first branchial grooves. These elevations will subsequently fuse on each side to form the **pinna (auricle)** of the **external ear.**

3. Urogenital system.

Aids: Fig. T; A, Figs. 599, 601, 603; M, Figs. 234, 235; PA, Figs. 59, 60, 64.

Return to the level of the cloacal membrane (Plate 52, Fig. 2) and trace sections posteriorly until the cloaca is reached. Note that the ventral (upper) portion of the cloaca broadens transversely. This broadened portion is the **urogenital sinus.** The urogenital sinus is continuous with the **mesonephric ducts** in more posterior sections (Fig. T; Plate 53, Fig. 1). Continue tracing sections posteriorly, following the mesonephric ducts. Note that they lie lateral to the colon (Plate 53, Fig. 2). They are quickly cut frontally, as they join another portion of the mesonephric ducts located in the ventral part of the large **mesonephric kidneys** (Plate 53, Fig. 3). The mesonephric ducts disappear a few sections more posteriorly.

Return to the level where the mesonephric ducts are cut frontally (Plate 53, Fig. 3) and trace that part of each mesonephric duct within the mesonephric kidney *anteriorly*. Note that numerous **mesonephric tubules** are continuous with it. Continue to trace sections *anteriorly*, until the mesonephric ducts can no longer be identified. The mesonephric duct on each side will form the **epididymis, vas deferens,** and **ejaculatory duct** of the adult male reproductive system; it will also give rise to an evagination that forms the **seminal vesicle.** The mesonephric ducts mainly degenerate in the female.

Note the tremendous size of the mesonephric kidneys relative to that of other structures of the pig embryo (see A, Fig. 599; M, Fig. 234; PA, Fig. 59). This large size probably counteracts the rather inefficient **placenta** of pig embryos (**diffuse, epitheliochorialis type** with a **placental membrane [barrier]** composed of many layers). The placenta apparently does not remove nitrogenous wastes from the bloodstream of pig embryos very readily; pig embryos therefore possess massive mesonephric kidneys to take care of this function for themselves. Examine a section cut through about the middle of the mesonephric kidneys (Plate 52). Note that this type of kidney consists mostly of **mesonephric tubules.** These tubules mainly degenerate in females. In males some mesonephric tubules persist as the **efferent ductules (vasa efferentia)** of the adult reproductive system; the remaining tubules degenerate. At the medial side of each mesonephric kidney, note several large spaces bounded by a very flat epithelium and filled with cells. These expanded spaces are the **glomerular (Bowman's) capsules** of the mesonephric tubules (Plate 52, Fig. 1). The cells within the glomerular capsules are capillaries, constituting the **glomeruli,** and contained blood cells (Plate 52, Fig. 2). Glomerular capsules and glomeruli of mesonephric kidneys later degenerate in both males and females.

The **gonad rudiments** are just forming at this stage as a thickening on the medial side of each mesonephric kidney (Plate 50, Fig. 2; Plate 51, Fig. 3; Plate 52, Fig. 2). Each gonad rudiment consists of a localized thickening of visceral peritoneum (that is, a localized thickening of the splanchnic mesoderm that covers the organs of the peritoneal cavity), called the **germinal epithelium,** and a subjacent region of condensed mesenchyme (Plate 50, Fig. 3). The gonad rudiments contain **primordial germ cells** (not readily identifiable), which in mammals originate from the **endoderm** of the caudal portion of the **yolk sac.** These cells then undergo an extensive migration through the splanchnic mesoderm of the yolk sac and the dorsal gut mesentery to reach the gonad rudiments.

Return to the level where the mesonephric ducts connect to the urogenital sinus (Plate 53, Fig. 1) and trace sections posteriorly. Note that a small duct emerges from the dorsal (lower) side of each mesonephric duct shortly after the urogenital sinus fades out (Plate 53, Fig. 3). These ducts are the ureters. Continue tracing sections posteriorly, noting that the **ureters** separate from the mesonephric ducts and that each eventually expands as the **renal pelvis** (Plate 54, Fig. 1). The distinct epithelial walls of these structures (that is, the layer next to the lumen) later bud repeatedly, forming the **major** and **minor calyces** and **collecting tubules** of the **metanephric kidneys.** The very dark mass of cells just outside each renal pelvis consists of condensed **nephrotome** (Plate 54, Fig. 1), which forms the **secretory tubules** of the **metanephric kidneys.** Thus, development of the metanephric kidneys involves both epithelial and mesenchymal components. It has been demonstrated experimentally that neither of these components can develop in the absence of the other. Therefore, development of the metanephric kidneys depends on **epithelial-mesenchymal interactions (inductions),** which are similarly involved in the development of many other structures whose rudiments consist of epithelial and mesenchymal components.

4. Circulatory system.

Aids: Figs. U–X; A–V#6, #7; A, Figs. 606, 607, 622, 623; M, Figs. 235, 236; PA, Figs. 66–68.

a. Arterial system. Begin with the most posterior section through the **bulbus cordis** (Plate 48, Fig. 1) and trace sections *anteriorly.* Observe that the cavity of the bulbus cordis becomes separated into two cavities by the approximation of two ingrowths of the bulbus cordis wall. These ingrowths are the **bulbar ridges** (Plate 47, Fig. 2); they are fused in more *anterior* sections as the **bulbar septum** (Plate 47, Fig. 1), which separates the bulbus cordis into two vessels. The vessel to the *right* (apparent left) is the **aortic trunk (ascending aorta);** the vessel to the *left* is the **pulmonary trunk.** Note that the pulmonary trunk extends dorsad at about this level, so as to be cut frontally, and is continuous with the two **sixth-aortic arches** (Plate 47, Fig. 1). The *left* (apparent right) sixth aortic arch is usually larger in diameter than is the *right.* Continue tracing sections *anteriorly* and observe that the sixth aortic arches join the **dorsal aortae** (Plate 46, Figs. 2, 1). The distal end of the *left* sixth aortic arch (that is, the portion that connects to the *left* dorsal aorta) is the **ductus arteriosus** (Fig. U); it persists until birth as an important blood channel acting as a shunt, enabling much of the blood to bypass the functionless lungs. The ductus arteriosus is converted after birth into a fibrous ligament, the **ligamentum arteriosum.** The distal end of the *right* sixth aortic arch soon degenerates. The *right* (apparent left) dorsal aorta is usually smaller than the *left* at the level where the sixth aortic arches join the dorsal aortae. This level of the *right* dorsal aorta becomes part of the adult **right subclavian artery,** carrying blood mainly to the right foreleg, whereas this level of the *left* dorsal aorta becomes part of the adult **arch of the aorta,** carrying blood to most regions of the body (Fig. U).

Return to the level where the pulmonary trunk gives rise to the sixth aortic arches (Plate 47, Fig. 1) and trace sections *posteriorly.* Identify the **pulmonary arteries** as the sixth aortic arches fade out (Plate 47, Fig. 2). These arteries originated as caudal outgrowths from the sixth aortic arches. Try to trace the pulmonary arteries back toward the lung buds.

Return to the level of the bulbar septum (Plate 47, Fig. 1) and trace sections *anteriorly,* noting the disappearance of the pulmonary trunk after it gives rise to the sixth aortic arches (Plate 46, Fig. 3). (The **fifth aortic arches** are rudimentary and have degenerated by this stage.) Identify the **fourth aortic arches** (Plate 45, Fig. 3), continuous with the aortic trunk, and note that they quickly join the dorsal aortae (Plate 45, Figs. 3, 2). The *left* (apparent right) fourth aortic arch is typically larger than the *right.* The former is incorporated into the adult **arch of the aorta;** the latter into the adult **right subclavian artery** (Fig. U). Observe that the aortic trunk terminates cranially by dividing into the two **third-aortic arches** (Plate 45, Fig. 2). (The **first** and **second aortic arches** have degenerated or are degenerating by this stage.) Try to identify a pair of small vessels extending ventrad from the third aortic arches at about this level. These vessels are the **external carotid arteries;** attempt to trace them into the developing lower jaw (that is, the mandibular processes).

Return to the level where the third aortic arches join the dorsal aortae (Plate 45, Fig. 2) and trace sections *anteriorly.* Note that the third aortic arches join the dorsal aortae (Plate 44, Fig. 1). The third aortic arches form the adult **common carotid arteries** and part of the adult **internal carotid arteries.** The remainder of each internal carotid artery is formed from an extension of each dorsal aorta, cranial to the connection between the third aortic arch and dorsal aorta (Fig. U). Observe that the portion of each dorsal aorta lying between its connection to the fourth and third aortic arches is considerably reduced in diameter (Fig. U; Plate 44, Figs. 1–3). This level of each dorsal aorta, the **ductus caroticus,** will soon completely degenerate. Following this degeneration, blood passing from the aortic trunk into the *third* aortic arches will flow cranially through the **internal carotid arteries,** whereas blood passing from the aortic trunk into the *fourth* aortic arches will flow caudally through the **right subclavian artery** and the **arch of the aorta.**

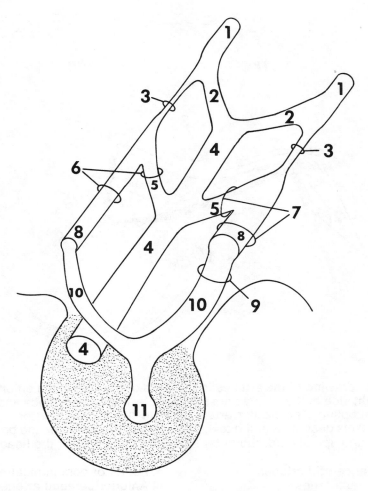

Fig. U. Drawing of a reconstruction of the aortic arches of the 10-mm pig embryo. (Because this reconstruction was made directly from transverse sections, the *right* side of the embryo is drawn on the apparent left side of the reconstruction and the *left* side of the embryo is drawn on the apparent right side of the reconstruction.)

1. Internal carotid artery
2. Third aortic arch
3. Ductus caroticus
4. Aortic trunk
5. Fourth aortic arch
6. Two components of adult right subclavian artery
7. Two components of adult arch of the aorta
8. Dorsal aorta
9. Ductus arteriosus
10. Sixth aortic arch
11. Pulmonary trunk

Continue tracing sections *anteriorly,* following the internal carotid arteries (that is, the cranial extensions of the dorsal aortae). They are quickly cut frontally (Fig. V, level a; Plate 43, Fig. 3) and disappear a few sections more *anteriorly*. Return to the level where the internal carotid arteries are cut frontally (Fig. V, level a; Plate 43, Fig. 3). Shift your attention to the lower end of each internal carotid artery (that is, the end nearest the diencephalon) and trace sections *posteriorly*. The internal carotid arteries gradually move downward toward the diencephalon (Fig. V, level b; Plate 44, Figs. 1–3), where each joins another vessel cut frontally. These latter vessels are the cranial ends of the internal carotid arteries (Fig. V, level c). Each is continuous at its lower end with a small **anterior cerebral artery** (Plate 44, Fig. 3). Continue tracing sections *posteriorly,* watching the anterior cerebral arteries. They are difficult to follow because they are just developing, but they can usually be identified in more *posterior* sections lateral to the diencephalon (Plate 45, Fig. 3).

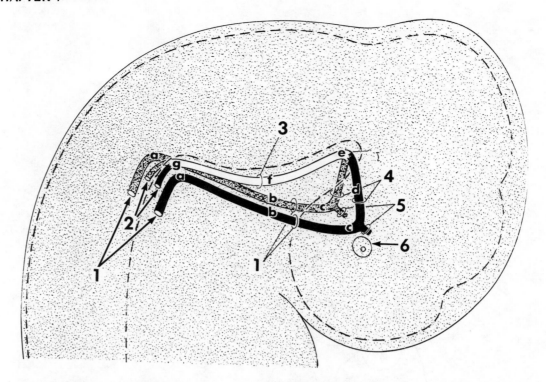

Fig. V. Schematic drawing of the arteries in the head of the 10-mm pig embryo. Arteries on the right side of the embryo are indicated by heavy black lines and on the left side by stippling. The basilar artery (3) is in the midline. Letters a-g indicate specific levels described in the text. The dashed line indicates the boundaries of the brain and spinal cord; the outer line, the boundaries of the head.

1. Internal carotid arteries
2. Vertebral arteries
3. Basilar artery

4. Posterior communicating arteries
5. Anterior cerebral arteries
6. Eye

Return to the level where the internal carotid and anterior cerebral arteries on each side are continuous (Plate 44, Fig. 3) and trace sections *anteriorly,* watching the cranial end of each internal carotid artery (that is, the portion that is cut frontally). The **posterior communicating arteries** quickly appear in place of these latter, frontally cut vessels (Fig. V, level d; Plate 44, Fig. 1). (The anterior cerebral and posterior communicating arteries will later become components of the **arterial circle of Willis,** a complex of blood vessels delivering blood to the ventral surface of the brain.) Continue tracing sections *anteriorly,* following the posterior communicating arteries. They first lie lateral to the infundibulum (Plate 43, Fig. 3) and then ventral to the mesencephalon (Plate 43, Figs. 2, 1; Plate 42, Fig. 3). Note that they approach a vessel lying in the midline, just beneath the rhombencephalon, the **basilar artery,** and the three vessels become continuous (Fig. V, level e). (The exact region where the two posterior communicating arteries and basilar artery become continuous is difficult to identify.)

Reverse direction and trace sections *posteriorly,* following the basilar artery. As the rhombencephalon begins to fade out, identify a single vessel lying in the midline, just above the rhombencephalon (Plate 43, Figs. 1, 2). This vessel is part of the basilar artery; in more posterior sections, the rhombencephalon fades out and the two parts of the basilar artery join and are cut frontally (Fig. V, level f; Plate 44, Fig. 1). The basilar artery fades out in more posterior sections.

Return to the level where the basilar artery is cut frontally (Fig. V, level f; Plate 44, Fig. 1) and trace sections *anteriorly,* following the upper portion of the basilar artery. Note that it lengthens dorsoventrally and is continuous with two vessels, the **vertebral arteries** (Fig. V, level g; Plate 43, Fig. 1), which extend dorsad. The vertebral arteries are irregularly shaped in this region. Trace sections *posteriorly,* following the vertebral arteries beneath the spinal cord. (In the adult, each vertebral artery receives its blood directly from a **subclavian artery.**)

Return to the level of the stomach (Plate 49, Fig. 3) and identify the **descending aorta.** Trace sections posteriorly. At about the level where the stomach fades out, or, more commonly, in slightly more posterior sections, identify a single midline vessel continuous with the descending aorta ventrally, the **celiac artery** (see A, Fig. 622). It originated by fusion of a pair of **vitelline arteries** at an earlier stage. Continue tracing sections posteriorly and identify paired vessels continuous with the descending aorta dorsolaterally; these are the **intersegmental arteries.** (The adult **left subclavian artery** is derived exclusively from a left intersegmental artery at the level of the foreleg buds. The adult **right subclavian artery** is derived from a right intersegmental artery at the level of the foreleg buds [Plate 48, Fig. 3], part of the right dorsal aorta, and part of the right fourth aortic arch; see Fig. U.)

Continue to trace sections posteriorly and identify small ventrolateral branches of the descending aorta. These are the **mesonephric (lateral) arteries,** which carry blood to the glomeruli of the mesonephric kidneys (see A, Fig. 623). Identify a large midline vessel continuous with the descending aorta ventrally in sections at about the level of the caudal end of the liver (Plate 51, Fig. 3). This vessel is the **superior mesenteric artery** (see A, Fig. 606); it also originated by fusion of a pair of **vitelline arteries.** The distal end of the superior mesenteric artery can be identified within the umbilical cord at about this level (Plate 51, Fig. 3). Trace sections *posteriorly* until the two portions of the superior mesenteric artery join and are cut frontally (Plate 52, Fig. 2).

Quickly trace sections posteriorly until the descending aorta is cut frontally due to the tail flexure (Plate 54, Fig. 2). The descending aorta disappears in more posterior sections. Return to the level at which the descending aorta is cut frontally (Plate 54, Fig. 2) and trace sections *anteriorly,* following the lower part of this vessel. Identify the right and left **umbilical arteries** continuous with the descending aorta (Plate 54, Fig. 2). A smaller midline portion of the descending aorta can be traced into the tail as the **caudal artery** (Plate 54, Figs. 2, 1). Try to identify a small lateral branch from each umbilical artery; these branches are the **external iliac arteries** (Plate 54, Fig. 1). Continue tracing sections *anteriorly.* The umbilical arteries first lie at the base of the hindleg buds (Plate 53, Figs. 3, 2). This portion of the umbilical arteries forms part of the adult **internal iliac arteries.** The umbilical arteries can be identified within the umbilical cord in more *anterior* sections (Plate 52, Figs. 2, 1; Plate 51, Figs. 3, 1).

b. Heart. Return to the most posterior section through the bulbar septum (Plate 47, Fig. 1) and trace sections posteriorly. Identify the **right** and **left atria** and the muscular **left ventricle** (Plate 47, Figs. 2, 3). Continue tracing sections posteriorly and watch the two atria approach each other and become continuous (Plate 48, Fig. 1). The bulbus cordis and muscular **right ventricle** are also continuous at about this level. The cavities of the right and left atria are partially separated by a partition, the **septum primum (septum I).** This septum is incomplete dorsally as the **foramen secundum (foramen II).** (Earlier there existed a more ventral opening in the septum primum, the **foramen primum [foramen I],** which is now closed.) In slightly more posterior sections, the septum primum seems to separate completely the two atria (Plate 48, Fig. 2). Continue tracing sections posteriorly and observe that the cavities of the atrium and ventricle on each side are continuous via an **atrioventricular canal** (Plate 48, Fig. 3). (The **tricuspid valve** *later* develops within the *right* atrioventricular canal; the **bicuspid [mitral] valve** develops within the *left.*) The atrioventricular canals lie on either side of a midline mass of lightly stained tissue, the **endocardial cushion.** Identify the prominent **interventricular septum,** partially separating the cavity of the ventricle into right and left sides. At this stage the interventricular septum is incomplete dorsally as the **interventricular foramen.** (This foramen will later be closed by the **septum membranaceum,** derived from outgrowths from the endocardial cushion and part of the bulbar septum.)

Return to the level of the foramen secundum (Plate 48, Fig. 1) and trace sections posteriorly. Identify the **sinus venosus** lying above the *right* atrium (Plate 48, Figs. 2, 3) and the **sinoatrial valve** projecting into the cavity of the *right* atrium (Plate 48, Fig. 2). The sinus venosus is eventually absorbed by the wall of the *right* atrium as the **pacemaker** of the adult heart. The sinoatrial valve consists of right and left **valve flaps,** which are usually in contact with one another. The *left* (apparent right) valve flap forms part of the **septum secundum (septum II),** which will therefore lie to the *right* (apparent left) of the septum primum. An opening, the **foramen ovale,** persists between the septum secundum and endocardial cushion (Plate 48, Fig. 2). The foramen ovale is staggered with respect to the opening in the septum primum (that is, the **foramen secundum**). The positioning of these two foramina and atrial septa is such that the septum primum acts as a flutter valve allowing blood to pass only *from the right to the left* atrium.

The wall of the heart consists of three layers (difficult to distinguish from one another). The inner layer of the heart (the one that immediately encloses blood cells) is the **endocardium.** The middle (and thickest) layer is the **myocardium.** The outer layer is the **epicardium (visceral pericardium).** Although the exact origin of the epicardium is unknown in pig embryos, in chick and mouse embryos this layer originates from the region of the **sinus venosus,** near the **dorsal mesocardium.** The epicardium grows downward from this region as a cellular sheet, eventually covering the outer surface of the entire myocardium.

c. Venous system. Return again to the level of the foramen secundum (Plate 48, Fig. 1) and trace sections posteriorly. Identify a single **pulmonary vein** continuous with the *left* atrium shortly before it fades out (Plate 48, Fig. 3). (This vein will later branch to form four **pulmonary veins,** which will open directly into the *left* atrium in the adult.)

Quickly trace sections posteriorly until the umbilical cord can be identified (Plate 51, Fig. 1). Identify the right and left **umbilical (allantoic) veins** within the umbilical cord (Plate 51, Figs. 1, 3; Plate 52, Figs. 1, 2). The *right* (apparent left) umbilical vein is smaller than the *left* because it is degenerating. After this degeneration occurs, all oxygenated blood will flow from the **placenta** to the embryo via the *left* umbilical vein. Each umbilical vein is cut across twice. The two portions of each vein become continuous and are cut frontally as sections are traced posteriorly (Plate 52, Fig. 3; Plate 53, Fig. 1). The umbilical veins fade out in more posterior sections.

Return to the level where the umbilical veins are cut frontally (Plate 53, Fig. 1; Plate 52, Fig. 3) and trace sections *anteriorly,* following the upper portion of the umbilical veins. In addition, observe the region between the two mesonephric kidneys, just beneath the descending aorta. Right and left **subcardinal veins** may be located there (Plate 51, Figs. 3, 1), or the subcardinal veins may have fused to form a **subcardinal anastomosis** (Plate 52). (The subcardinal veins are fused at several localized levels in some embryos, forming multiple subcardinal anastomoses.) Continue tracing sections *anteriorly* and note that the *left* (apparent right) umbilical vein enters the liver (Plate 51, Fig. 1). (The right umbilical vein usually joins the left shortly before the latter enters the liver, but the right umbilical vein also enters the liver in younger embryos.) Also note that as sections are traced *anteriorly,* the *left* (apparent right) subcardinal vein fades out, and the *right* continues as part of the **inferior vena cava** (Figs. W, X, level a; Plate 50, Fig. 3).

Return to the level where the left umbilical vein enters the liver (Plate 51, Fig. 1). Identify a vessel lying above and to the *left* (apparent right) of the duodenum at about this level. This vessel shifts to the *right* of the duodenum in slightly more *anterior* sections (Plate 50, Fig. 3). This vessel constitutes the **superior mesenteric vein,** when it lies to the *left* of the duodenum (Plate 51, Fig. 1), and the **portal vein,** when it lies in the midline and to the *right* of the duodenum (Plate 50, Fig. 3). Continue to trace sections *anteriorly* and note that the portal vein enters the right dorsal lobe of the liver and that the inferior vena cava begins to shift ventrad toward the liver (Plate 50, Figs. 2, 1). The inferior vena cava enters the right dorsal lobe of the liver in more *anterior* sections (Figs. W, X, level b; Plate 49, Fig. 3). The **ductus venosus** can be identified at about this level. It is formed by the enlargement of hepatic sinusoids.

Return again to the level where the left umbilical vein enters the liver (Plate 51, Fig. 1) and trace sections *anteriorly.* Try to trace the left umbilical vein (and possibly also the right) until it joins the ductus venosus. (The exact boundary between the left umbilical vein and ductus venosus is impossible to distinguish. The latter is irregularly shaped; the former is circular in transverse section.) Also try to trace the portal vein until it joins the ductus venosus (this happens at a section level between Plate 50, Fig. 1 and Plate 49, Fig. 3). The inferior vena cava and ductus venosus become continuous in slightly more *anterior* sections (Figs. W, X, level c; Plate 49, Fig. 2). This fused vessel narrows in more anterior sections, indicating the level of the inferior vena cava (Figs. W, X, level d; Plate 49, Fig. 1). Continue tracing sections *anteriorly* and note that the inferior vena cava exits from the liver (Figs. W, X, level e) and opens into the sinus venosus.

Return to a level where the portal vein can be identified within the right dorsal lobe of the liver (Plate 50, Figs. 1, 2) and trace sections *posteriorly.* It quickly leaves the liver and lies between the dorsal and ventral pancreatic rudiments to the *right* (apparent left) of the duodenum (Plate 50, Fig. 3). Note that it then shifts to the left of the duodenum to become the superior mesenteric vein

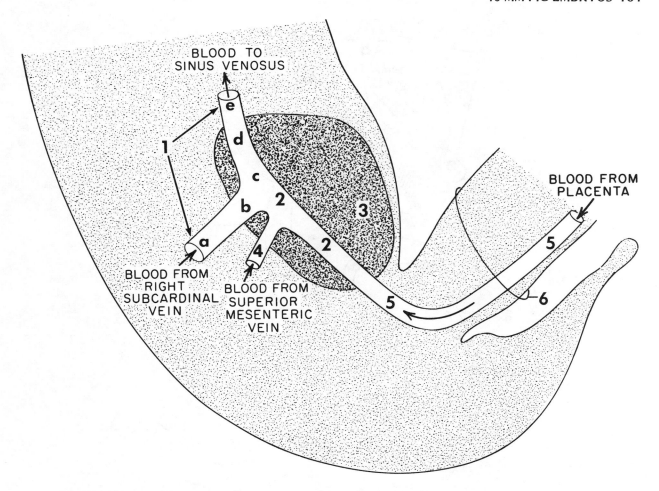

Fig. W. Schematic drawing of the major veins associated with the liver in the 10-mm pig embryo. The *right* umbilical vein is not shown. Letters a-e indicate specific levels of the inferior vena cava (1) described in text. The outer line indicates the boundaries of the caudal two-thirds of the embryo and of the umbilical cord. Arrows indicate direction of blood flow.

1. Inferior vena cava
2. Ductus venosus
3. Liver
4. Portal vein
5. Left umbilical vein
6. Umbilical cord

(Plate 51, Fig. 1), one of the main branches of the portal vein in the adult. Trace sections posteriorly, following the superior mesenteric vein. It soon joins a prominent **common vitelline vein** (Plate 51, Fig. 3). (The superior mesenteric, portal, and common vitelline veins are derived from a pair of **vitelline veins** present earlier. The superior mesenteric vein is derived from the proximal part of the *left* vitelline vein, the portal vein from the proximal part of the *right* vitelline vein and from a cross connection between right and left vitelline veins, and the common vitelline vein from an anastomosis between the distal ends of the right and left vitelline veins.) In more posterior sections, the superior mesenteric and common vitelline veins can be traced into the umbilical cord and are cut frontally—first the common vitelline vein, and then the superior mesenteric vein (Plate 52, Fig. 2). These veins then disappear. Return to the levels at which the superior mesenteric (Plate 52, Fig. 2) and the common vitelline veins are cut frontally and trace sections *anteriorly,* following the lower portion of each vein within the umbilical cord. Trace these vessels as far as possible.

Return to a section where the **precardial veins** can first be identified (Plate 42, Fig. 3). These veins are cut frontally at about this level. Trace sections *posteriorly,* following the lower portion of each precardial vein until it fades out ventrolateral to the diencephalon. (The adult **superior vena**

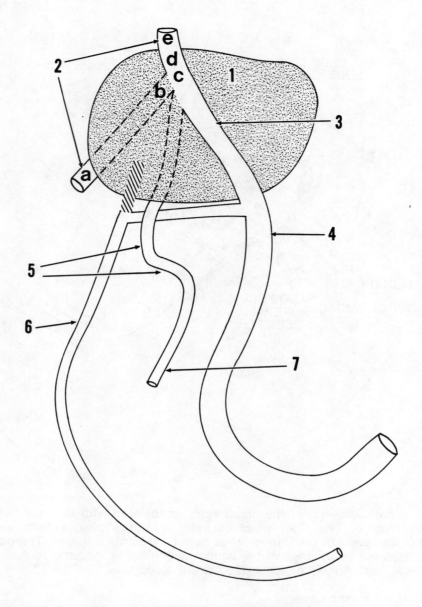

Fig. X. Drawing of a reconstruction of the major veins associated with the liver in the 10-mm pig embryo. This drawing is similar to Fig. W, but the vessels are viewed from the front rather than the side. Letters a-e indicate specific levels of the inferior vena cava (2) described in the text.

1. Liver
2. Inferior vena cava
3. Ductus venosus
4. Left umbilical vein
5. Portal vein
6. Right umbilical vein
7. Superior mesenteric vein

cava is derived in part from a portion of the *right* precardinal vein. The adult **internal jugular veins** are derived from the cranial ends of both precardinal veins.)

Return again to a section where the precardinal veins can first be identified (Plate 42, Fig. 3) and quickly trace sections posteriorly, following the *upper* portion of each precardinal vein. Note that the precardinal veins are closely approximated to the nodose ganglia (Plate 44, Fig. 3). The precardinal veins gradually move ventrad in more posterior sections (Plate 45, Fig. 3; Plate 46, Fig. 3; Plate 47, Fig. 3). They elongate dorsoventrally at about the level of the foreleg buds (Plate 48, Figs. 1, 2), indicating that sections are now cutting through the **common cardinal veins.** (The adult **superior vena cava** is derived from the *right* common cardinal vein, as well as from the *right* precardinal vein. The left common cardinal vein forms the adult **coronary sinus** and **oblique vein of the left atrium.**) The *right* common cardinal vein quickly enters the sinus venosus (Plate 48, Fig. 2). Similarly, the *left* common cardinal vein enters the sinus venosus, but in more posterior sections, by means of a narrow connection beneath the trachea (use high magnification and carefully trace sections to observe this connection). Try to identify the irregularly shaped **subclavian veins** just developing at the base of the foreleg buds (Plate 47, Fig. 3; Plate 48, Fig. 1).

Return to the level where the *right* common cardinal vein enters the sinus venosus (Plate 48, Fig. 2) and trace sections posteriorly. Identify the **postcardinal veins** quickly appearing in place of the common cardinal veins (Plate 48, Fig. 3). Continue tracing sections posteriorly, following the postcardinal veins as far as possible. Note that they first lie dorsolateral to the mesonephric kidneys (Plate 49, Fig. 1). They are cut across frontally in more posterior sections (Plate 54, Fig. 2). Reverse direction and trace sections *anteriorly,* following the lower portion of each postcardinal vein located at the base of a hindleg bud (Plate 54, Fig. 2) into the tail (Plate 53, Fig. 3). (The *left* postcardinal vein later mainly degenerates. The proximal part of the *right* postcardinal vein forms part of the adult **azygos vein.**)

C. SUMMARY OF THE CONTRIBUTIONS OF THE GERM LAYERS TO STRUCTURES PRESENT IN THE 10-MM PIG EMBRYO, BUT NOT PRESENT IN THE 72-HOUR CHICK EMBRYO.

Ectoderm
autonomic ganglia
brachial plexus
cornea
cranial ganglia:
   VII. geniculate
   VIII. acoustic
   IX. petrosal
   X. nodose
cranial nerves:
   VI. abducens
   VIII. auditory
   X. vagus
   XI. spinal accessory
   XII. hypoglossal
Froriep's ganglia
glioblasts
lamina terminalis
pigment granules (within
   pigmented retinas)
rudiments of the semicircular canals
sclera
spinal nerves

Mesoderm
cloacal septum
eye muscle rudiments
gonad rudiments
heart partitions:
   bulbar ridges and septum
   endocardial cushion
   interventricular septum
   septum primum
   septum secundum
mesenteries:
   falciform ligament
   mesocolon
mesonephric kidneys
pericardium
peritoneum
pleura
renal pelvis
septum transversum
sinoatrial valve
ureters
Wharton's jelly

Endoderm
caudal limb of the intestinal loop
colon
common bile duct
cranial limb of the intestinal loop
cystic duct
eparterial bronchus
gall bladder
hepatic cords
hepatic duct
larynx
pancreatic ducts and rudiments
rectum
thyroid gland
trachea
urogenital sinus

Ectoderm and Mesoderm
choroid
choroid plexus
genital eminence
mammary ridges
nasal processes
umbilical cord

Endoderm and Mesoderm
arytenoid swellings
epiglottis
tongue rudiments

BRIEF TECHNIQUES FOR PREPARING EMBRYOS FOR LIGHT MICROSCOPY

Although there are many different methods for preparing embryos for light microscopy, we describe here only those methods that routinely yield good results. Specific procedures for processing chick embryos are described. Similar (and in many cases identical) procedures are also adequate for amphibian and mammalian embryos. *Use extreme care when processing tissues for microscopy because many of the solvents are toxic. To be safe, use a fume hood whenever possible, wear protective (safety) eye glasses, and do not attempt any of the procedures without the direct supervision of an experienced person.*

A. WHOLE MOUNTS

Incubate fertile eggs at 38 °C and about 50 to 60% relative humidity (keeping incubator water pans filled throughout the entire period of incubation gives adequate humidity) until desired stages are obtained (that is, 18–25 hours—primitive streak, head process, and early neural fold stages; 26–29 hours—typical 24-hour embryos; 33–49 hours—typical 33-hour embryos; 50–56 hours—typical 48-hour embryos; about 72 hours—typical 72-hour embryos). Two procedures can be used to collect embryos; the first usually works best for embryos 24 hours or older, whereas the second works best for younger embryos. It is best to start with older embryos (which are easier to collect than are younger embryos) and then to progress to younger stages as your skills improve.

To do the first procedure, carefully crack eggs into finger bowls containing warm 123 mM saline (0.72% aqueous solution of NaCl). Take care not to break the yolk (its fragility increases with increased length of incubation) because breaking the yolk clouds the saline and usually results in lost embryos. To avoid this problem it is best to crack the egg against the side of the finger bowl, submerse the egg in the saline contained in the bowl, and gently separate the two halves of the shell. Then manipulate the yolk and attached blastoderm with fingertips until the blastoderm floats uppermost. Grasp the periphery of the blastoderm (that is, the area opaca) with a pair of fine forceps (watchmaker's or #5). Then use fine-pointed scissors to cut around the perimeter of the blastoderm. (Make sure you hold on to the periphery of the blastoderm with your forceps; also make sure that the blastoderm is floating uppermost, centered on the yolk—eccentrically positioned blastoderms are more difficult to remove without tearing.) After the entire perimeter of the blastoderm is cut free from the yolk, gently grasp the blastoderm with forceps and float it away from the yolk. Place an ordinary spoon beneath the blastoderm while you hold the latter with forceps. Slowly lift the spoon and the cuddled blastoderm out of the finger bowl and transfer them to a second bowl that contains fresh saline. Gently free the blastoderm from the spoon and remove the latter from the bowl. The blastoderm at this point is usually still covered dorsally by the vitelline membrane. (Although this latter structure seems to be a single membrane, it actually consists of both the inner and outer vitelline membranes.) To remove this membrane it is best to grasp the periphery of the blastoderm and gently waft the blastoderm back and forth in the saline until the vitelline membrane floats free. (The action involved is analogous to shaking out a rug, when you grasp one edge of the rug and the rug undulates in the air as you raise and lower your arms.)

To do the second procedure, use a dull pair of watchmaker's forceps to excise a cap of shell at the blunt end of the egg (hold the blunt end of the shell up, insert one tip of the forceps into the shell about one-third the distance from the top of the egg, and then hold the forceps stationary and rotate the egg around until the cap can be removed; this action is much the same as that used by an electric can opener). Also use forceps to remove chalazae (the white strands at the poles of the egg) and as much of the thick albumen as possible. Decant most of the thin albumen into a bowl and discard it. Pour the yolk, its attached blastoderm, and enveloping vitelline membranes into a bowl containing saline, and cut along the equator of the yolk (with the blastoderm floating uppermost) with a pair of fine scissors. Peel the vitelline membranes and attached blastoderm off the yolk and transfer them (with a spoon) to a petri dish filled with saline. Separate the blastoderm from the vitelline membranes by gently squirting saline between the blastoderm and membranes with a pipette.

After the blastoderm has been freed from its membranes (using either the first or second procedure), place a small dish (a dish approximately 50 mm in diameter works best) in the bowl of saline beneath the blastoderm and withdraw the dish slowly. This procedure results in removal of the blastoderm and some saline from the bowl. Use forceps to unwrinkle the blastoderm and to float it dorsal side up in the small dish. Remove excess saline from the dish with a pipette so that the blastoderm flattens onto the bottom of the dish; slowly replace the saline with fixative. (Begin by placing one drop directly onto the surface of the blastoderm and then slowly add several drops peripheral to the blastoderm until the latter is completely covered.) Many fixatives can be used. We prefer a mixture (1:2:7) of glacial acetic acid, 37% formaldehyde solution, and absolute ethanol because it consistently gives good results. Fix embryos for 2 hours to overnight in *covered* dishes. (Add enough fixative so that the embryo does not dry out as evaporation occurs.) Then trim the blastoderm (with a fine scissor or razor or scalpel blade) to a convenient size, removing most of the tissue peripheral to the area pellucida.

Next begin dehydrating the embryo with ethanol by removing the fixative and adding 70% ethanol. (To avoid damage to your embryo, it is best to transfer liquids to the dish containing the embryo rather than transfer the embryo to different dishes; remove most of the previous liquid with a pipette before adding the succeeding liquid, but be sure the embryo does not dry out between changes.) Embryos should be placed in two to three changes of 70% ethanol for 5 to 10 minutes each. Then stain the embryo with a borax carmine solution (add 3 g carmine and 4 g sodium borate to 100 ml distilled water; boil for 10 to 15 minutes; cool; add 100 ml 70% ethanol; add distilled water, if necessary, to bring the volume up to 200 ml; let the solution set for 2 days; then filter it twice). After staining the embryo overnight, partially destain it for about 6 hours with six changes of acid-alcohol (100 ml 70% ethanol containing 5 drops of concentrated hydrochloric acid); dehydrate it (95% ethanol, one change, 10 minutes; 100% ethanol, two changes, 10 minutes each); and finally clear it (xylene, toluene, or Histosol, two changes, 10 minutes each). Then transfer each embryo with forceps to a glass slide; immediately surround it with a large drop of mounting media (Permount, Pro-Texx, or the equivalent), and cover it with a circular cover slip (18 mm in diameter). For embryos older than about 33 hours, cover slips usually need to be supported with small pieces of a broken cover slip placed around the periphery of the blastoderm; otherwise, air bubbles will form between the slide and cover slip (such supports may also be needed for supporting 24- to 33-hour embryos—depending on the thickness of your mounting media—to prevent the coverslip from crushing the embryo).

B. SERIAL SECTIONS

Treat embryos as described for making whole mounts, with the following exceptions. After embryos are fixed and partially dehydrated with 70% ethanol, stain them for 30 seconds (to aid in locating and orienting them during subsequent processing) with an eosin solution (0.5g in 100 ml 70% ethanol). Then dehydrate and clear embryos as described. Infiltrate embryos with melted paraffin (Paraplast X-tra, 52°–54°C, seems to work best) in the following sequence (embryos being infiltrated with paraffin should be kept in an oven at about 58°C—do not allow the temperature to become higher!): three changes, 100% paraffin, 20 minutes each after paraffin has completely melted. Then orient embryos with a warm dissecting needle (for transverse or sagittal sections) in fresh 100% melted paraffin in molds (for example, Peel-A-Way molds) and leave them at room temperature until the blocks harden. Trim the blocks with razor blades and mount them in the chuck of a rotary microtome for serial sectioning at 8–10 μm. The microtome slices (sections) the entire embryo into thin sections and simultaneously fuses the section edges together (end-to-end) in the order in which they were cut, forming a delicate ribbon. Pick up the ribbons with forceps or fine paintbrushes and float them on glass slides coated with albumen fixative and flooded with distilled water (albumen fixative consists of a 50:50 mixture of egg albumen/glycerine; use your index finger to spread a *very light* film of fixative on each slide). Allow slides to dry overnight on hot plates at 40°C.

Process and stain sections in the following way (place groups of slides in slide racks and transfer slides to staining dishes containing the solutions listed below). First remove paraffin from sections with two changes of xylene, toluene, or Histosol (10 minutes each) and gradually hydrate sections (100% ethanol, two changes, 2 minutes each; 95% ethanol, 2 minutes; 70% ethanol, 2 minutes; water, 5 minutes). Then stain sections with Harris' hematoxylin (Harleco, Gibbstown, New Jersey; 30 seconds to 3 minutes), wash in running tap water (3 minutes), rinse in 2% aqueous sodium bicarbonate (2 minutes), wash in running tap water (3 minutes), and gradually dehydrate and clear (70% ethanol, 5 minutes; 95% ethanol, 5 minutes; 100% ethanol, two changes, 5 minutes each; xylene, toluene, or Histosol, two changes, 5 minutes each). Next, mount cover slips with Permount, Pro-Texx, or the equivalent.

Appendix II

BRIEF TECHNIQUES FOR PREPARING EMBRYOS FOR SCANNING ELECTRON MICROSCOPY

There are many different ways to prepare embryos for scanning electron microscopy. We describe here methods for producing the various types of images shown in the plates. *Use extreme care when processing tissues for microscopy because many of the solvents are toxic. To be safe, use a fume hood whenever possible, wear protective (safety) eyeglasses, and do not attempt any of the procedures without the direct supervision of an experienced person.*

A. INTACT SPECIMENS

Remove blastoderms from the yolk at desired stages and flatten them onto the bottoms of plastic or glass dishes, exactly as described in Appendix I. Next, fix the blastoderms for 2 hours with a solution of 2.5% glutaraldehyde in 0.1-M phosphate buffer (pH 7.2), trim them to isolate embryos from extraembryonic areas, and gradually dehydrate them (35% ethanol, 5 minutes; 50% ethanol, 5 minutes; 70% ethanol, 5 minutes; 80% ethanol, 5 minutes; 95% ethanol, two changes, 10 minutes each; 100% ethanol, two changes, 10 minutes each). Then dry embryos in a critical-point-drying apparatus. This device consists of a pressure chamber into which samples (infiltrated with 100% ethanol) are placed for drying. *This procedure can be dangerous because high pressures are generated during critical-point-drying. Do not attempt to use a critical-point-dryer without the direct supervision of an experienced person.* After placing samples in the pressure chamber, seal the chamber and then cool it with liquid carbon dioxide. Slowly leak liquid carbon dioxide into the chamber while the 100% ethanol is drained out. The liquid carbon dioxide quickly replaces the ethanol that formerly saturated the sample. Then heat the sealed pressure chamber. As the temperature of the chamber increases, so does its pressure. The "critical point" eventually is reached (that is, about 31 °C and 1,100 lb/sq in. pressure). Liquid carbon dioxide is converted to gaseous carbon dioxide at the critical point; carbon dioxide is then slowly bled off, eventually reducing the pressure of the chamber to atmospheric pressure. At the end of this process a dried sample is available for examination in the vacuum of a scanning electron microscope. (A vacuum must be used so that streams of electrons can flow to, and then be scanned across, the sample. Samples must be dry because wet samples give off water vapor that would destroy the vacuum. Critical-point-drying is used instead of simple air drying. The latter process grossly distorts the surfaces of cells, as evaporation occurs at the air-water interface.)

Affix the dried samples to stubs (usually made of aluminum) with conductive paint and coat the surfaces of the sample with a thin layer of metal (for example, gold) to make them conductive. This is done in a vacuum evaporator or a sputter coater. *Both these instruments generate high voltages, so use extreme care.* If the metal coating is insufficient, samples "charge" or glow in the scanning electron microscope as they are bombarded with electrons. Charging obscures the details of viewed samples.

B. SLICES

Slices of embryos are prepared in much the same way as intact specimens, except that embryos are cut with scissors or razor or scalpel blades after fixation. These cuts can be made transversely or sagittally, and the resulting slices can be dehydrated, dried, mounted to stubs, and coated with metal, as already described.

The internal morphology of embryos can be readily viewed in slices. One advantage of this technique is that the surfaces of cells are demonstrated (that is, the fracture plane generated by slicing passes *between* rather than through cells; this is not true of other techniques used to expose internal areas of embryos). One disadvantage of this technique is that slicing sometimes distorts embryos by displacing cells to ectopic areas, separating adjacent organ rudiments from one another, or tearing organ rudiments.

C. CRYOFRACTURES

Cryofractures are also prepared in much the same way as intact specimens. However, after embryos are dehydrated, and before they are critical-point-dried, place them in small cylinders fashioned from Parafilm. Crimp shut the two ends of each cylinder with a hemostat so that each cylinder contains an embryo surrounded by 100% ethanol. Next, plunge these cylinders into liquid nitrogen (*use extreme care when handling liquid nitrogen*), where they quickly freeze, and position a razor blade (gripped with a hemostat and cooled in liquid nitrogen) on each frozen cylinder at a desired level (that is, if a transverse cryofracture through the heart is desired, position the razor blade at a level estimated to overlie the heart). Then hit the razor blade briskly with a hammer, creating two cryofractures (that is, two fractured surfaces are produced with each blow of the hammer). Place both pieces in fresh 100% ethanol (at room temperature), and then critical-point-dry these pieces, mount them to stubs, and coat them with metal.

Cryofractures, like slices, readily show the internal morphology of embryos. Two advantages of this technique are that cells are rarely displaced to other areas by fracturing, and organ rudiments usually do not tear (although they sometimes chip or crack). One disadvantage of this technique is that the fracture plane passes *through* cells rather than between them. Thus, the surfaces of cells are not revealed in the plane of the fracture, and the fractured surface characteristically has a flat appearance. A second disadvantage is that it is difficult to obtain fractures exactly through desired areas because so many attempts must be made.

D. SECTIONED BLOCKS

The internal morphology of embryos can be revealed in yet a third way: embryos can be embedded in paraffin and the blocks sectioned until desired levels are reached. Paraffin can then be removed from the remainder of the sectioned block, creating a cut surface suitable (after appropriate processing) for viewing with scanning electron microscopy.

The specific procedure for producing sectioned blocks is to fix and dehydrate embryos exactly as described for intact embryos. Clear embryos in xylene, toluene, or Histosol and embed them in paraffin. Next, cut sections for light microscopy until the desired areas are reached. Place sectioned blocks in several changes of xylene, toluene, or Histosol to remove the paraffin, and finally into two changes of 100% ethanol (10 minutes each). Then critical-point-dry the dehydrated, partially sectioned tissue blocks, mount them to stubs, and coat them with metal as already described.

One advantage of using sectioned blocks to examine the internal aspects of embryos is that precise areas within embryos can be readily exposed, unlike the situation with cryofractures. Thus, sectioned blocks are particularly useful for demonstrating sagittal views of embryos. Sectioned blocks have a disadvantage shared by cryofractures: the section plane passes *through* cells rather than between them. Therefore, the cut surface of a sectioned block appears to be flat.

ABRIDGED HAMBURGER AND HAMILTON STAGE SERIES FOR MAJOR STAGES COVERED IN THIS GUIDE

PLATE A

The Hamburger and Hamilton (1951) stage series is the most widely used system for staging avian embryos. Illustrations and brief descriptions of the major stages covered in this guide appear below (for additional details see H, pp. 78–91, or V. Hamburger and H. L. Hamilton [1951]. A series of normal stages in the development of the chick embryo. *J. Morphol.* **88**:49–92). The number in the lower lefthand corner of each illustration indicates its Hamburger and Hamilton stage.

Stage 1. Prestreak stage; not illustrated. The primitive streak has not yet formed. The hypoblast is forming but is not readily visible from the dorsal surface. The egg is usually laid at this stage.

Stage 2. Initial streak stage; not illustrated. The primitive streak has just formed and consists of a short conical density, almost as wide as it is long. (6–7 hours of incubation)

Stage 3. Intermediate streak stage. The primitive streak now has greater length than width but has not yet fully elongated (that is, it does not yet extend craniad beyond about the center of the area pellucida). A primitive groove may (late Stage 3) or may not (early Stage 3) be present. (12–13 hours of incubation)

Stage 4. Definitive streak stage. Typical 18-hour embryo. The primitive streak has elongated fully and the primitive knot, pit, and ridges are distinct. A short tongue of cells extends slightly craniad from the primitive knot (arrow). (18–19 hours of incubation)

Stage 5. Head process stage. Typical 18-hour embryo. A distinct, rodlike head process (notochord) has formed and the primitive knot is regressing. The head fold of the body has not yet formed. (19–22 hours of incubation)

Stage 6. Head-fold stage. Typical 18-hour embryo. The head fold of the body (arrows) has formed cranial to the tip of the head process. Somites have not yet formed. (23–25 hours of incubation)

Stage 7. One-somite stage. The first pair of somites (arrows) has formed just cranial to the primitive knot. Stages 7–14 are designated principally by the number of somite pairs. A numbered stage is assigned to embryos when they acquire each third somite pair. Thus, embryos at Stage 8 have 4 somites, and embryos at Stage 9 have 7 somites. Pluses and minuses are used to designate intermediate stages. Therefore, embryos at stage 7 + have 2 somite pairs, and those at 8 − have 3 somite pairs. (23–26 hours of incubation)

Stage 8. Four-somite stage. Typical 24-hour embryo. Neural folds have fused at the mesencephalon level. (26–29 hours of incubation)

Stage 8 +. Five-somite stage. Typical 24-hour embryo. Neurulation is more advanced than at Stage 8.

Stage 9. Seven-somite stage. Optic vesicle formation is under way. (29–33 hours of incubation)

PLATE B

Stage 10. Ten-somite stage. Typical 33-hour embryo. (33–38 hours of incubation)

Stage 11. Thirteen-somite stage. Typical 33-hour embryo. (40–45 hours of incubation)

Stage 12. Sixteen-somite stage; not illustrated. Typical 33-hour embryo. (45–49 hours of incubation)

Stage 13. Nineteen-somite stage; not illustrated. (48–52 hours of incubation)

Stage 14. Twenty-two-somite stage; not illustrated. The cranial flexure has partially formed so that the longitudinal axes of the fore- and hindbrain meet in the midbrain at about a right angle. (50–53 hours of incubation)

Stage 15. Twenty-four- to twenty-seven-somite stage. Typical 48-hour embryo. The longitudinal axes of the fore- and hindbrain meet in the midbrain at an acute angle. The lateral body folds extend to the cranial border of the wing buds (that is, to about somite 15). (50–55 hours of incubation)

Stage 16. Twenty-six- to twenty-eight-somite stage; not illustrated. Typical 48-hour embryo. The lateral body folds extend to a level midway between the wing and leg buds (that is, to about somite 20). (51–56 hours of incubation)

Stage 17. Twenty-nine- to thirty-two-somite stage. Typical 72-hour embryo. The cervical flexure is well formed so that the longitudinal axes of the brain and spinal cord meet at about a right angle. (52–64 hours of incubation)

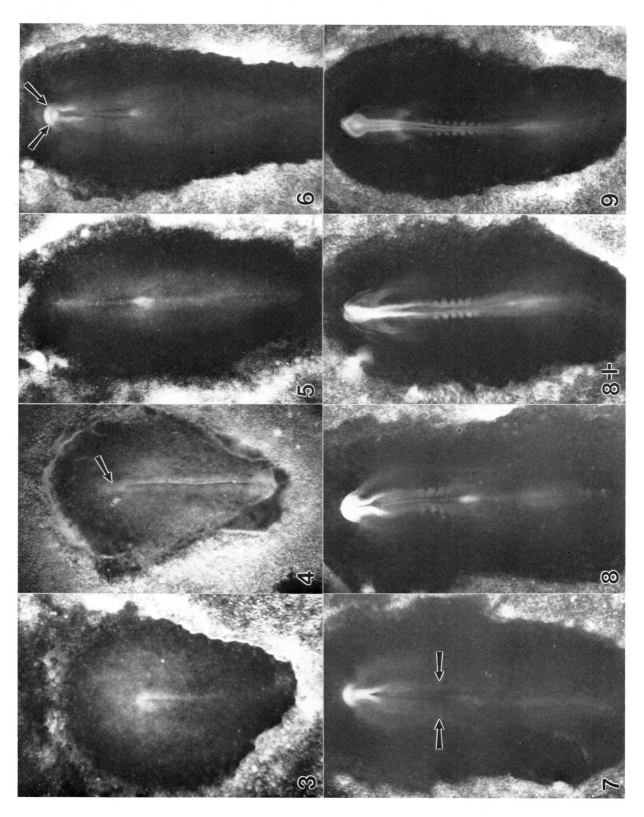

Plate A

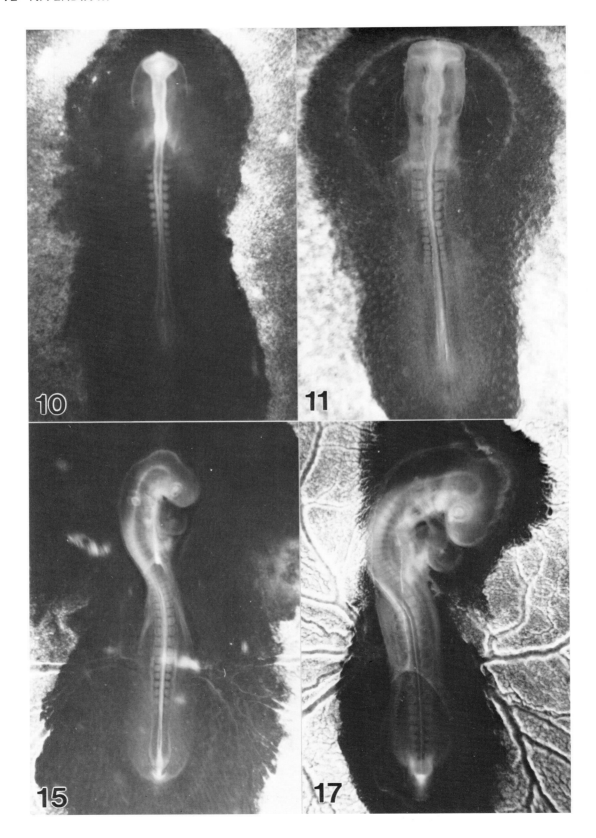

Plate B

PART II

Atlas for
Vertebrate
Embryology

Plates **1-6**

EARLY FROG EMBRYOS

PLATE 1
FROG: BLASTULA, GASTRULAE, AND NEURULA

FIGURE 1:
Blastula (sagittal section)

FIGURE 2:
Dorsal lip gastrula (sagittal section)

FIGURE 3:
Yolk plug gastrula (sagittal section)

FIGURES 4, 5:
Neural plate neurula (transverse section)

(Figure 5 is an enlargement of dorsal portion of Figure 4.)

AP Animal pole
D Dorsal side
V Ventral side
VP Vegetal pole

1. Pigmented cortex
2. Vitelline membrane
3. Blastocoel
4. Area of gray crescent
5. Shrinkage spaces
6. Nuclei
7. Blastomeres
8. Outer ectodermal layer
9. Inner ectodermal layer
10. Archenteron roof (mesoderm, except at cranial end where roof formed from endoderm)
11. Direction of epiboly
12. Dorsal blastoporal lip
13. Blastopore
14. Archenteron
15. Yolk-filled endodermal cells
16. Yolk plug
17. Ventral blastoporal lip
18. Neural plate
19. Skin ectoderm
20. Lateral plate mesoderm
21. Directions of cellular migration to form endodermal roof of archenteron
22. Segmental plate mesoderm
23. Notochord
24. Archenteron roof (endoderm)

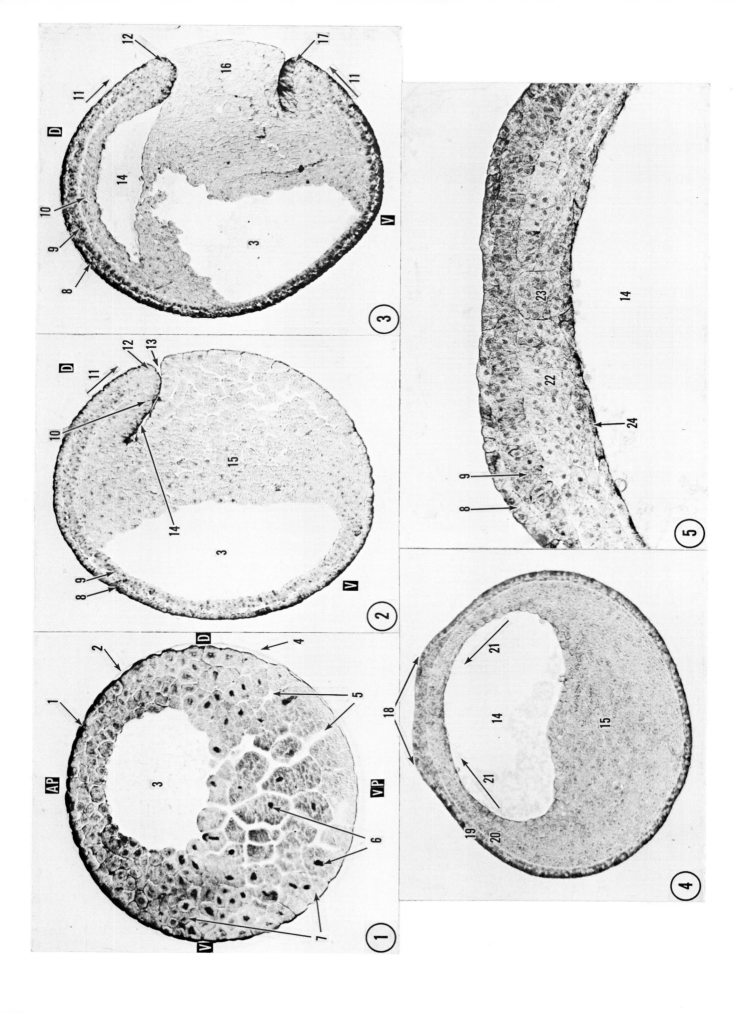

PLATE 2

FROG: NEURULA AND 4-MM EMBRYO SERIAL TRANSVERSE SECTIONS

FIGURES 1,2:
Neural fold neurula (transverse section)

FIGURES 3, 4:
4-mm embryo serial transverse sections

(Figure 2 is an enlargement of dorsal portion of Figure 1.)

1. Neural groove
2. Skin ectoderm
3. Lateral plate mesoderm
4. Archenteron
5. Yolk-filled endodermal cells
6. Neural fold
7. Outer ectodermal layer
8. Inner ectodermal layer
9. Segmental plate mesoderm
10. Notochord
11. Archenteron roof (endoderm)

12. Pineal gland
13. Prosencephalon
14. Nasal placode
15. Mesencephalon
16. Pigmented retina of optic cup
17. Sensory retina of optic cup
18. Optic stalk
19. Rudiment of the anterior pituitary gland
20. Head mesenchyme
21. Stomodeum

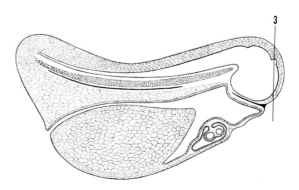

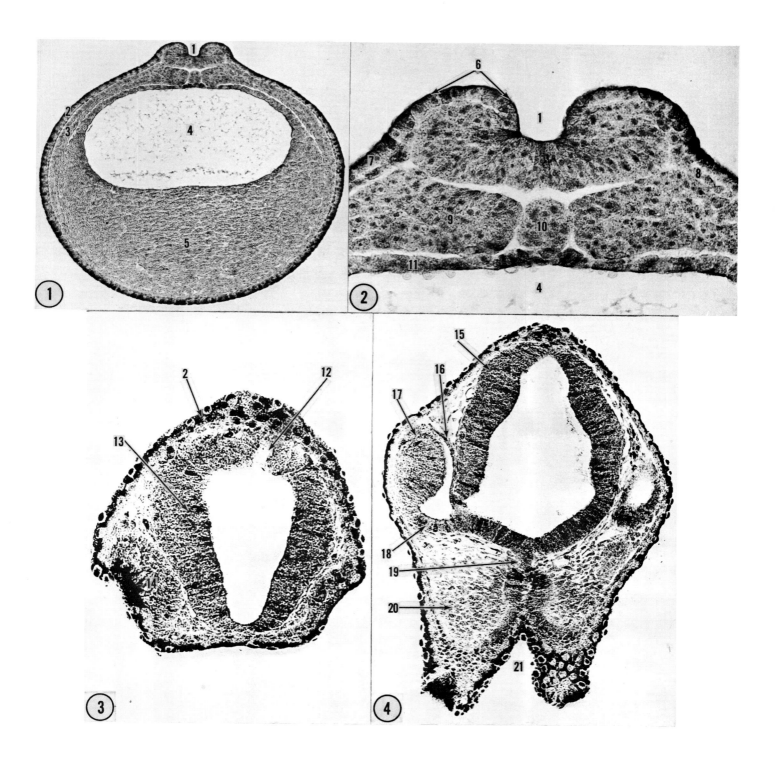

PLATE 3
4-MM FROG EMBRYO SERIAL TRANSVERSE SECTIONS

 1. Mesencephalon
 2. Future corneal epithelium
 3. Lens placode
 4. Rudiment of the anterior pituitary gland
 5. Foregut
 6. Oral membrane
 7. Adhesive gland
 8. Stomodeum
 9. Rhombencephalon
10. Skin ectoderm
11. Semilunar ganglion
12. Infundibulum
13. Auditory vesicle
14. Notochord
15. Dorsal aorta
16. Pharynx
17. First aortic arch
18. Bulbus cordis
19. Duodenum
20. Liver rudiment
21. Dorsal mesocardium
22. Pericardial cavity
23. Endocardium of ventricle
24. Myocardium of ventricle
25. Parietal pericardium

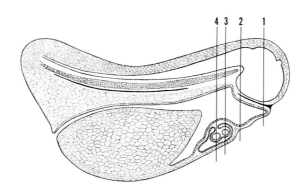

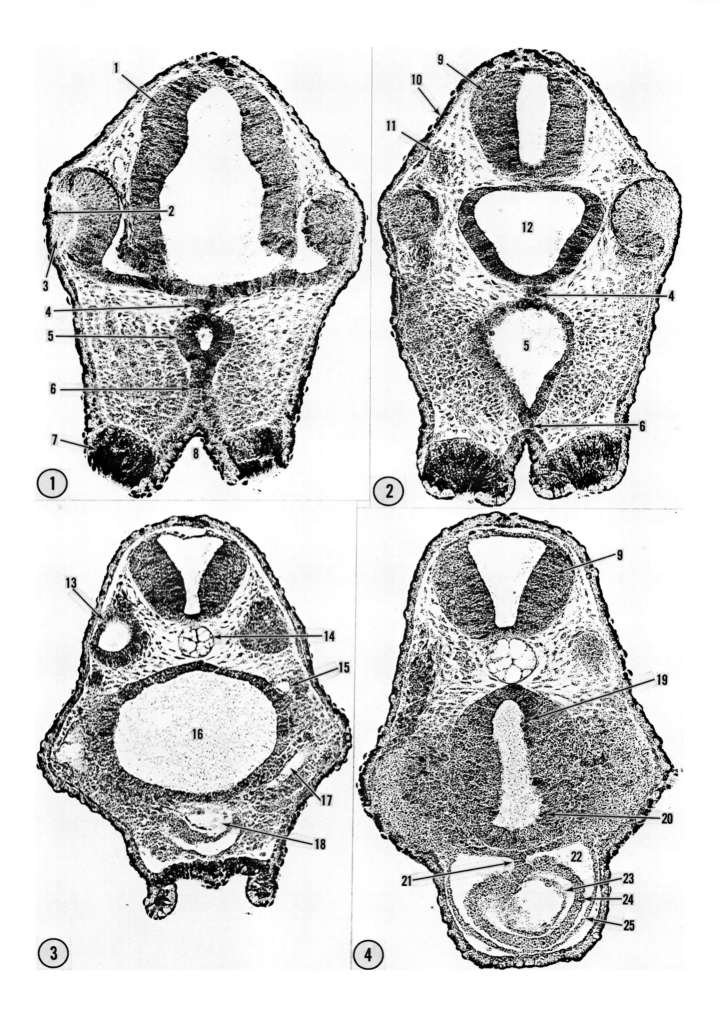

PLATE 4
4-MM FROG EMBRYO SERIAL TRANSVERSE SECTIONS

1. Roof plate
2. Neural crest cells
3. Spinal cord
4. Floor plate
5. Dorsal aorta
6. Pronephric tubule
7. Pronephric duct
8. Pronephric ridge
9. Midgut
10. Yolk-filled endodermal cells

11. Skin ectoderm
12. Liver rudiment
13. Dorsal fin
14. Somite
15. Notochord
16. Subnotochordal rod
17. Hindgut
18. Proctodeum
19. Ventral fin

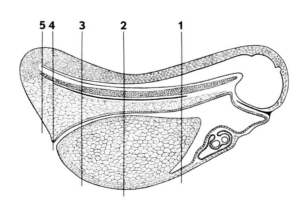

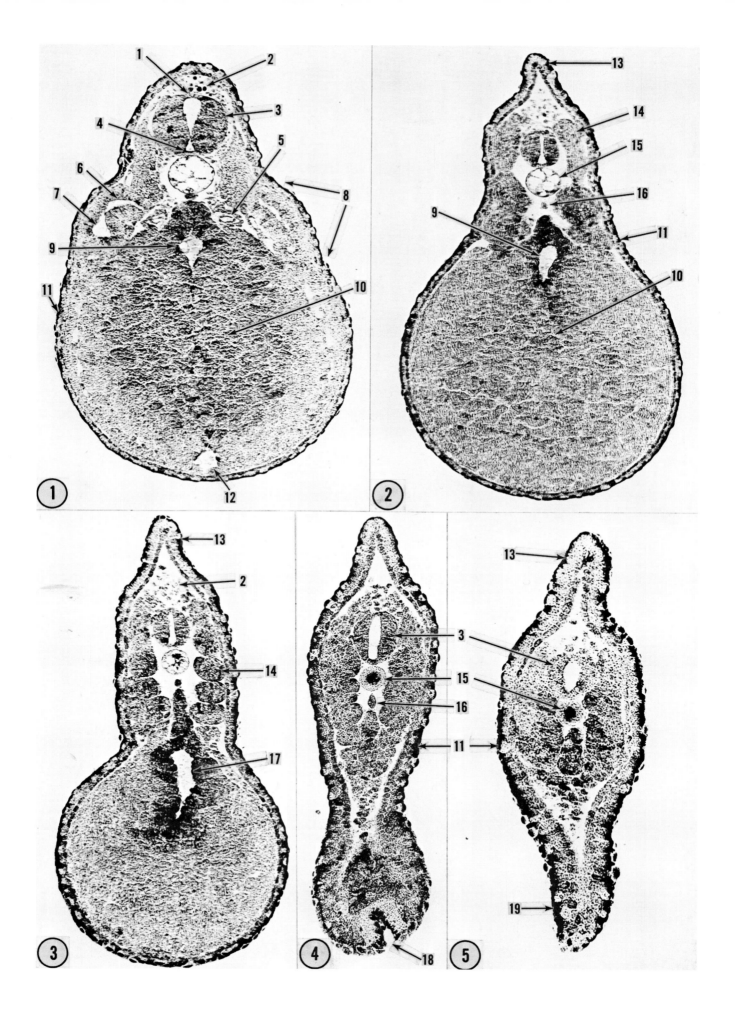

PLATE 5
FROG: EARLY CLEAVAGE STAGES AND BLASTULAE—SCANNING
ELECTRON MICROGRAPHS

FIGURE 1:
Two-cell stage (viewed from side)

FIGURE 2:
Four-cell stage (viewed from animal pole and side)

FIGURE 3:
Eight-cell stage (viewed from animal pole and side)

FIGURE 4:
Sixteen-cell stage (viewed from animal pole and side;
all macromeres are not visible)

FIGURE 5:
Early blastula (viewed from animal pole and side)

FIGURE 6:
Late blastula (viewed from animal pole)

AP animal pole
VP Vegetal pole

1. Cleavage furrow
2. Blastomere
3. Micromere (blastomere)
4. Macromere (blastomere)

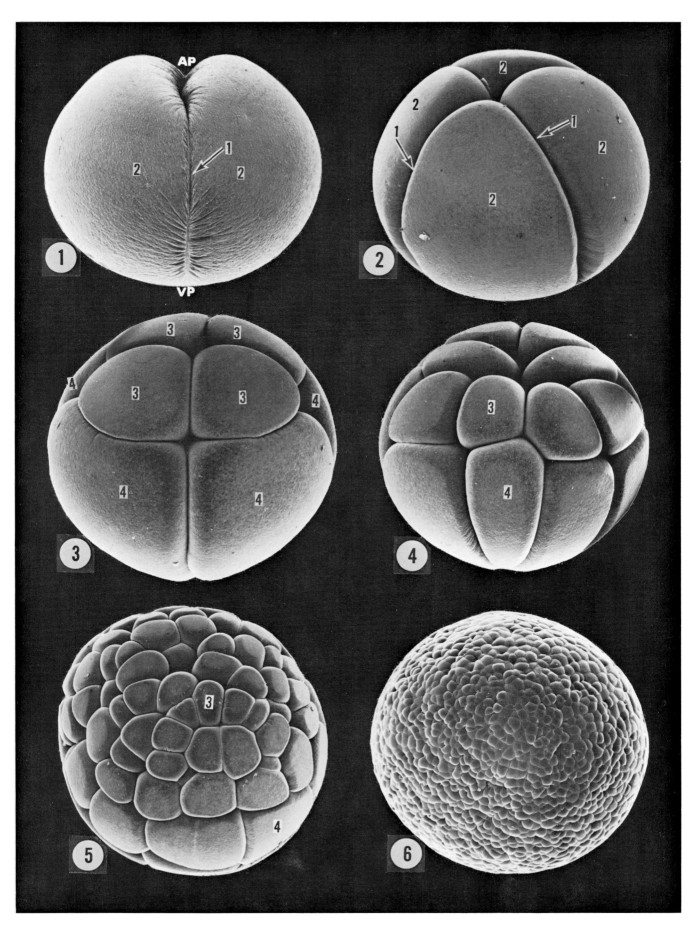

PLATE 6

FROG: GASTRULA, EARLY EMBRYO, AND 4-MM EMBRYO—SCANNING ELECTRON MICROGRAPHS

FIGURE 1:
Gastrula (dorsal view)

FIGURE 2:
Early embryo (dorsolateral view)

FIGURE 3:
4-mm embryo (lateral view)

D Dorsal side
H Head (cranial) end
R Right side
T Tail (caudal) end

1. Yolk plug
2. Dorsal blastoporal lip

3. Lateral blastoporal lip
4. Neural tube
5. Ciliary tufts
6. Developing eye
7. Dorsal fin
8. Ventral fin
9. Stomodeum

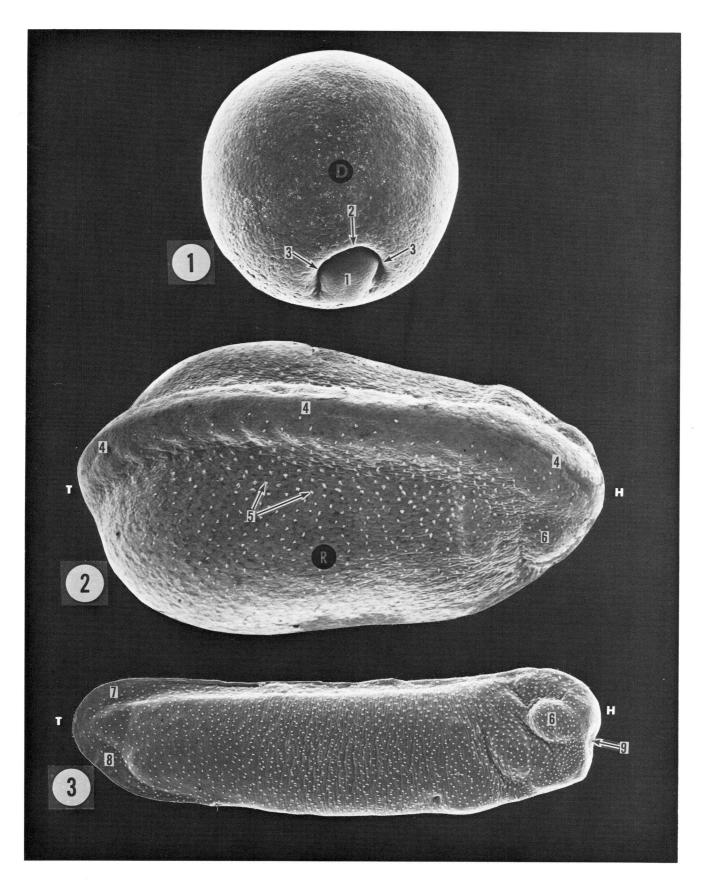

Plates **7-40**

EARLY CHICK EMBRYOS

PLATE 7
33-HOUR CHICK EMBRYO WHOLE MOUNTS

(Figures 1-4 are dorsal views; Figure 5 is a ventral view.)

1. Area vasculosa
2. Blood islands
3. Somites
4. Spinal cord region of neural tube
5. Segmental plates
6. Neural folds
7. Region of the primitive streak
8. Infundibulum
9. Proamnion
10. Mesencephalon region of neural tube
11. Caudal extent of the subcephalic pocket
12. Metencephalon region of neural tube
13. Neuromeres of myelencephalon region of neural tube
14. 5th intersomitic furrow
15. Notochord beneath broadened neural groove
16. Optic vesicle(s)
17. Notochord beneath mesencephalon
18. First somite
19. Area pellucida
20. Continuity between a neural fold (upper arrow) and primitive ridge (lower arrow)
21. Remnant of the cranial neuropore
22. Skin ectoderm
23. Head mesenchyme
24. Foregut
25. Ventricle
26. Sinoatrial region
27. Cranial intestinal portal
28. Bulbus cordis
29. Continuity between sinoatrial region and vitelline vein
30. Telencephalon region of the neural tube
31. Diencephalon region of the neural tube

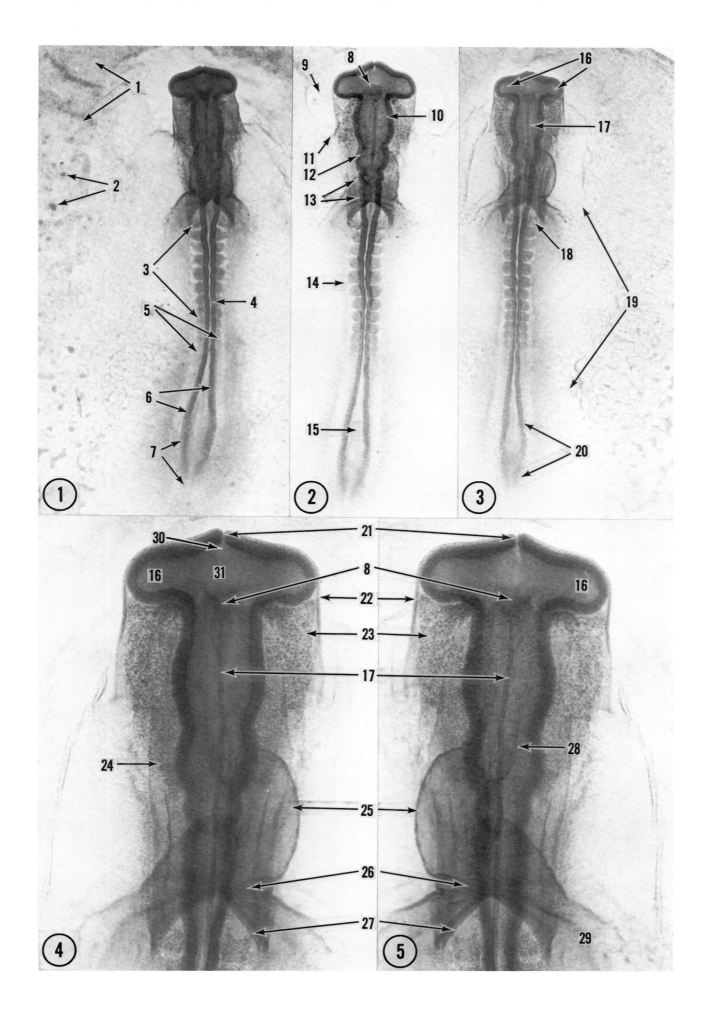

PLATE 8

33-HOUR CHICK EMBRYO SERIAL TRANSVERSE SECTIONS

1. Diencephalon
2. Future lens ectoderm
3. Optic vesicle
4. Infundibulum
5. Foregut
6. Subcephalic pocket
7. Proamnion
8. Head mesenchyme
9. Dorsal aorta
10. First aortic arch
11. Ventral aorta
12. Oral membrane

13. Notochord
14. Mesencephalon
15. Coelom
16. Splanchnic mesoderm
17. Endoderm
18. Bulbus cordis
19. Somatic mesoderm
20. Skin ectoderm
21. Somatopleure
22. Metencephalon
23. Neural crest cells

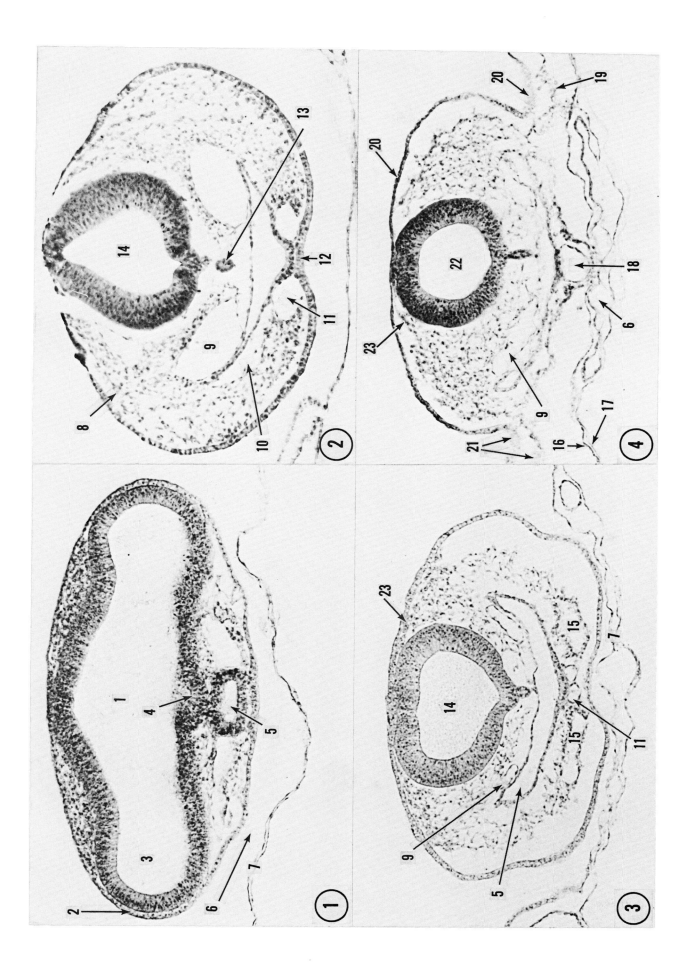

PLATE 9

33-HOUR CHICK EMBRYO SERIAL TRANSVERSE SECTIONS AND SAGITTAL SECTION

(Figures 1-5 are serial transverse sections; Figure 6 is a midsagittal section.)

1. Skin ectoderm
2. Foregut
3. Ventricle
4. Pericardial cavity region of the coelom
5. Myocardium
6. Endocardium
7. Thyroid rudiment
8. Dorsal aorta
9. Myelencephalon
10. Auditory placode
11. Junction between somatic and splanchnic mesoderm
12. Sinoatrial region
13. Roof plate

14. Spinal cord
15. Floor plate
16. Pronephric cord
17. Splanchnopleure of the lateral plate
18. Notochord
19. Endoderm
20. Splanchnic mesoderm
21. Somite
22. Neural groove
23. Neural folds
24. Segmental plate
25. Primitive groove
26. Primitive ridges
27. Primitive streak

28. Infundibulum
29. Mesencephalon
30. Metencephalon
31. Cranial intestinal portal
32. Bulbus cordis
33. Proamnion
34. Oral membrane
35. Subcephalic pocket
36. Prosencephalon
37. Somatic mesoderm
38. Somatopleure of the lateral plate
39. Nephrotome (buds off pronephric cords)
40. Coelom

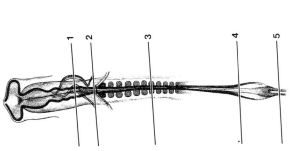

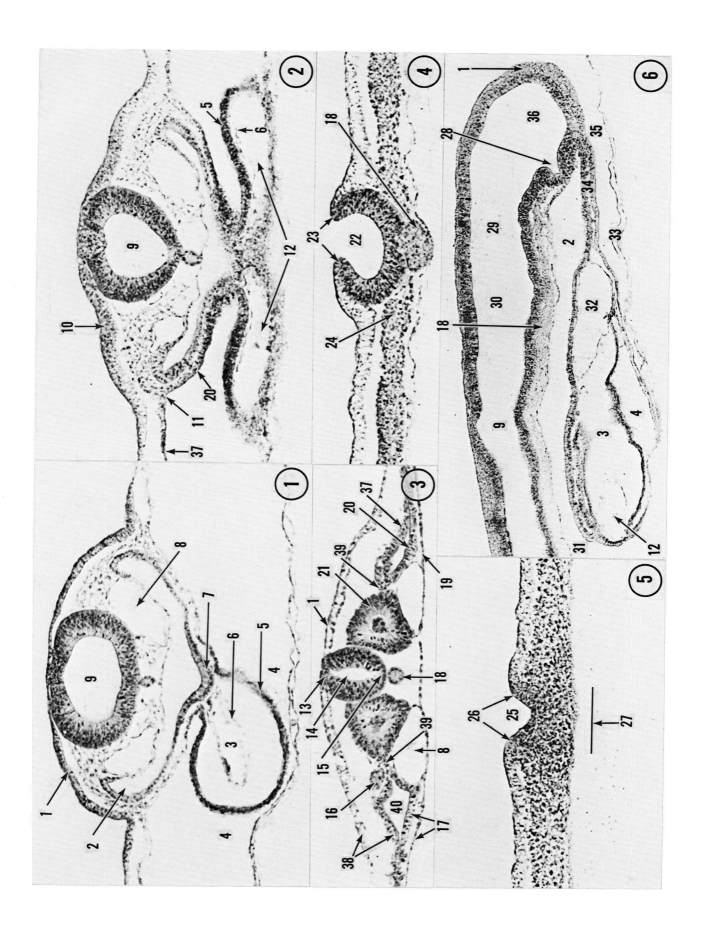

PLATE 10

33-HOUR CHICK EMBRYOS—SCANNING ELECTRON MICROGRAPHS

FIGURE 1:
Intact embryo (dorsal view)

FIGURE 2:
Intact embryo (dorsal view of caudal end)

FIGURE 3:
Intact embryo (cranial end)

FIGURE 4:
Transverse slice (The skin ectoderm and subjacent mesenchyme
have been removed on the left side of the micrograph.)

FIGURE 5:
Enlargement of the lateral portion of a transverse slice

Asterisk: Artifactual crack in blastoderm

1. Head (cranial) end of embryo
2. Auditory placodes
3. Neural fold
4. Neural groove
5. Primitive groove (flanked by primitive ridges)
6. Remnant of the cranial neuropore
7. Optic vesicle (covered by skin ectoderm in Fig. 3)
8. Ventral surface of head
9. Continuity between optic vesicle and diencephalon
10. Infundibulum
11. Future lens ectoderm

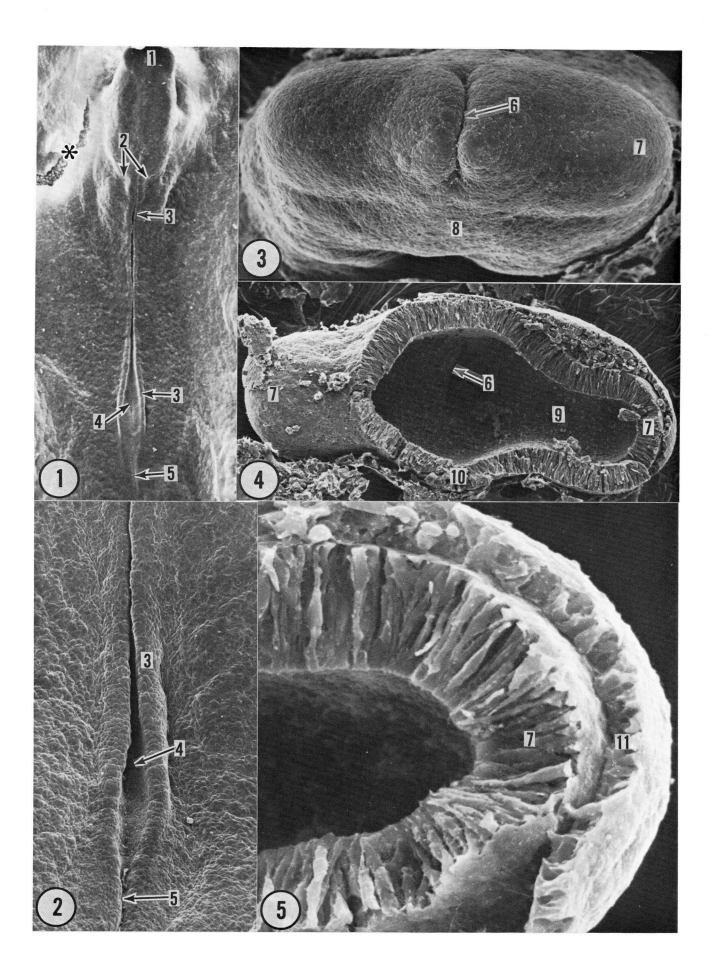

PLATE 11

33-HOUR CHICK EMBRYOS—SCANNING ELECTRON MICROGRAPHS

FIGURE 1:
Cut surface of a block sectioned transversely

FIGURE 2:
Transverse slice (tilted to show the heart; splanchnopleure removed)

FIGURE 3:
Transverse cryofracture

FIGURE 4:
Enlargement of the cardiac jelly from a transverse cryofracture

FIGURE 5:
Enlargement of the auditory vesicle from an intact specimen

FIGURE 6:
Transverse slice

1. Metencephalon (cranial end)
2. Dorsal aorta
3. Foregut
4. Skin ectoderm
5. Somatic mesoderm
6. Somatopleure
7. Bulbus cordis
8. Dorsal mesocardium
9. Pericardial cavity
10. Ventricle
11. Splanchnopleure
12. Metencephalon (caudal end)
13. Sinoatrial region
14. Myelencephalon
15. Auditory vesicle (invaginated auditory placode)
16. Notochord
17. Thyroid rudiment
18. Endocardium of ventricle
19. Myocardium of ventricle
20. Cardiac jelly
21. Spinal cord
22. Somite
23. Nephrotome
24. Coelom
25. Endoderm

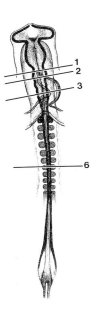

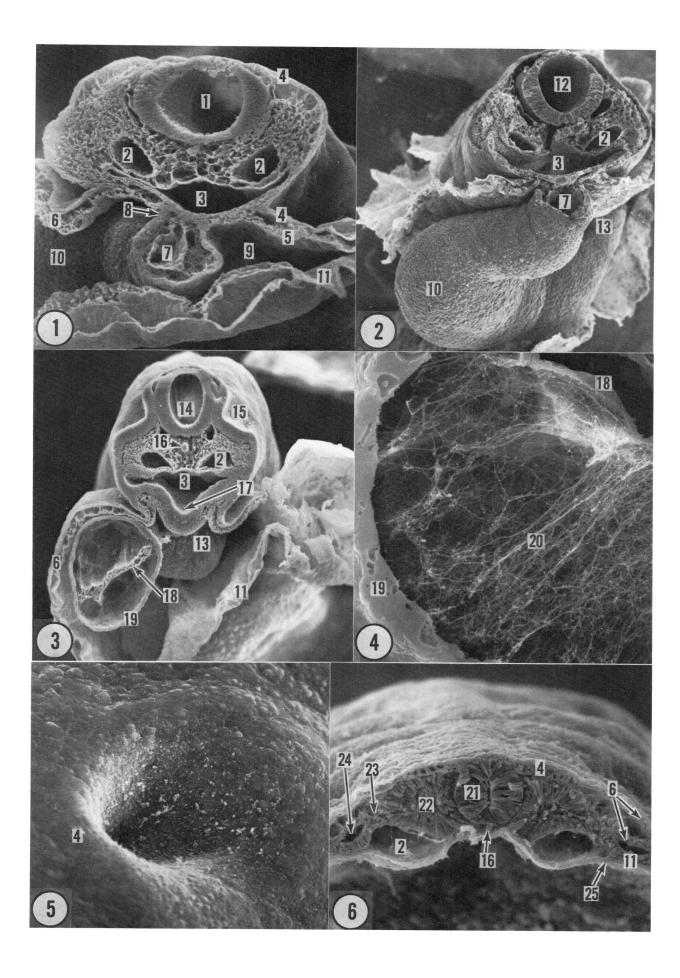

PLATE 12

33-HOUR CHICK EMBRYOS—SCANNING ELECTRON MICROGRAPHS

FIGURE 1:
Transverse slice

FIGURE 2:
Transverse cryofracture

FIGURE 3:
Transverse slice

FIGURE 4:
Cut surface of a block sectioned sagittally
(This embryo is slightly more developed than most 33-hour embryos.)

1. Skin ectoderm
2. Somite
3. Spinal cord
4. Notochord
5. Dorsal aorta (endothelium ruptured on left side of micrograph)
6. Endoderm
7. Neural fold
8. Neural groove
9. Segmental plate
10. Primitive streak
11. Mesoderm
12. Primitive groove
13. Primitive ridge (poorly defined)

14. Diencephalon
15. Optic vesicle
16. Infundibulum
17. Mesencephalon
18. Metencephalon
19. Myelencephalon
20. Notochord
21. Cranial intestinal portal
22. Foregut
23. Sinoatrial region
24. Oral membrane
25. Subcephalic pocket
26. Ectoderm of proamnion

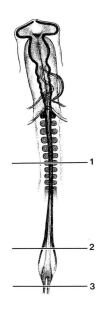

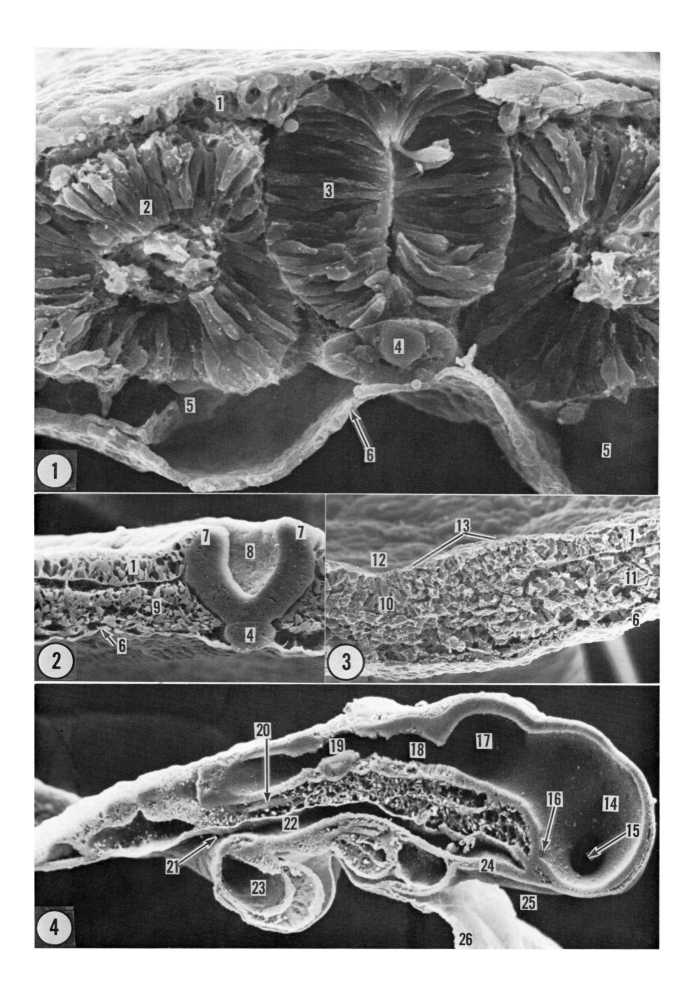

PLATE 13

18-HOUR CHICK EMBRYO WHOLE MOUNTS

FIGURE 1:
Definitive primitive streak stage

FIGURES 2, 3:
Head process stage

FIGURE 4:
Early head fold stage

1. Area pellucida
2. Primitive streak
3. Head process (future cranial part of the notochord)
4. Primitive knot
5. Primitive groove
6. Primitive ridge
7. Primitive pit
8. Proamnion
9. Head fold of the body

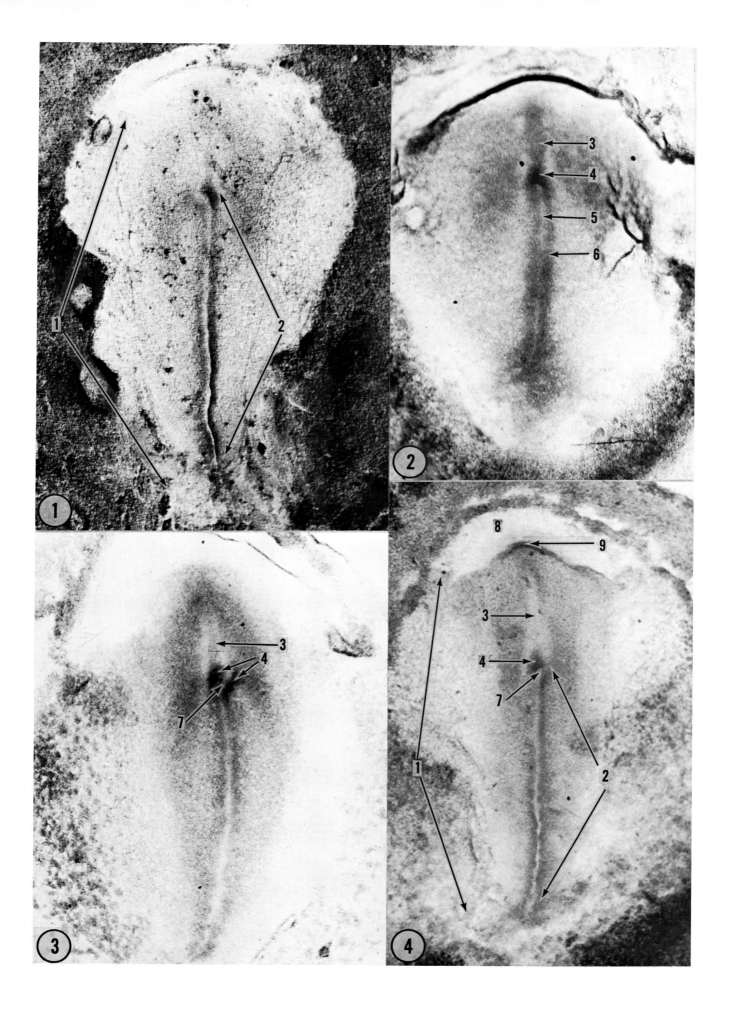

PLATE 14

18-HOUR CHICK EMBRYOS—SCANNING ELECTRON MICROGRAPHS

FIGURE 1:
Intact embryo, definitive primitive streak stage (dorsal view)

FIGURE 2:
Intact embryo, head process stage (dorsal view)

FIGURE 3:
Intact embryo, early head fold stage (dorsal view)

FIGURE 4:
Slightly parasagittal slice, early head fold stage

FIGURE 5:
Transverse slice through neural plate, early head fold stage

1. Primitive knot
2. Primitive pit
3. Primitive groove
4. Primitive ridges
5. Head process (beneath neural plate)

6. Neural plate
7. Early head fold of the body
8. Ectoderm
9. Endoderm
10. Mesoderm

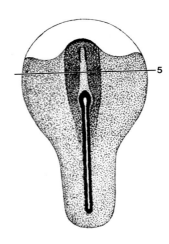

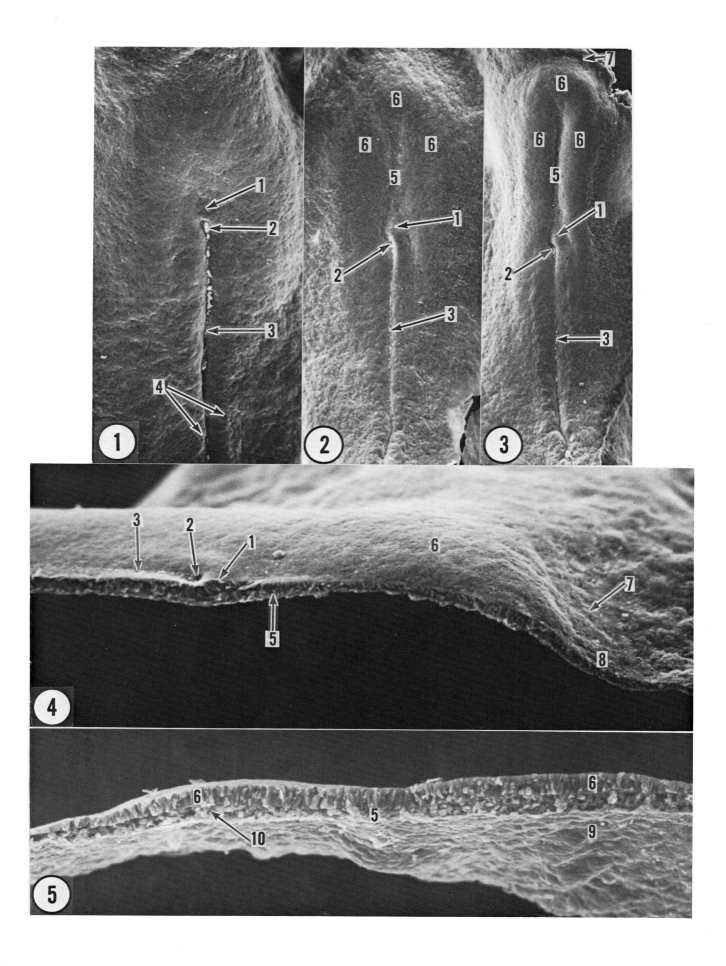

PLATE 15

18-HOUR CHICK EMBRYOS, EARLY HEAD FOLD STAGE— SCANNING ELECTRON MICROGRAPHS

FIGURE 1:
Transverse slice through primitive knot
(The background of the figure shows more *caudal* levels.)

FIGURE 2:
Transverse slice through primitive pit

FIGURE 3:
Transverse slice through primitive groove and ridges
(The background of the figure shows more *cranial* levels.)

1. Primitive knot
2. Primitive pit
3. Primitive groove
4. Epiblast
5. Mesoderm

6. Endoderm
7. Ingressing prospective mesodermal cells
8. Primitive ridge
9. Early neural goove

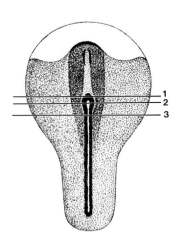

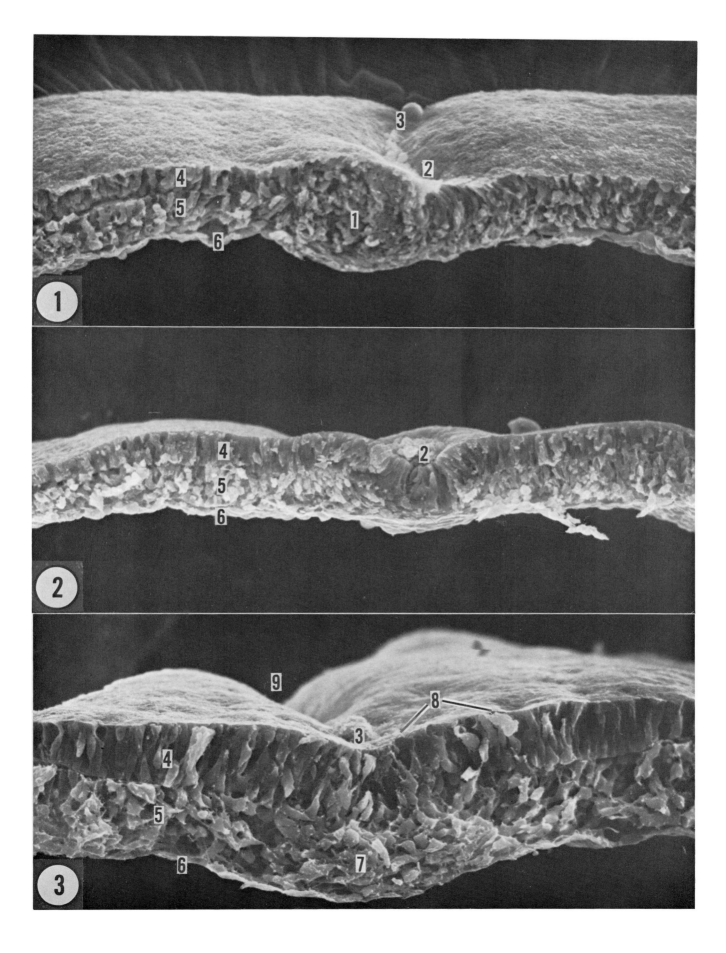

PLATE 16
24-HOUR CHICK EMBRYO WHOLE MOUNTS

(Figures 3 and 4 are enlargements of embryo illustrated in Figure 2.)

1. Proamnion
2. Caudal extent of the subcephalic pocket
3. Neural folds
4. Somites
5. Cranial neuropore
6. Primitive streak
7. Neural tube
8. Cranial intestinal portal
9. Area opaca

10. Intersomitic furrows
11. Notochord
12. Area pellucida
13. Skin ectoderm
14. Head mesenchyme
15. Lateral margin of foregut
16. Neural groove
17. Second somite
18. Third intersomitic furrow
19. Segmental plate

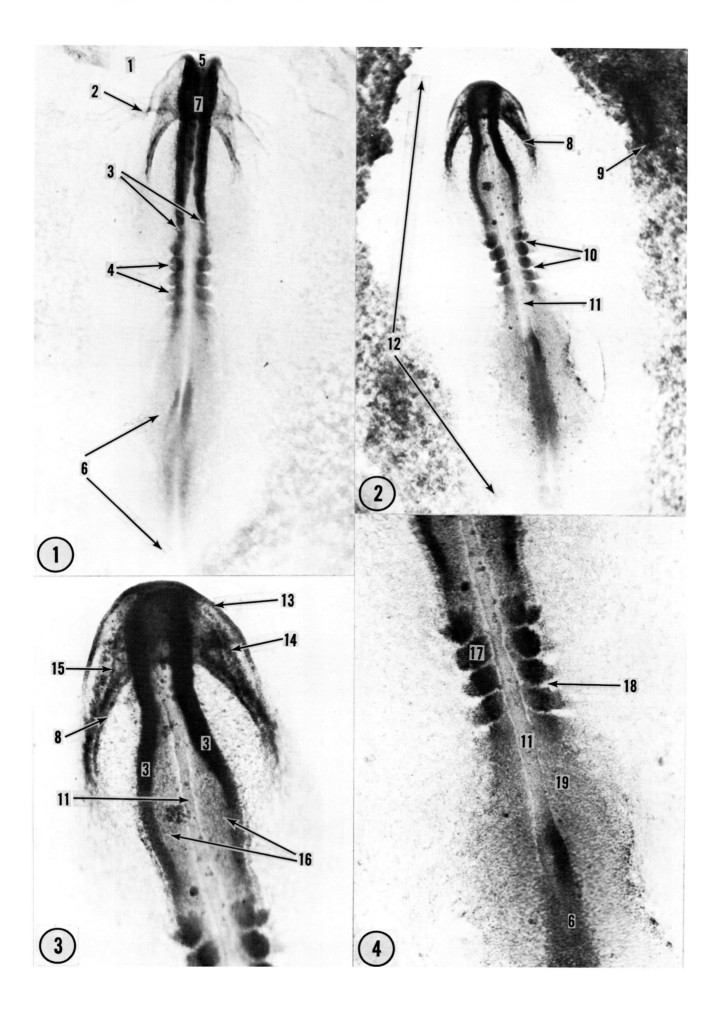

PLATE 17

24-HOUR CHICK EMBRYO SERIAL TRANSVERSE SECTIONS AND SAGITTAL SECTIONS

FIGURES 1-4:
Serial transverse sections

FIGURE 5:
Midsagittal section

FIGURE 6:
Sagittal section just lateral to the midline

(Unlabeled arrows in Figure 2 indicate lateral body fold.)

1. Neural tube
2. Skin ectoderm
3. Head mesenchyme
4. Foregut
5. Coelom
6. Proamnion
7. Subcephalic pocket
8. Notochord
9. Somatopleure

10. Splanchnopleure
11. Rudiment of the pericardial cavity (portion of coelom)
12. Cranial intestinal portal
13. Cardiac primordia
14. Endoderm
15. Splanchnic mesoderm
16. Somatic mesoderm
17. Neural groove
18. Neural ectoderm

19. Somite
20. Neural fold
21. Beginning coelom formation in lateral plate
22. Nephrotome
23. Neural plate
24. Segmental plate
25. Oral membrane
26. Cranial neuropore

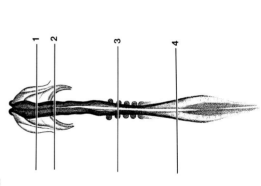

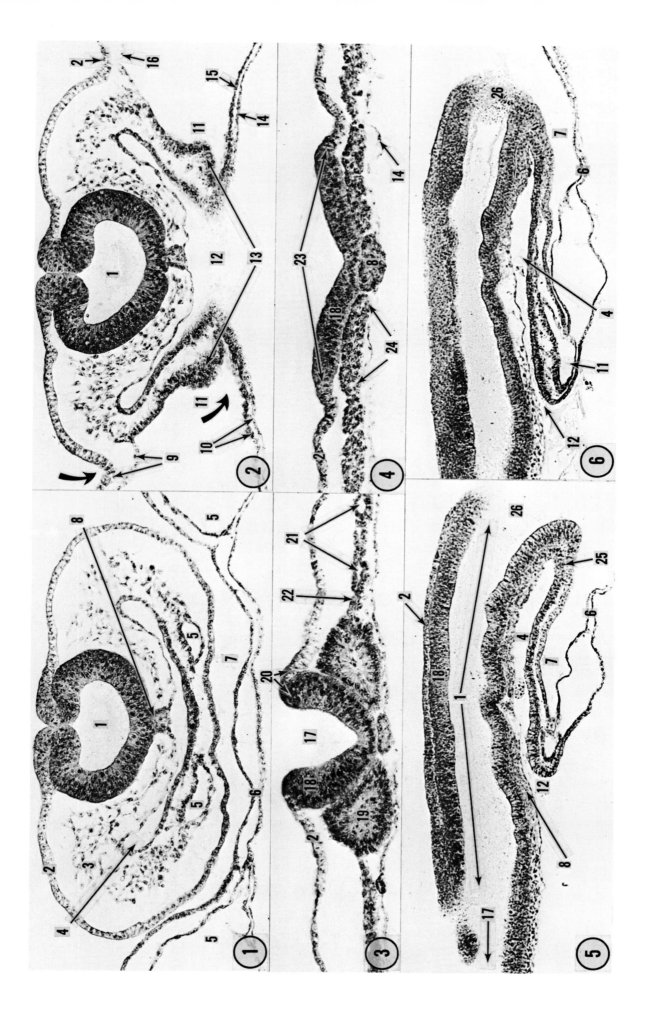

PLATE 18

21- AND 24-HOUR CHICK EMBRYOS—SCANNING ELECTRON MICROGRAPHS

FIGURE 1:
21-hour intact embryo (dorsal view)

FIGURES 2, 3:
24-hour intact embryos (dorsal views)

FIGURE 4:
Midsagittal slice of a 24-hour embryo

1. Head fold of the body
2. Neural plate
3. Skin ectoderm
4. Primitive pit
5. Primitive groove
6. Primitive ridges
7. Neural groove of the future mesencephalon region
8. Neural fold
9. Primitive streak

10. Cranial neuropore
11. Neural tube of the mesencephalon region
12. Lateral extent of the head fold of the body
13. Neural groove of the future spinal cord
14. Foregut
15. Cranial intestinal portal
16. Subcephalic pocket

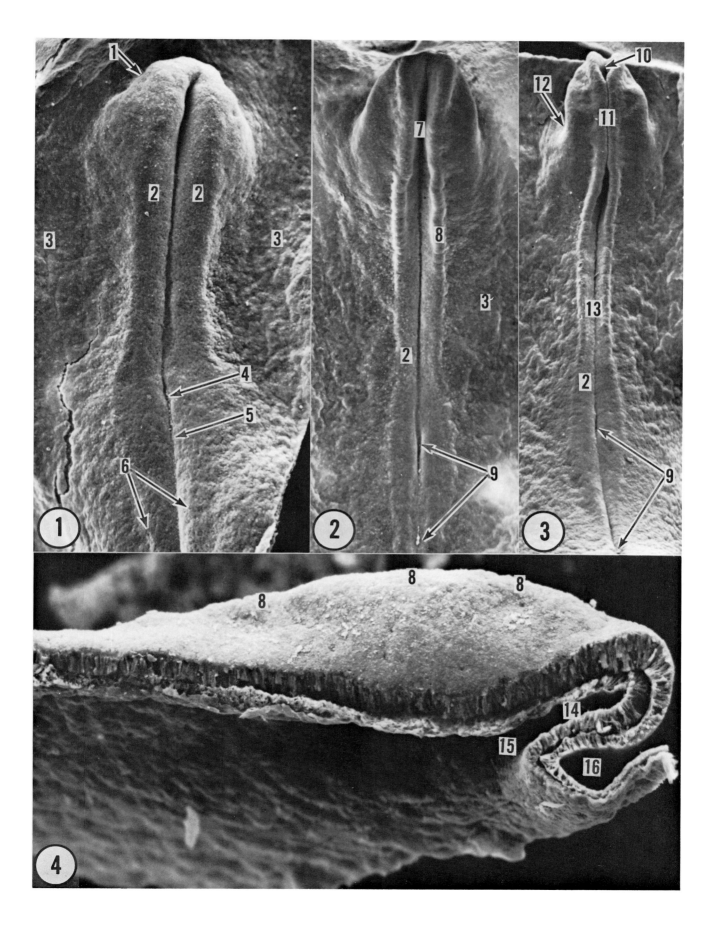

PLATE 19
24-HOUR CHICK EMBRYOS—SCANNING ELECTRON MICROGRAPHS

FIGURE 1:
Intact embryo (cranial end)

FIGURES 2-5:
Transverse cryofractures

(Figures 2 and 3 are located at about the same craniocaudal level;
Figure 2 is from a less developed 24-hour embryo than is Figure 3.
Because Figures 2 and 3 are from less developed 24-hour embryos
than the one shown in the drawing below,
the levels of Figures 2 and 3 are not indicated on this drawing.)

Arrows: Artifactual discontinuities in cryofractured tissues

1. Neural fold
2. Cranial neuropore
3. Neural groove
4. Notochord
5. Head mesenchyme
6. Foregut
7. Cranial intestinal portal
8. Skin ectoderm
9. Lateral plate mesoderm (split into somatic and splanchnic mesoderm)
10. Endoderm

11. Subcephalic pocket
12. Proamnion (folded and cracked)
13. Neural tube (just about to form at level shown in Figure 3)
14. Coelom
15. Splanchnopleure (component of lateral body fold)
16. Somatopleure
17. Somite
18. Nephrotome
19. Lateral plate mesoderm (not yet split into somatic and splanchnic mesoderm)

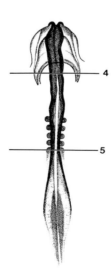

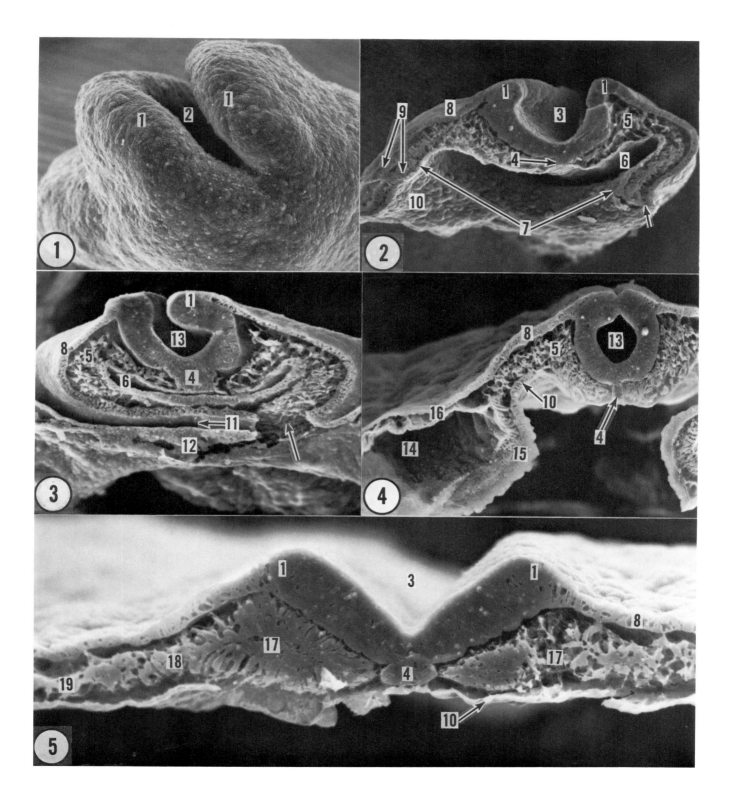

PLATE 20

48-HOUR CHICK EMBRYO WHOLE MOUNTS

(Asterisk in Figure 2 indicates the cranial flexure.)

1. Stomodeum
2. Optic cup
3. Maxillary process
4. Notochord
5. Isthmus
6. Mandibular process
7. Auditory vesicle
8. Second branchial groove
9. Third branchial groove
10. Caudal intestinal portal
11. Caudal boundary of body
12. Cranial intestinal portal
13. Cranial liver rudiment
14. Ventricle
15. Bulbus cordis
16. Optic fissure

17. Metencephalon
18. Roof plate of myelencephalon
19. First branchial groove
20. Second branchial arch
21. Third branchial arch
22. Boundary of amniotic folds
23. Spinal cord
24. Telencephalon
25. Foregut
26. Diencephalon
27. Mesencephalon
28. Myelencephalon
29. Somites
30. Vitelline artery
31. Tail bud

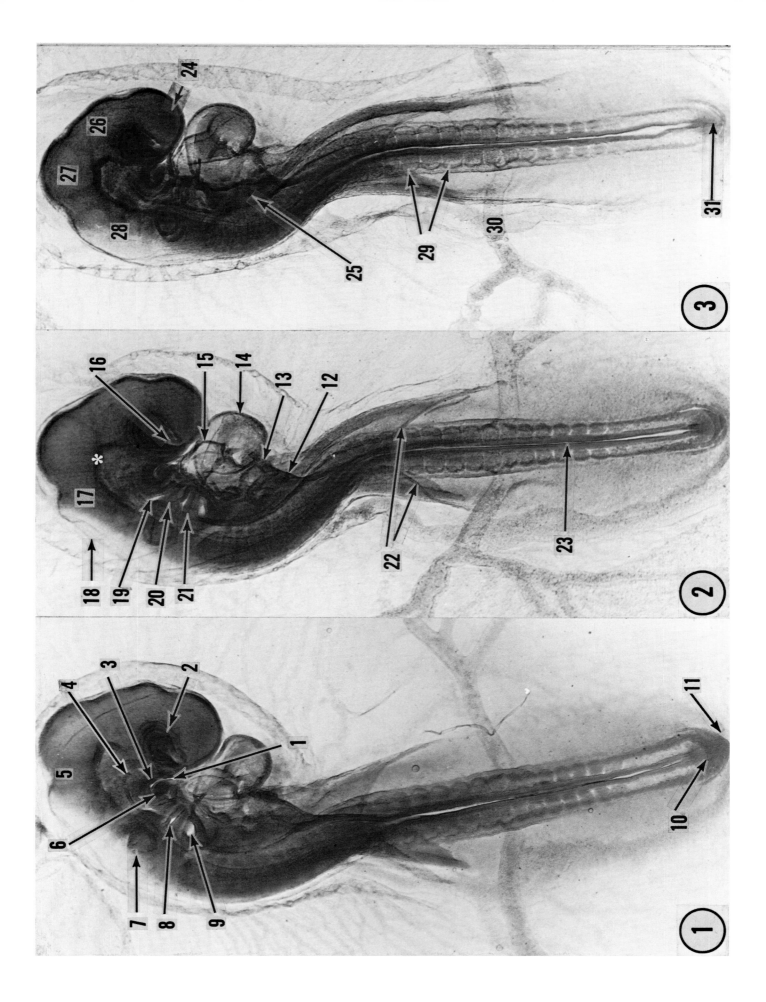

PLATE 21

48-HOUR CHICK EMBRYO WHOLE MOUNTS—INJECTED

(The cranial half of the embryo illustrated in Figure 1 is shown in Figure 2.)

1. Right vitelline vein
2. Plexus of head blood vessels
3. Left vitelline vein
4. Plexus of vitelline blood vessels
5. Descending aorta
6. Right dorsal aorta
7. Right vitelline artery
8. Right vitelline vein entering sinus venosus
9. Sinus venosus
10. Common cardinal and left vitelline veins entering sinus venosus
11. Ventricle
12. Bulbus cordis
13. Atrium
14. Aortic sac
15. First aortic arch
16. Continuity between dorsal aorta and first aortic arch (dashed line)
17. Precardinal vein
18. Second aortic arch
19. Third aortic arch
20. Intersegmental arteries

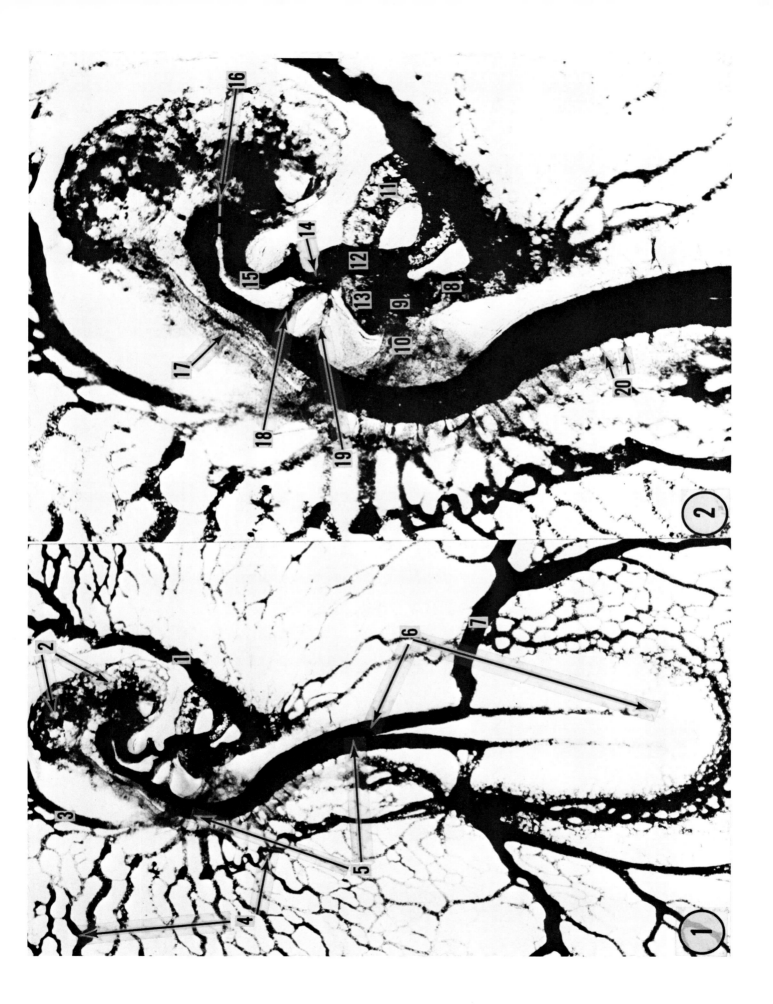

PLATE 22
48-HOUR CHICK EMBRYO SERIAL TRANSVERSE SECTIONS

1. Myelencephalon
2. Metencephalon
3. Isthmus
4. Head mesenchyme
5. Mesencephalon
6. Diencephalon
7. Roof plate of myelencephalon
8. Semilunar ganglion
9. Notochord
10. Amnion
11. Yolk sac
12. Precardinal vein

13. Acousticofacialis ganglion
14. Dorsal aorta
15. Foregut endoderm
16. Auditory vesicle
17. First pharyngeal pouch
18. First branchial groove
19. Pharynx
20. First aortic arch
21. Chorion
22. Rathke's pouch
23. Infundibulum
24. First closing plate

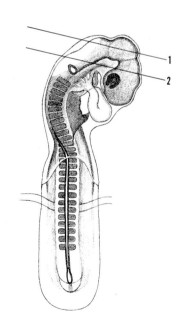

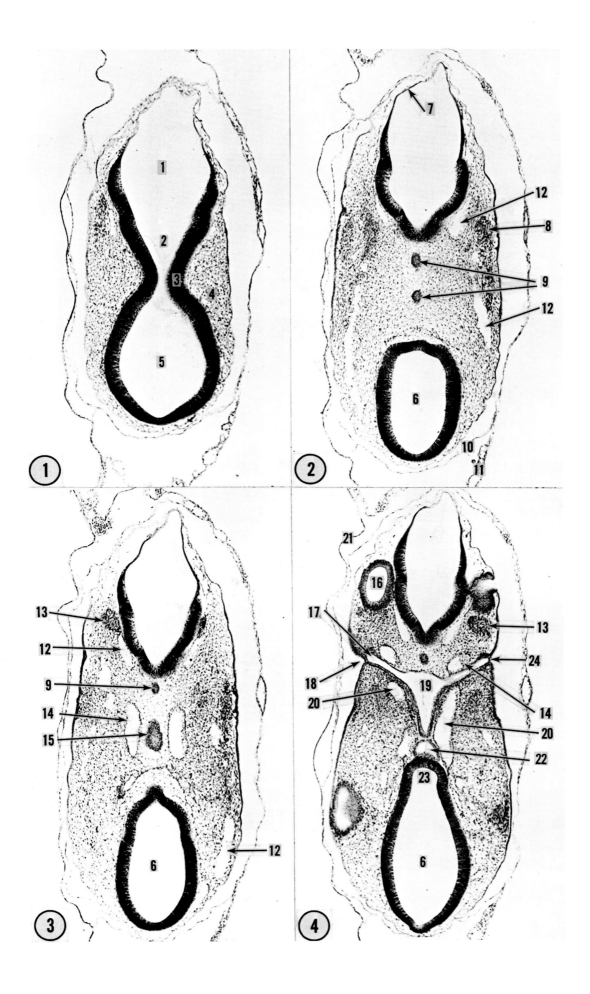

PLATE 23
48-HOUR CHICK EMBRYO SERIAL TRANSVERSE SECTIONS

1. Myelencephalon
2. Superior ganglion
3. Auditory vesicle
4. Acousticofacialis ganglion
5. First pharyngeal pouch
6. Pharynx
7. First branchial groove
8. First aortic arch
9. Mandibular process
10. Maxillary process
11. Oral membrane
12. Stomodeum
13. Rathke's pouch (continuous with stomodeum)
14. Infundibulum
15. Optic cup
16. Epibranchial placode (contributes cells to facialis part of acoustico-facialis ganglion)
17. Opticoel
18. Precardinal vein
19. Notochord
20. Dorsal aorta
21. Second aortic arch
22. Pigmented retina
23. Continuity between skin ectoderm and lens vesicle
24. Sensory retina
25. Skin ectoderm
26. Second pharyngeal pouch
27. Aortic sac
28. Vitelline blood vessel
29. Second closing plate
30. Chorion
31. Amnion
32. Yolk sac
33. Optic stalk
34. Thyroid rudiment
35. Diencephalon

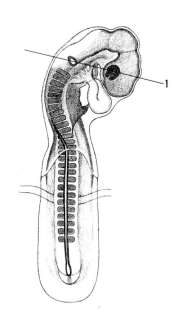

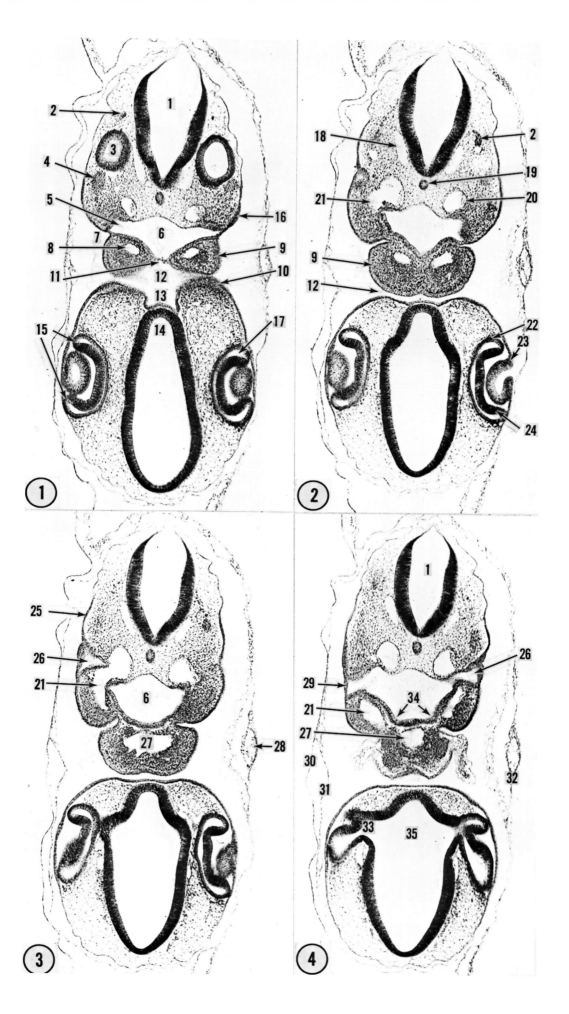

PLATE 24
48-HOUR CHICK EMBRYO SERIAL TRANSVERSE SECTIONS

1. Somite # 1
2. Chorion
3. Precardinal vein
4. Dorsal aortae
5. Amniotic cavity
6. Third pharyngeal pouch
7. Third closing plate
8. Pharynx
9. Third aortic arch
10. Endocardium of bulbus cordis
11. Myocardium of bulbus cordis
12. Aortic sac
13. Nasal placode
14. Telencephalon
15. Dermatome
16. Myotome
17. Sclerotome

18. Atrium
19. Descending aorta
20. Foregut
21. Amnion
22. Splanchnic mesoderm
23. Pericardial cavity
24. Bulbus cordis
25. Ventricle
26. Spinal cord
27. Pleural cavity
28. Postcardinal vein
29. Common cardinal vein
30. Beginning of lung bud
31. Dorsal mesocardium
32. Sinus venosus
33. Vitelline blood vessel
34. Cranial liver rudiment

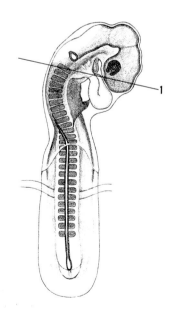

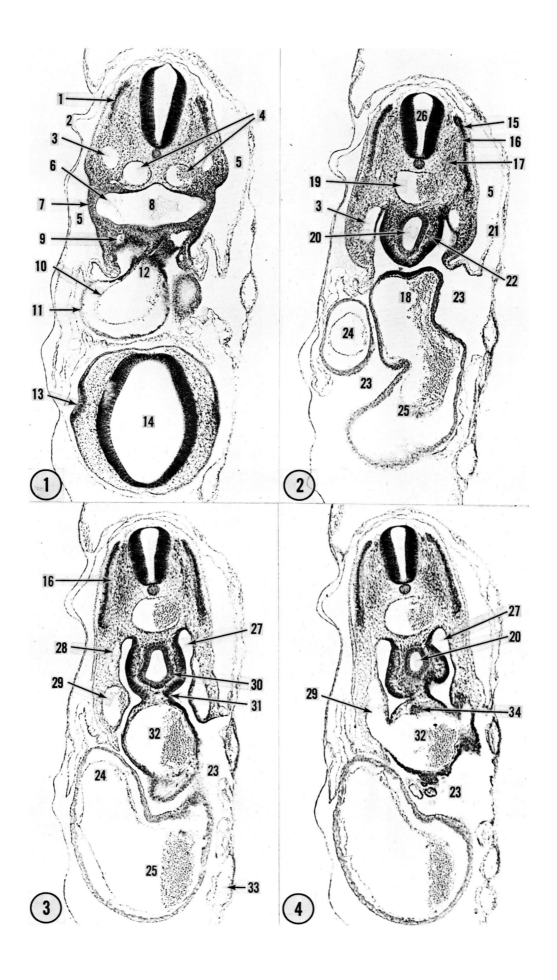

PLATE 25
48-HOUR CHICK EMBRYO SERIAL TRANSVERSE SECTIONS

1. Spinal cord
2. Notochord
3. Intersegmental artery
4. Descending aorta
5. Postcardinal vein
6. Duodenum
7. Cranial liver rudiment
8. Vitelline vein
9. Caudal liver rudiment
10. Rudiment of the peritoneal cavity
11. Mesonephric duct rudiment (cavitated)
12. Cranial intestinal portal
13. Yolk sac
14. Mesonephric tubule rudiment
15. Ectoderm of lateral amniotic fold
16. Somatic mesoderm of lateral amniotic fold
17. Chorion
18. Amnion
19. Amniotic cavity
20. Dorsal aortae
21. Extraembryonic coelom
22. Mesonephric duct rudiment (noncavitated)
23. Sclerotome
24. Myotome
25. Dermatome
26. Vitelline blood vessel
27. Floor plate
28. Roof plate
29. Dorsal aorta
30. Vitelline artery
31. Ectoderm of lateral body fold
32. Somatic mesoderm of lateral body fold
33. Endoderm

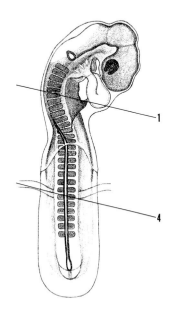

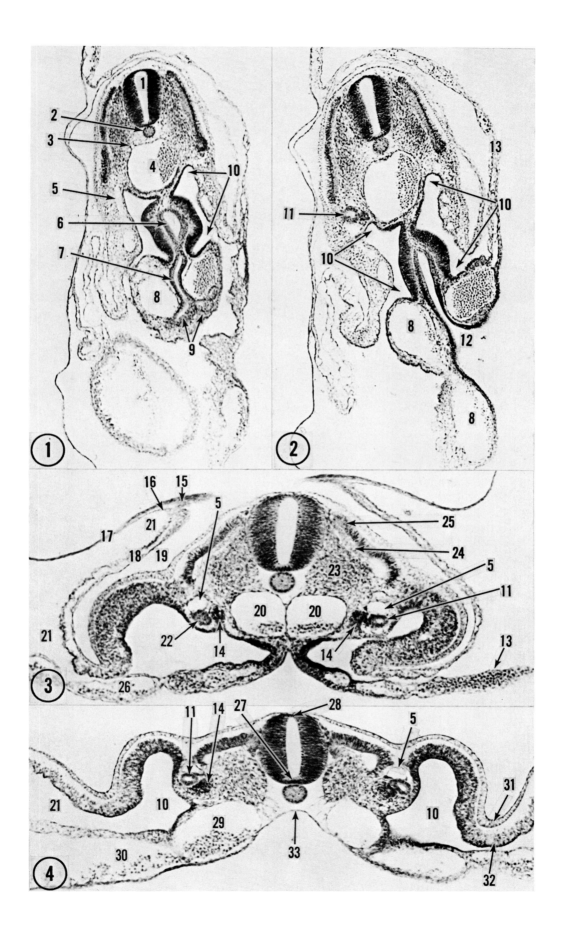

PLATE 26
48-HOUR CHICK EMBRYO SERIAL TRANSVERSE SECTIONS AND
SAGITTAL SECTIONS

FIGURES 1, 2:
Serial transverse sections

FIGURE 3:
Midsagittal section

FIGURE 4:
Parasagittal section at level of the optic cup

1. Tail bud
2. Somatopleure
3. Vitelline blood vessel
4. Caudal intestinal portal
5. Skin ectoderm
6. Extraembryonic coelom
7. Splanchnopleure (of yolk sac)
8. Allantois rudiment
9. Roof plate of myelencephalon
10. Isthmus
11. Myelencephalon
12. Metencephalon
13. Mesencephalon
14. Notochord
15. Infundibulum
16. Rathke's pouch
17. Stomodeum

18. Diencephalon
19. Preoral gut
20. Oral membrane
21. Pharynx
22. Mandibular process
23. First aortic arch
24. Telencephalon
25. Bulbus cordis
26. Ventricle
27. Aortic sac
28. Sensory retina
29. Pigmented retina
30. Lens vesicle
31. Opticoel (continuous with cavity of diencephalon)
32. Optic fissure
33. Head mesenchyme

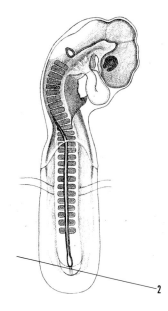

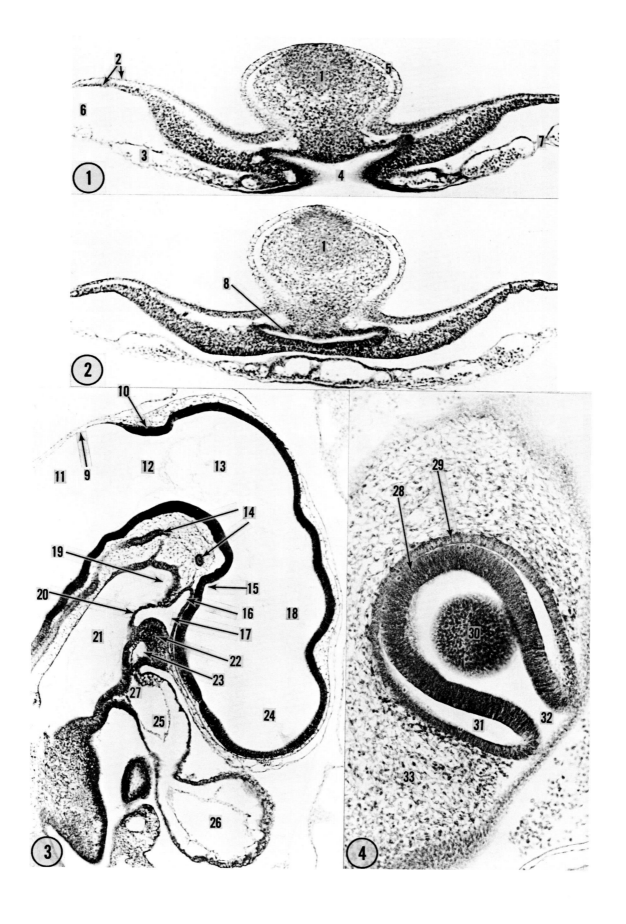

PLATE 27

48-HOUR CHICK EMBRYO—SCANNING ELECTRON MICROGRAPH
OF THE CUT SURFACE
OF A BLOCK SECTIONED TRANSVERSELY

1. Myelencephalon
2. Acousticofacialis ganglion
3. Yolk sac
4. Amnion
5. Notochord
6. Precardinal vein
7. Dorsal aorta
8. Chorion
9. Extraembryonic coelom
10. Amniotic cavity
11. Pharynx
12. First pharyngeal pouch
13. First branchial groove
14. Second branchial arch
15. First branchial arch
16. First aortic arch
17. Rathke's pouch
18. Infundibulum
19. Diencephalon
20. Optic cup
21. Sensory retina
22. Pigmented retina
23. Lens vesicle
24. Continuity between skin ectoderm and lens vesicle
25. Skin ectoderm

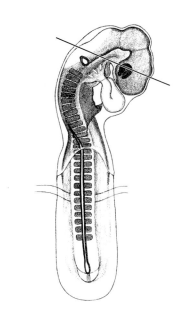

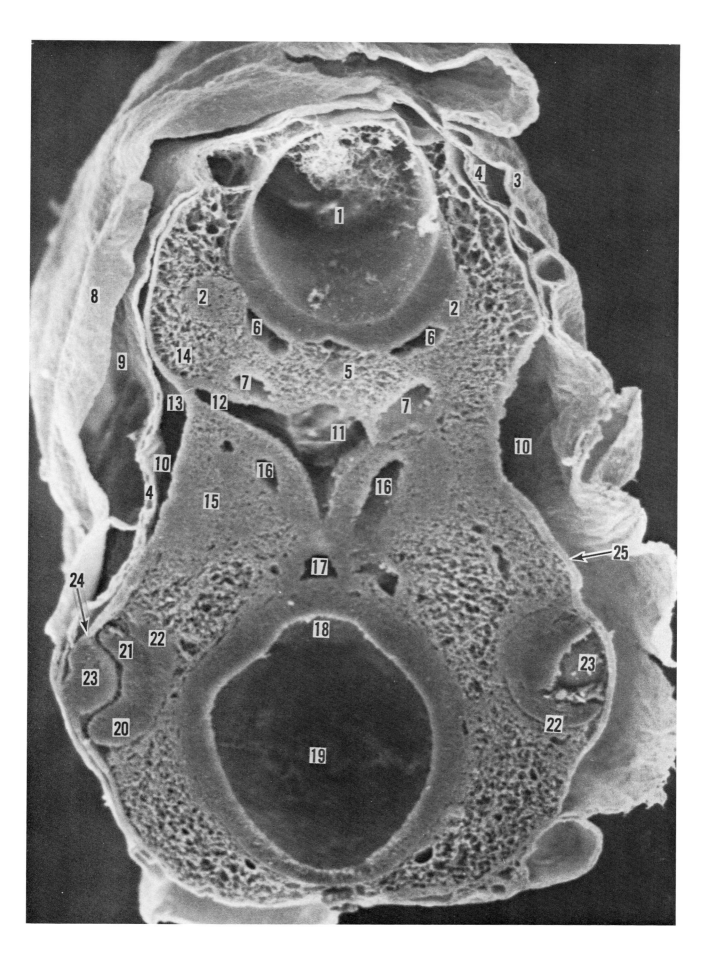

PLATE 28

48-HOUR CHICK EMBRYOS—SCANNING ELECTRON MICROGRAPHS

FIGURE 1:
Transverse slice (mid-portion of spinal cord, just cranial to
level shown in Plate 25, Fig. 3; background shows more *cranial* levels)

FIGURE 2:
Transverse cryofracture (caudal portion of spinal cord;
background shows more *caudal* levels)

1. Skin ectoderm
2. Spinal cord
3. Notochord
4. Dorsal aorta
5. Coelom
6. Endoderm
7. Lateral body fold
8. Caudal extent of the continuous cranial and lateral amniotic folds
9. Yolk sac (splanchnopleure)
10. Amnion (somatopleure)
11. Amniotic cavity
12. Endothelial cells forming an intersegmental artery in an intersomitic furrow
13. Neural crest cells
14. Postcardinal vein
15. Somite
16. Allantois rudiment (opening cranially as the caudal intestinal portal)
17. Somatopleure of lateral plate
18. Splanchnopleure of lateral plate

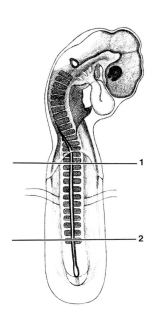

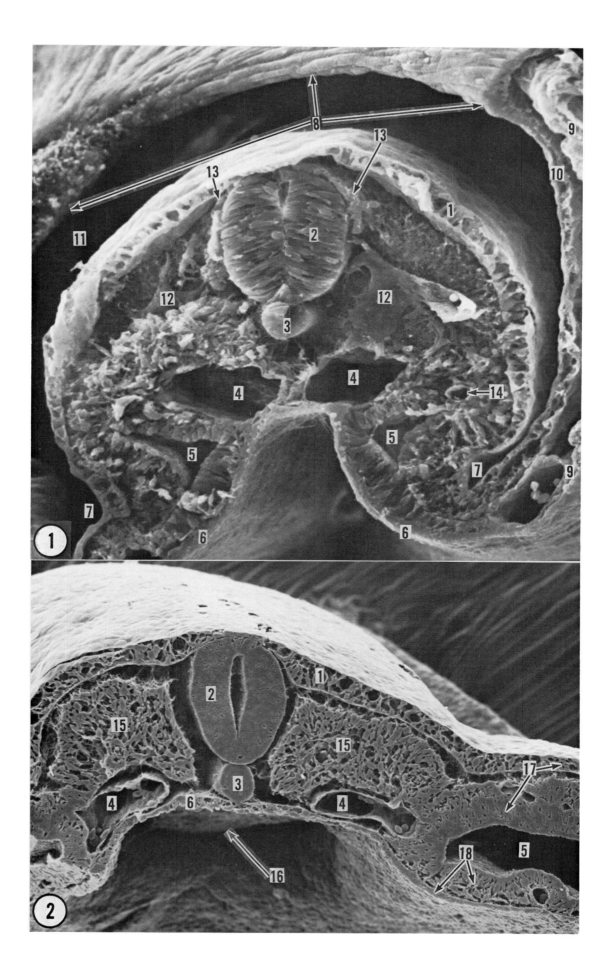

PLATE 29

**48-HOUR CHICK EMBRYO—SCANNING ELECTRON MICROGRAPH
OF THE
CUT SURFACE OF A BLOCK SECTIONED SAGITTALLY**

(Note that the cut surface is parasagittal.)

1. Telencephalon
2. Diencephalon
3. Optic stalk
4. Infundibulum
5. Mesencephalon
6. Metencephalon
7. Myelencephalon

8. Dorsal aorta
9. First aortic arch
10. Precardinal vein
11. Pharynx
12. Mandibular process
13. Atrium

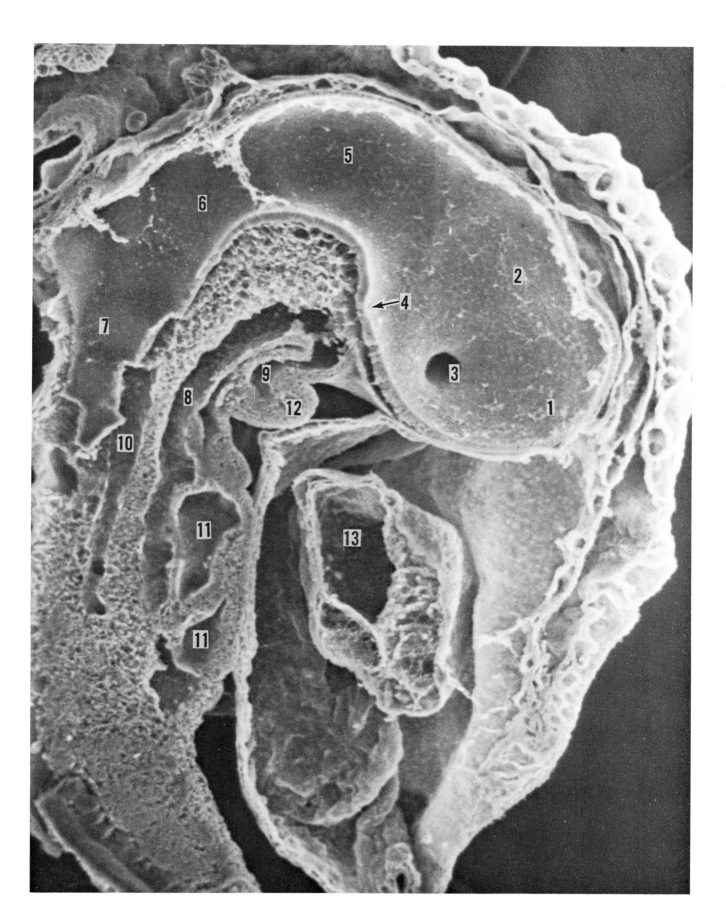

PLATE 30

72-HOUR CHICK EMBRYO WHOLE MOUNTS

1. Ventricle
2. Cerebral hemisphere of telencephalon
3. Pineal gland
4. Diencephalon
5. Mesencephalon
6. Isthmus
7. Metencephalon
8. Myelencephalon
9. Endolymphatic duct
10. Auditory vesicle
11. Wing bud
12. Cervical flexure
13. Vitelline artery
14. Caudal intestinal portal
15. Boundary of amniotic folds
16. Nasal pit
17. Semilunar ganglion
18. Acousticofacialis ganglion

19. Cranial intestinal portal
20. Tail flexure
21. First branchial groove
22. Roof plate of myelencephalon
23. Third branchial arch
24. Atrium
25. Leg bud
26. Allantois
27. Tail
28. Maxillary process
29. Optic cup
30. Mandibular process
31. Lens vesicle
32. Second branchial arch
33. Second branchial groove
34. Third branchial groove
35. Bulbus cordis
36. Sinus venosus

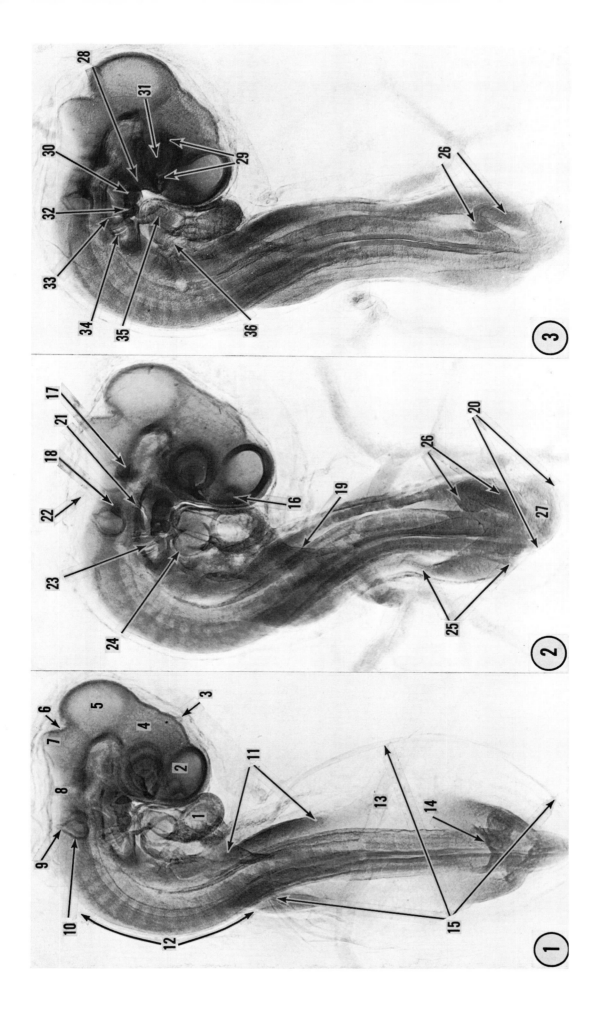

PLATE 31
72-HOUR CHICK EMBRYO WHOLE MOUNT

(Enlargement of head region)

1. Second branchial arch
2. Mandibular process
3. Pharynx
4. Semilunar ganglion
5. Rathke's pouch
6. Infundibulum
7. Stomodeum
8. Lens vesicle
9. Diencephalon
10. Cerebral hemisphere of telencephalon

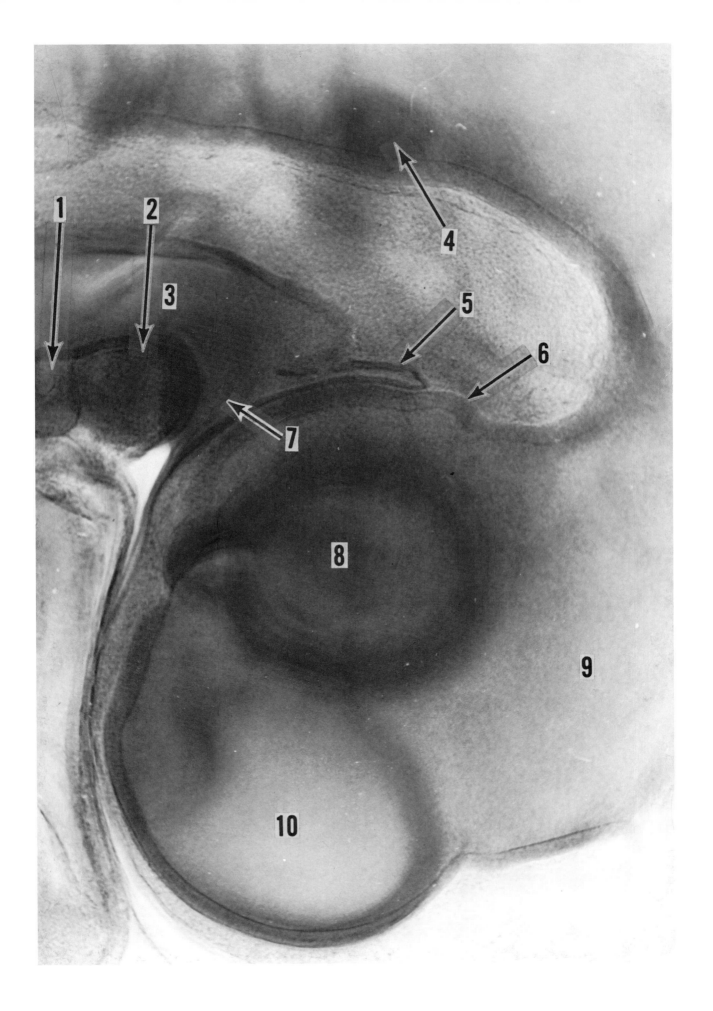

PLATE 32

72-HOUR INJECTED CHICK EMBRYO WHOLE MOUNT AND MOST ANTERIOR TRANSVERSE SECTION ILLUSTRATED

FIGURES 1, 2:

Injected embryo whole mounts. Figure 2 is an enlargement of the heart and aortic arch region of the embryo illustrated in Figure 1.

FIGURE 3:

Most anterior transverse section illustrated

1. First aortic arch
2. Second aortic arch
3. Third aortic arch
4. Internal carotid artery
5. Dorsal aorta
6. Descending aorta
7. Vitelline artery
8. Fourth aortic arch

9. Aortic sac
10. Bulbus cordis
11. Ventricle
12. Yolk sac
13. Somite # 1
14. Superior ganglion
15. Myelencephalon
16. Auditory vesicle

17. Acousticofacialis ganglion
18. Precardinal vein
19. Neuromeres
20. Amniotic cavity
21. Semilunar ganglion
22. Metencephalon
23. Mesencephalon

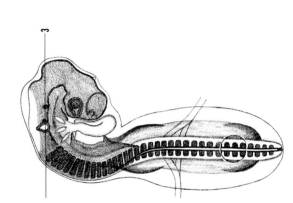

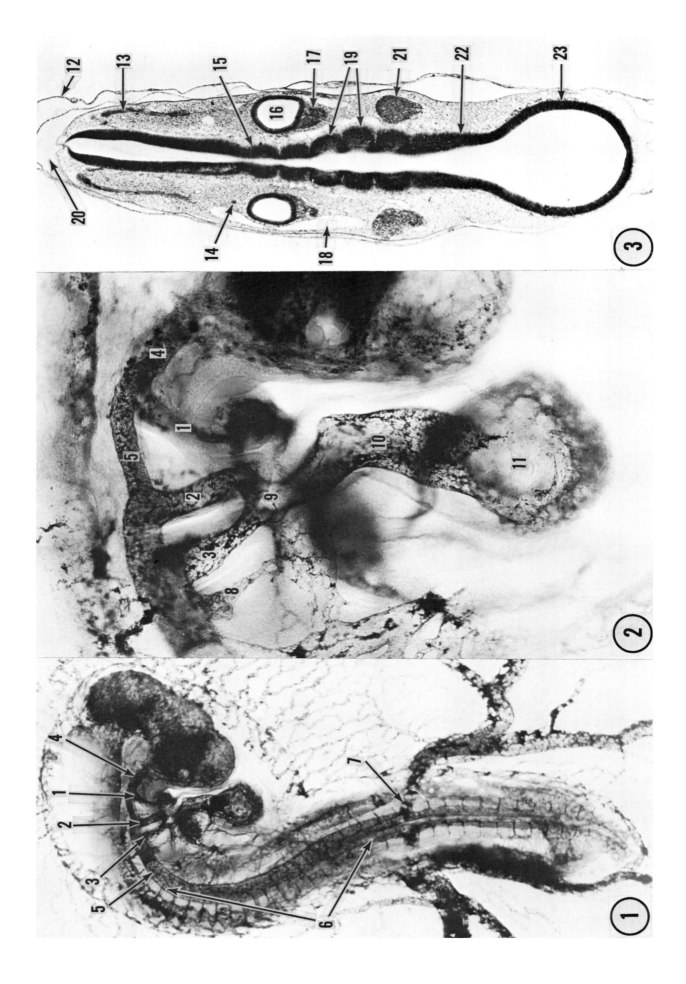

PLATE 33

72-HOUR CHICK EMBRYO SERIAL TRANSVERSE SECTIONS

1. Amnion
2. Yolk sac
3. Amniotic cavity
4. Somite
5. Notochord
6. Precardinal vein
7. Glossopharyngeal nerve
8. Epibranchial placode (contributes cells to facialis part of acousticofacialis ganglion)
9. Facial nerve
10. Trigeminal nerve—maxillary branch
11. Trigeminal nerve—mandibular branch
12. Trigeminal nerve—ophthalmic branch
13. Mesencephalon
14. Extraembryonic coelom

15. Skin ectoderm
16. Dorsal aorta
17. Second pharyngeal pouch
18. First pharyngeal pouch
19. First branchial cleft
20. Internal carotid artery
21. Third branchial arch
22. Jugular ganglion
23. Third aortic arch
24. Epibranchial placode (contributes cells to petrosal ganglion)
25. Second closing plate
26. Second aortic arch
27. Second branchial arch
28. Pharynx
29. First branchial groove
30. First closing plate
31. First aortic arch

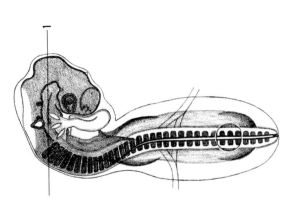

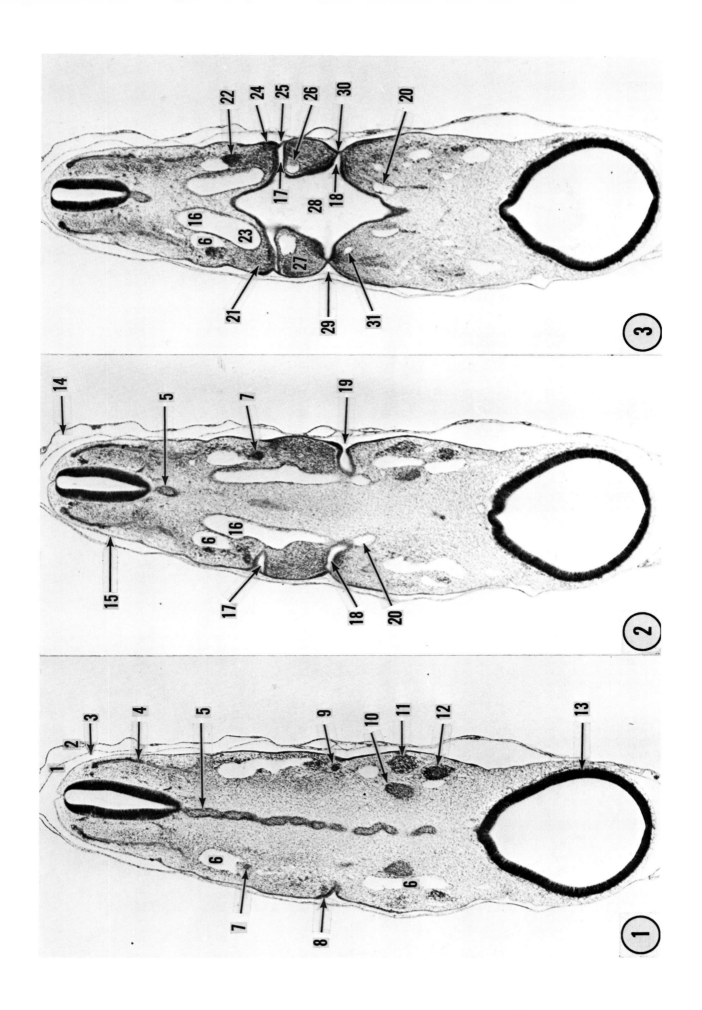

PLATE 34

72-HOUR CHICK EMBRYO SERIAL TRANSVERSE SECTIONS

1. Descending aorta
2. Dorsal aorta
3. Third pharyngeal pouch
4. Third aortic arch
5. Pharynx
6. Second pharyngeal pouch
7. Second branchial groove
8. Second aortic arch
9. First pharyngeal pouch
10. First aortic arch
11. Preoral gut
12. First branchial arch
13. Precardinal vein
14. Mesencephalon
15. Intersegmental artery
16. Fourth aortic arch
17. Third closing plate
18. Third branchial arch

19. Thyroid rudiment
20. Second branchial arch
21. Fourth branchial arch
22. Mandibular process
23. Maxillary process
24. Stomodeum
25. Rathke's pouch
26. Infundibulum
27. Spinal ganglion
28. Spinal cord
29. Notochord
30. Fourth closing plate
31. Fourth pharyngeal pouch
32. Vitelline blood vessel
33. Chorion
34. Amnion
35. Diencephalon

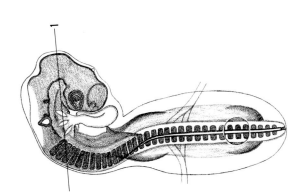

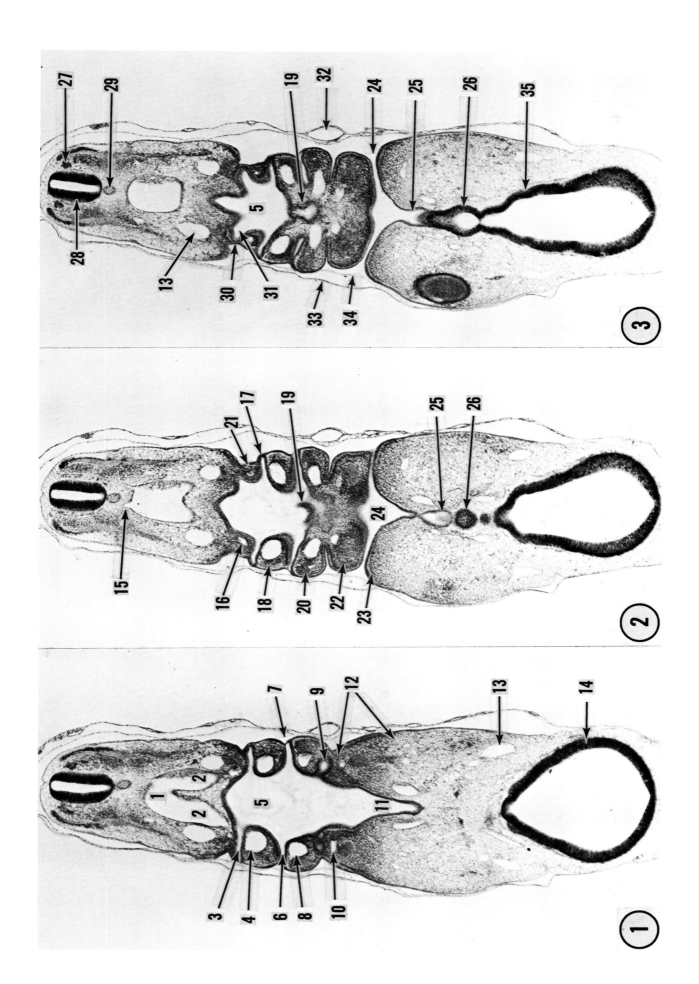

PLATE 35

72-HOUR CHICK EMBRYO SERIAL TRANSVERSE SECTIONS

1. Spinal cord
2. Postcardinal vein
3. Descending aorta
4. Common cardinal vein
5. Pharynx
6. Laryngotracheal groove
7. Aortic sac
8. Future corneal epithelium
9. Lens epithelium
10. Lens fibers
11. Ventral lip of optic cup
12. Dorsal lip of optic cup
13. Diencephalon
14. Spinal ganglion
15. Extraembryonic coelom
16. Atrium
17. Optic fissure (note lack of ventral lip of optic cup)
18. Pigmented retina
19. Sensory retina
20. Head mesenchyme
21. Lung bud
22. Sinus venosus
23. Pericardial cavity
24. Myocardium of bulbus cordis
25. Endocardium of bulbus cordis
26. Optic stalk

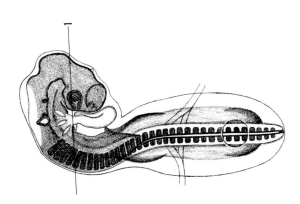

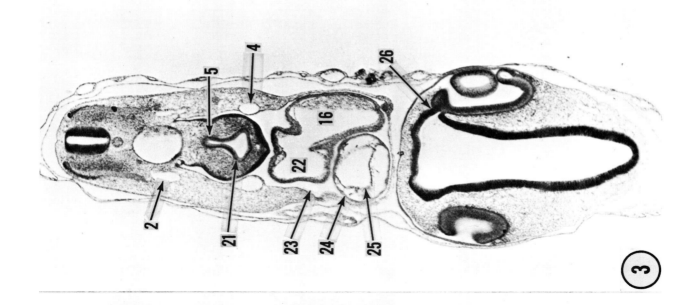

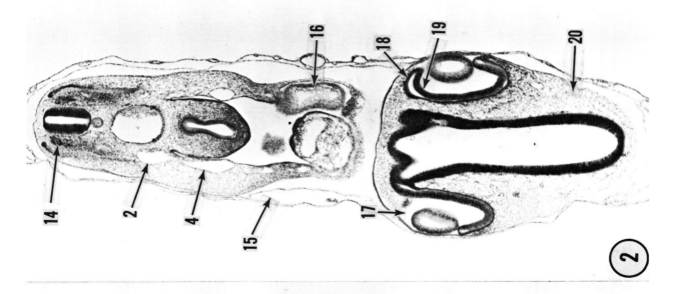

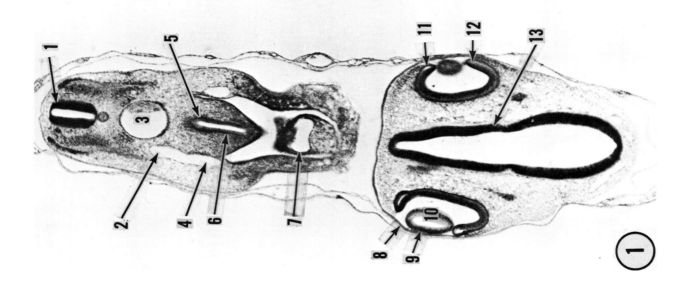

PLATE 36

72-HOUR CHICK EMBRYO SERIAL TRANSVERSE SECTIONS

1. Descending aorta
2. Postcardinal vein
3. Esophagus
4. Lung bud
5. Common cardinal vein
6. Sinus venosus
7. Atrium (continuous with ventricle below)
8. Bulbus cordis
9. Diencephalon
10. Mesoesophagus
11. Pleural cavity
12. Dorsal mesocardium
13. Somite
14. Notochord

15. Pericardial cavity
16. Cerebral hemisphere of telencephalon
17. Mesonephric duct (degenerating portion)
18. Dorsal mesogaster
19. Stomach
20. Hepatogastric ligament
21. Cranial liver rudiment
22. Ductus venosus
23. Endocardium of ventricle
24. Myocardium of ventricle
25. Nasal pit
26. Pineal gland

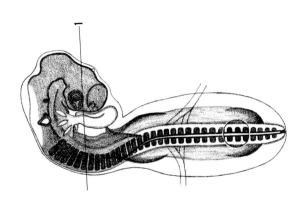

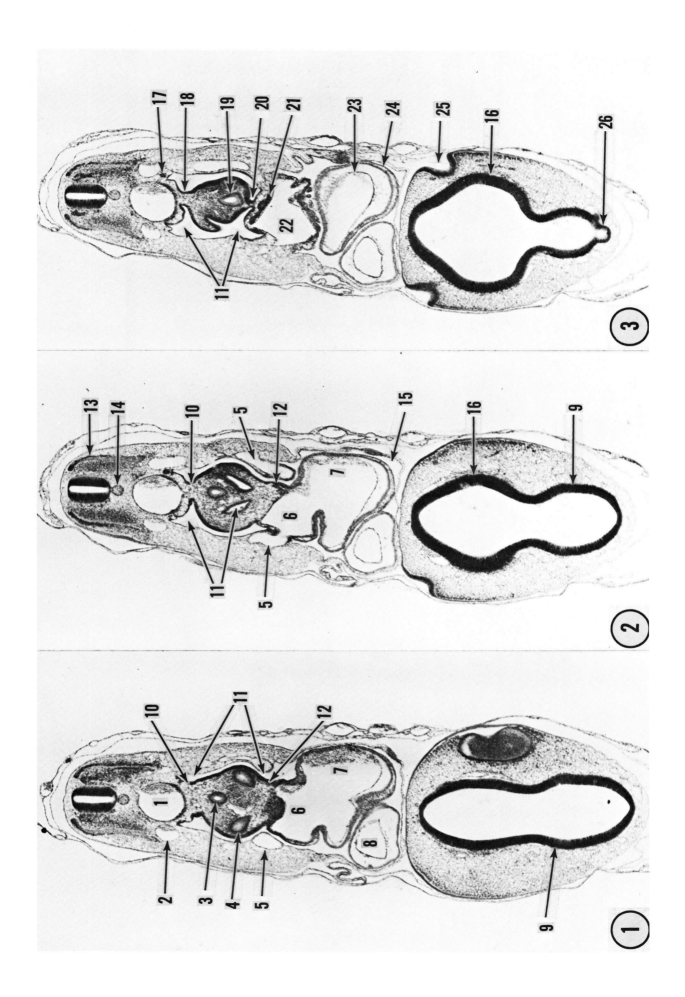

PLATE 37

72-HOUR CHICK EMBRYO SERIAL TRANSVERSE SECTIONS

1. Spinal ganglion
2. Postcardinal vein
3. Mesonephric duct (degenerating portion)
4. Mesoduodenum
5. Duodenum
6. Cranial liver rudiment
7. Peritoneal cavity
8. Ductus venosus
9. Caudal liver rudiment
10. Bulbus cordis
11. Ventricle
12. Cerebral hemisphere of telencephalon

13. Hepatoduodenal ligament
14. Spinal cord
15. Yolk sac
16. Amnion
17. Descending aorta
18. Dorsal pancreatic rudiment
19. Vitelline vein
20. Chorion
21. Dermatome
22. Myotome
23. Sclerotome
24. Intersegmental artery
25. Cranial intestinal portal

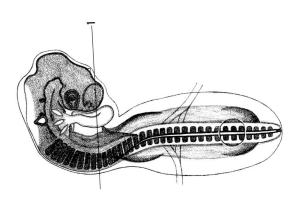

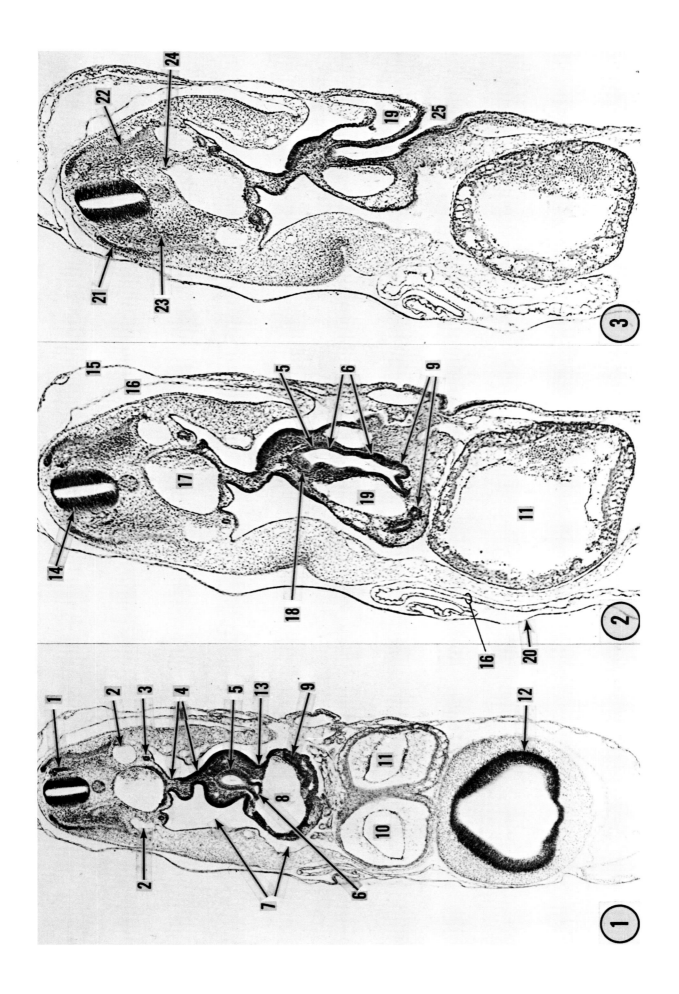

PLATE 38

72-HOUR CHICK EMBRYO SERIAL TRANSVERSE SECTIONS

1. Dermatome
2. Myotome
3. Sclerotome
4. Somatic mesoderm of *wing* bud
5. Mesonephric duct
6. Mesonephric tubule
7. Mesonephric tubule rudiment
8. Descending aorta
9. Apical ectodermal ridge of *wing* bud
10. Vitelline blood vessels
11. Postcardinal vein
12. Dorsal aortae
13. Somatic mesoderm of *leg* bud
14. Chorion

15. Amnion
16. Amniotic cavity
17. Extraembryonic coelom
18. Yolk sac
19. Lateral amniotic fold
20. Peritoneal cavity
21. Hindgut
22. Cloaca
23. Apical ectodermal ridge of *leg* bud
24. Splanchnic mesoderm of allantois
25. Endoderm of allantois
26. Cloacal membrane
27. Subcaudal pocket (amniotic cavity)

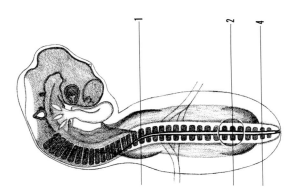

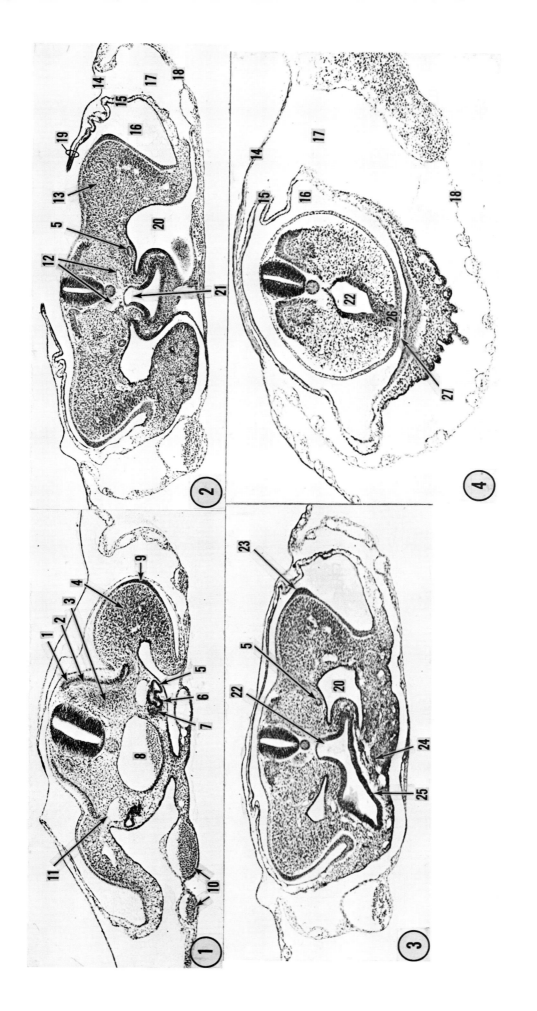

PLATE 39

72-HOUR CHICK EMBRYO MIDSAGITTAL SECTION

(Enlargement of head region)

1. Isthmus
2. Myelencephalon
3. Notochord
4. Metencephalon
5. Mesencephalon
6. Preoral gut
7. Amniotic cavity
8. Rathke's pouch

9. Pharynx
10. Mouth opening
11. Stomodeum
12. Infundibulum
13. Diencephalon
14. Pineal gland
15. Telencephalon

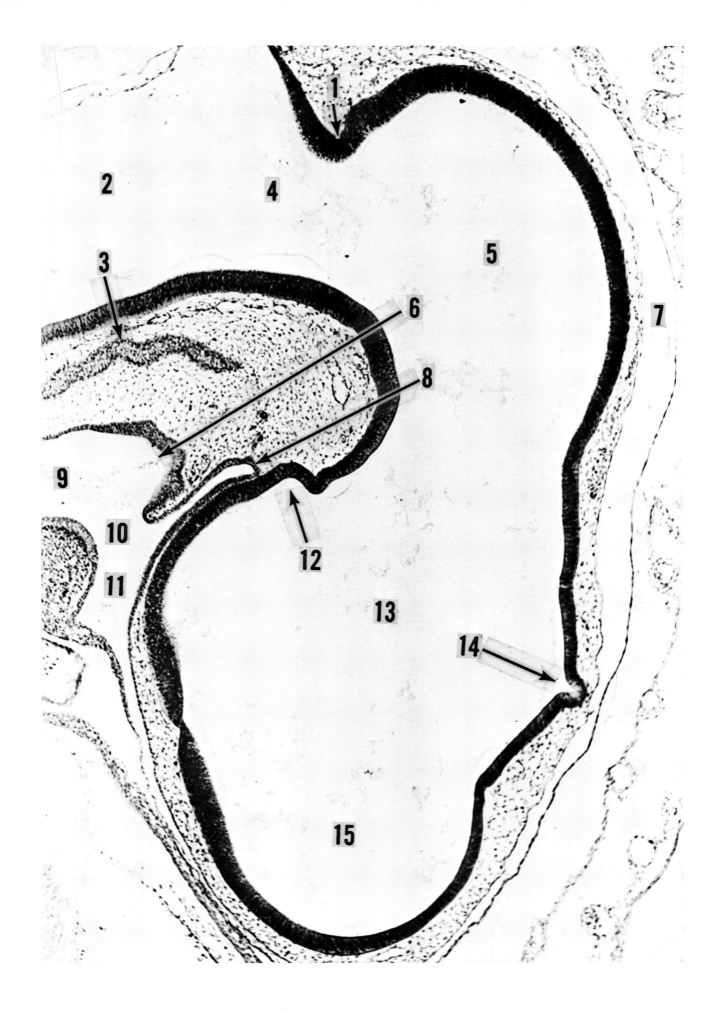

PLATE 40

72-HOUR CHICK EMBRYO—SCANNING ELECTRON MICROGRAPH OF THE
CUT SURFACE OF A BLOCK SECTIONED SAGITTALLY

(Note that the cut surface is mostly midsagittal.)

1. Cerebral hemisphere of telencephalon
2. Diencephalon
3. Optic stalk
4. Infundibulum
5. Rathke's pouch
6. Mesencephalon
7. Isthmus
8. Wall of metencephalon
9. Myelencephalon
10. Notochord
11. Dorsal aorta
12. Pharynx
13. Mouth opening
14. Stomodeum
15. Amniotic cavity
16. Amnion
17. Mandibular process
18. Thyroid rudiment
19. Pharyngeal pouches
20. Aortic sac
21. Bulbus cordis
22. Ventricle
23. Atrium

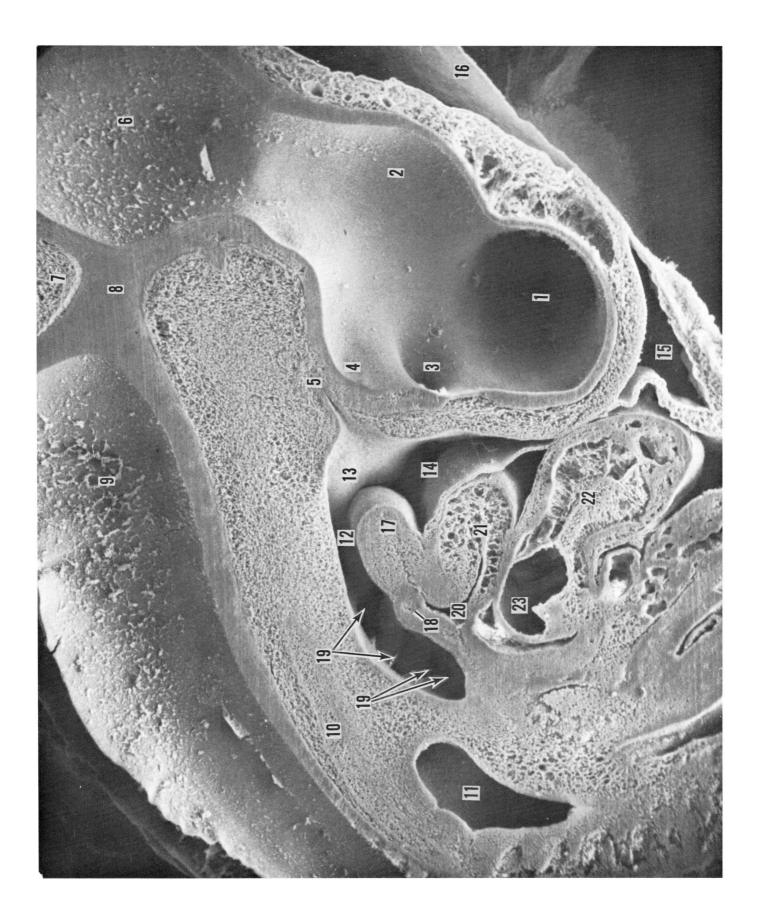

Plates 41-54

10-MM PIG EMBRYOS

PLATE 41

10-MM PIG EMBRYO SERIAL TRANSVERSE SECTIONS

1. Amnion
2. Myelencephalon
3. Fourth ventricle
4. Metencephalon
5. Isthmus
6. Mesencephalon
7. Cerebral aqueduct
8. Ventricular zone

9. Intermediate zone
10. Marginal zone
11. Roots of the spinal accessory nerve
12. Pia mater
13. Endolymphatic duct
14. Spinal accessory nerve
15. Sensory root of the vagus nerve
16. Auditory vesicle (future utriculus)

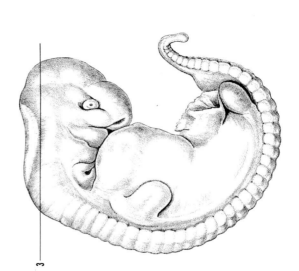

3

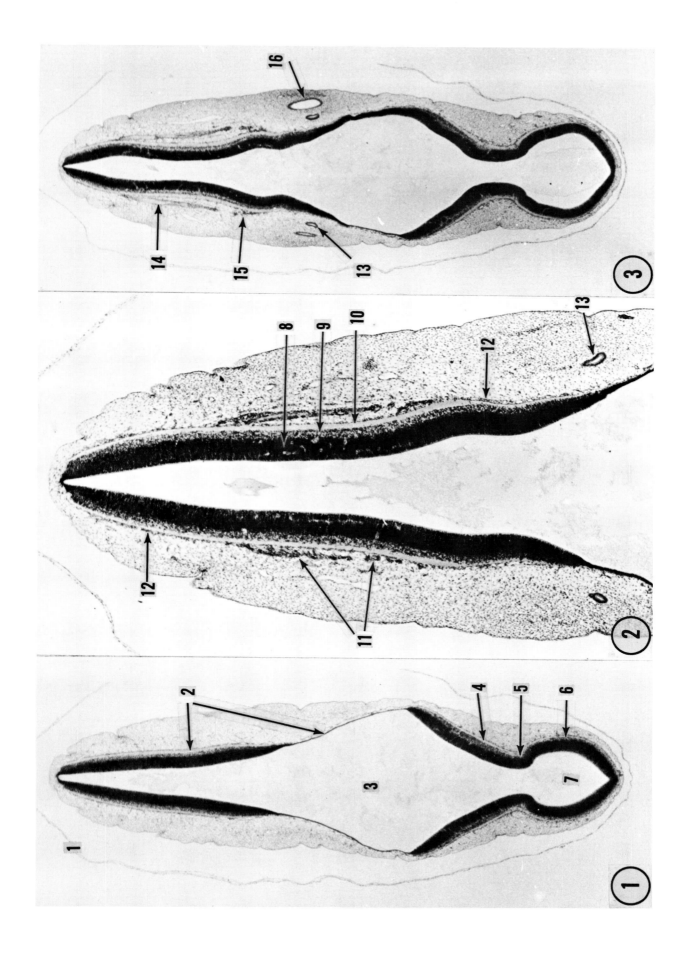

PLATE 42

10-MM PIG EMBRYO SERIAL TRANSVERSE SECTIONS

1. Spinal accessory nerve
2. Myelencephalon
3. Jugular ganglion
4. Sensory root of the glossopharyngeal nerve
5. Auditory vesicle (future utriculus)
6. Endolymphatic duct
7. Neuromeres
8. Metencephalon
9. Mesencephalon
10. Froriep's ganglion
11. Roots of the hypoglossal nerve
12. Superior ganglion
13. Amniotic cavity
14. Rudiment of the posterior semicircular canal
15. Rudiment of the anterior semicircular canal
16. Sensory root of the trigeminal nerve
17. Fourth ventricle
18. Cerebral aqueduct
19. Vagus nerve
20. Glossopharyngeal nerve
21. Precardinal vein
22. Auditory vesicle (future sacculus)
23. Acoustic ganglion
24. Geniculate ganglion
25. Semilunar ganglion
26. Rhombencephalon
27. Basilar artery
28. Oculomotor nerve
29. Posterior communicating artery

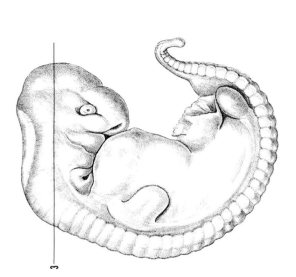

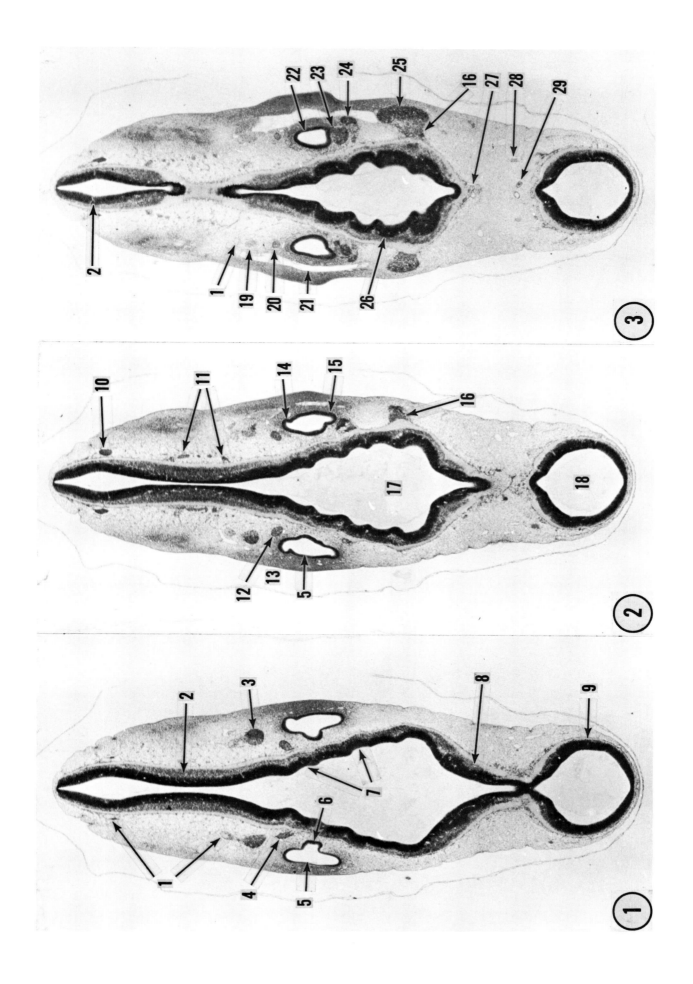

PLATE 43

10-MM PIG EMBRYO SERIAL TRANSVERSE SECTIONS

1. Roots of the hypoglossal nerve
2. Vertebral artery
3. Basilar artery
4. Precardinal vein
5. Acoustic ganglion
6. Sensory root of the facial nerve
7. Rhombencephalon
8. Semilunar ganglion
9. Oculomotor nerve
10. Posterior communicating artery
11. Mesencephalon
12. Spinal ganglion
13. Petrosal ganglion

14. Auditory vesicle (future cochlea)
15. Facial nerve
16. Abducens nerve
17. First closing plate
18. First pharyngeal pouch (future tympanic cavity)
19. Internal carotid artery (near level a, Fig. V)
20. First branchial groove
21. Infundibulum
22. Diencephalon
23. Third ventricle (major part)

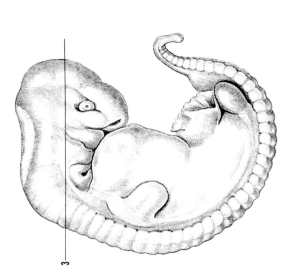

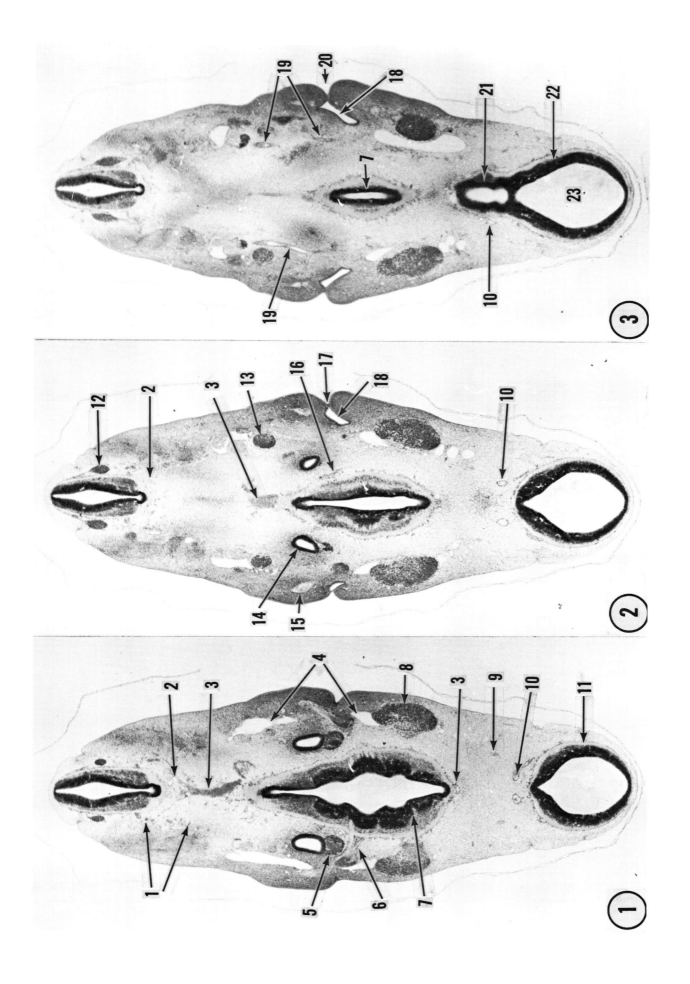

PLATE 44

10-MM PIG EMBRYO SERIAL TRANSVERSE SECTIONS

1. Ductus caroticus
2. Third aortic arch
3. Second pharyngeal pouch
4. Pharynx
5. Second branchial arch
6. Facial nerve
7. First pharyngeal pouch (future Eustachian tube, continuous below with the future tympanic cavity)
8. Basilar artery (near level f, Fig. V)
9. Internal carotid artery (near level b, Fig. V)
10. Mandibular branch of the trigeminal nerve
11. Semilunar ganglion
12. Posterior communicating artery
13. Glossopharyngeal nerve
14. Nodose ganglion
15. Second branchial groove
16. Copula
17. Tuberculum impar
18. Eye muscle rudiments
19. Rathke's pouch
20. Infundibulum
21. Diencephalon
22. Precardinal vein
23. Spinal accessory nerve
24. Lateral lingual swelling
25. Internal carotid artery (near level c, Fig. V)
26. Anterior cerebral artery
27. Third ventricle (major part)

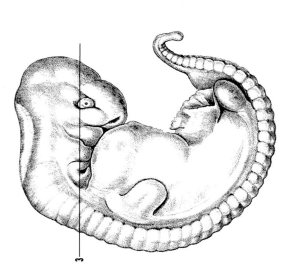

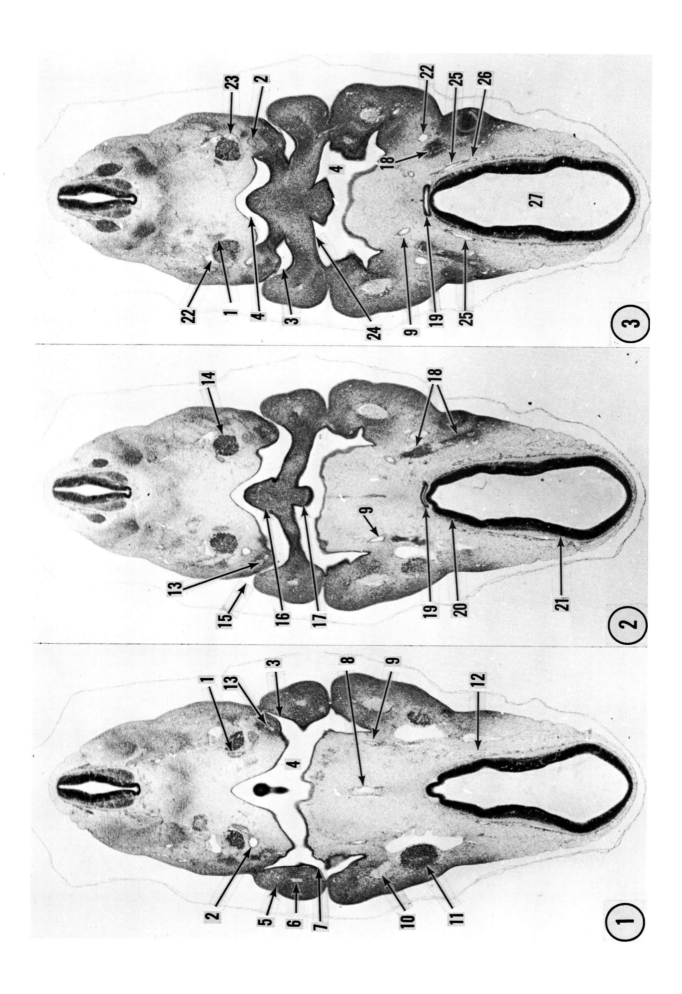

PLATE 45

10-MM PIG EMBRYO SERIAL TRANSVERSE SECTIONS

1. Epiglottis
2. Third pharyngeal pouch (inferior parathyroid rudiment)
3. Third aortic arch
4. Third branchial arch
5. Second branchial arch
6. Mandibular branch of the trigeminal nerve
7. Stomodeum
8. Sensory retina
9. Pigmented retina
10. Diencephalon
11. Third ventricle (major part)
12. Spinal cord
13. Spinal ganglion
14. Dorsal aorta
15. Fourth aortic arch
16. Cervical sinus
17. Third closing plate
18. Thyroid gland
19. Mandibular process
20. Maxillary process
21. Lens vesicle
22. Glottis
23. Arytenoid swelling
24. Precardinal vein
25. Fourth branchial arch
26. Third pharyngeal pouch (thymus rudiment)
27. Aortic trunk
28. Optic stalk
29. Optic fissure
30. Future corneal epithelium
31. Anterior cerebral artery
32. Pharynx

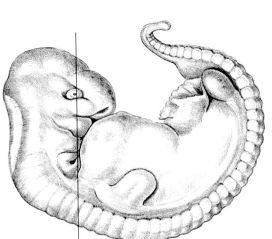

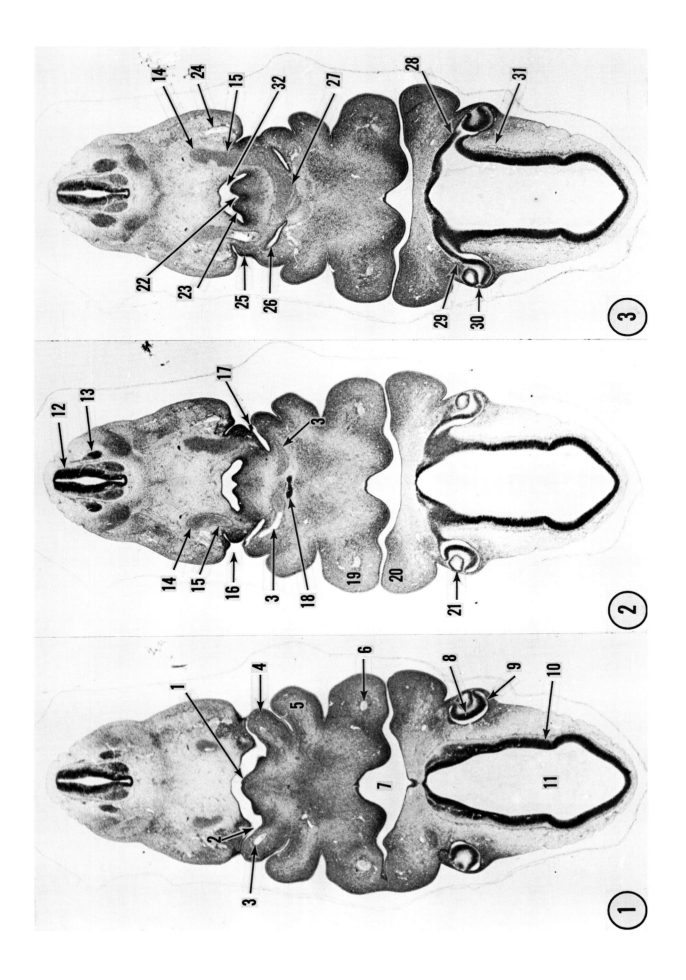

PLATE 46

10-MM PIG EMBRYO SERIAL TRANSVERSE SECTIONS

1. Dorsal aorta
2. Fifth pharyngeal pouch
3. Fourth pharyngeal pouch
4. Larynx
5. Aortic trunk
6. Stomodeum
7. Diencephalon
8. Third ventricle (major part)
9. Vertebral artery

10. Glottis
11. Pharynx
12. Sixth aortic arch
13. Esophagus
14. Precardinal vein
15. Nasal pit
16. Cerebral hemisphere of telencephalon
17. Third ventricle (minor part)

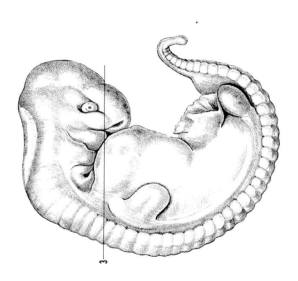

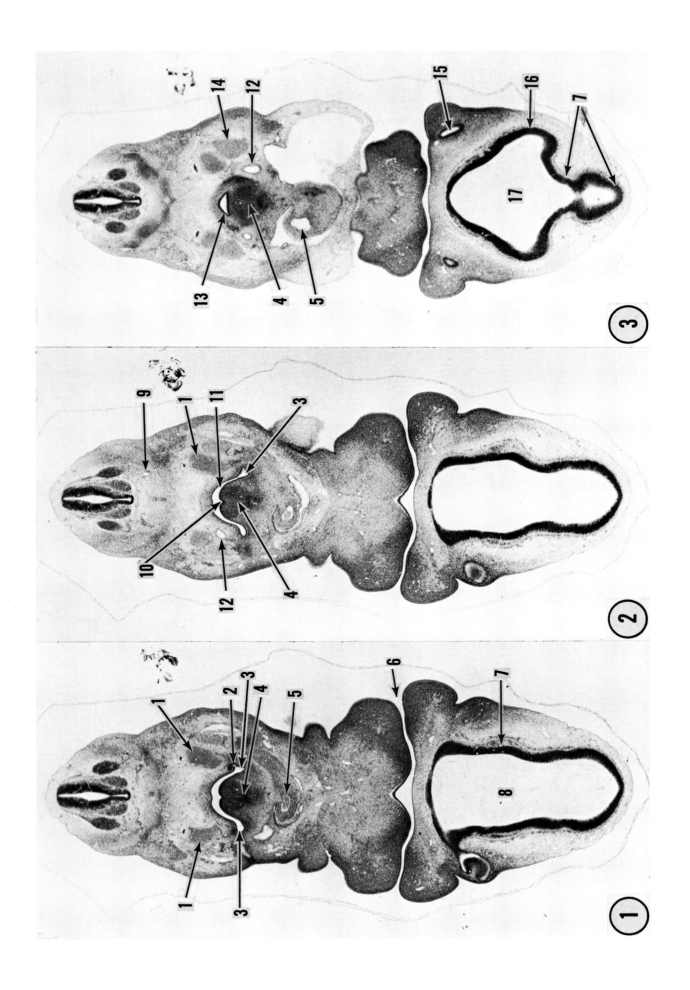

PLATE 47

10-MM PIG EMBRYO SERIAL TRANSVERSE SECTIONS

1. Spinal cord
2. Spinal ganglion
3. Dorsal aorta
4. Precardinal vein
5. Sixth aortic arch
6. Amniotic cavity
7. Aortic trunk
8. Pulmonary trunk
9. Bulbus cordis
10. Bulbar septum
11. Cerebral hemisphere of telencephalon
12. Third ventricle (minor part)
13. Diencephalon
14. Sympathetic chain ganglion

15. Esophagus
16. Trachea
17. Pulmonary artery
18. Left atrium
19. Bulbar ridges
20. Nasal pit
21. Amnion
22. Subclavian vein
23. Right atrium
24. Right ventricle
25. Left ventricle
26. Pericardial cavity
27. Medial nasal process
28. Lateral nasal process
29. Lateral ventricles

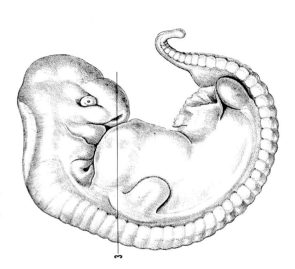

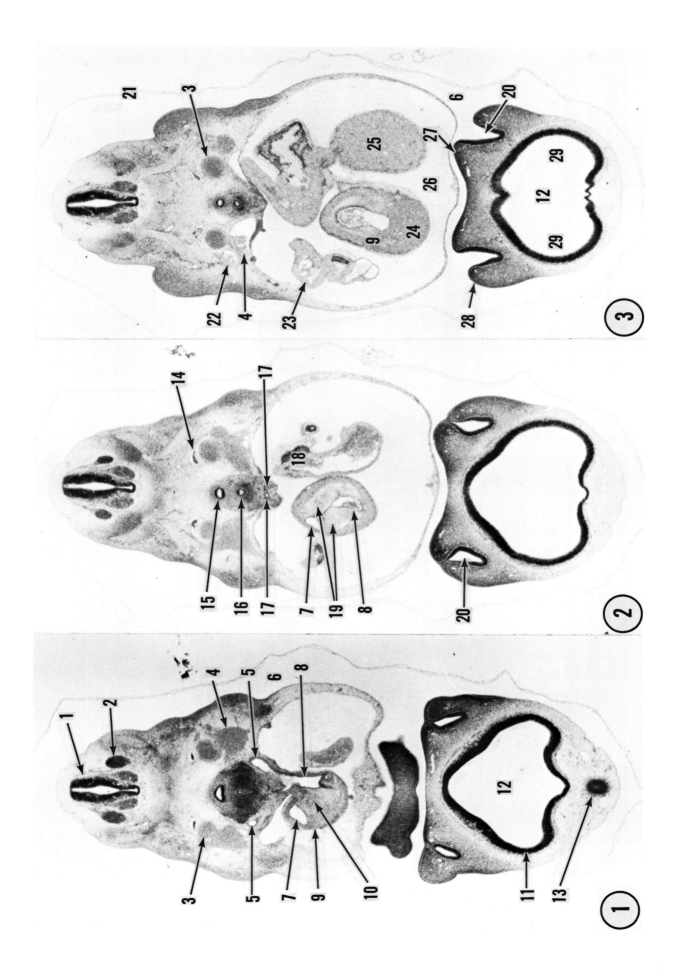

PLATE 48

10-MM PIG EMBRYO SERIAL TRANSVERSE SECTIONS

1. Subclavian vein
2. Dorsal aorta
3. Common cardinal vein
4. Trachea
5. Foramen secundum
6. Septum primum
7. Left atrium
8. Right atrium
9. Bulbus cordis
10. Right ventricle
11. Nasal pit
12. Cerebral hemisphere of telencephalon
13. Esophagus
14. Vagus nerve
15. Eparterial bronchus
16. Sinus venosus
17. Sinoatrial valve

18. Foramen ovale
19. Endocardial cushion
20. Left ventricle
21. Lamina terminalis
22. Lateral ventricles
23. Intersegmental artery (forms part of adult right subclavian artery)
24. Postcardinal vein
25. Pleural cavity
26. Pulmonary vein continuous with left atrium
27. Atrioventricular canal
28. Interventricular foramen
29. Interventricular septum
30. Pericardial cavity
31. Parietal pleura
32. Visceral pleura

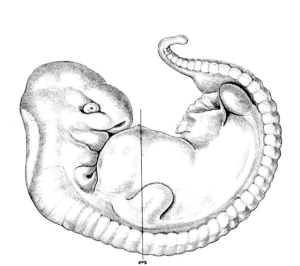

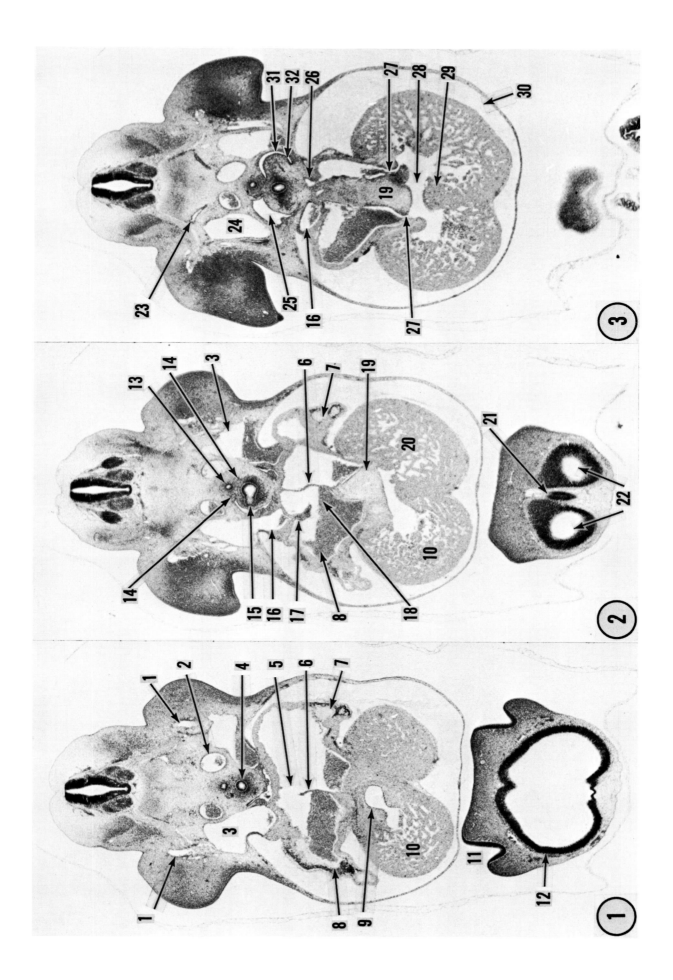

PLATE 49

10-MM PIG EMBRYO SERIAL TRANSVERSE SECTIONS

1. Spinal cord
2. Spinal ganglion
3. Brachial plexus
4. Postcardinal vein
5. Somatic mesoderm of foreleg bud
6. Esophagus
7. Lung bud
8. Peritoneal cavity (continuous medially with pleural cavity)
9. Apical ectodermal ridge of foreleg bud
10. Pleural cavity
11. Visceral pleura
12. Septum transversum
13. Inferior vena cava
14. Ventricle
15. Mesoesophagus
16. Descending aorta
17. Mesonephric kidney
18. Left dorsal lobe of liver
19. Left ventral lobe of liver
20. Ductus venosus
21. Yolk sac
22. Dorsal mesogaster
23. Stomach
24. Mammary ridge
25. Omental bursa
26. Hepatogastric ligament
27. Peritoneal cavity
28. Hepatic cords
29. Hepatic sinusoids

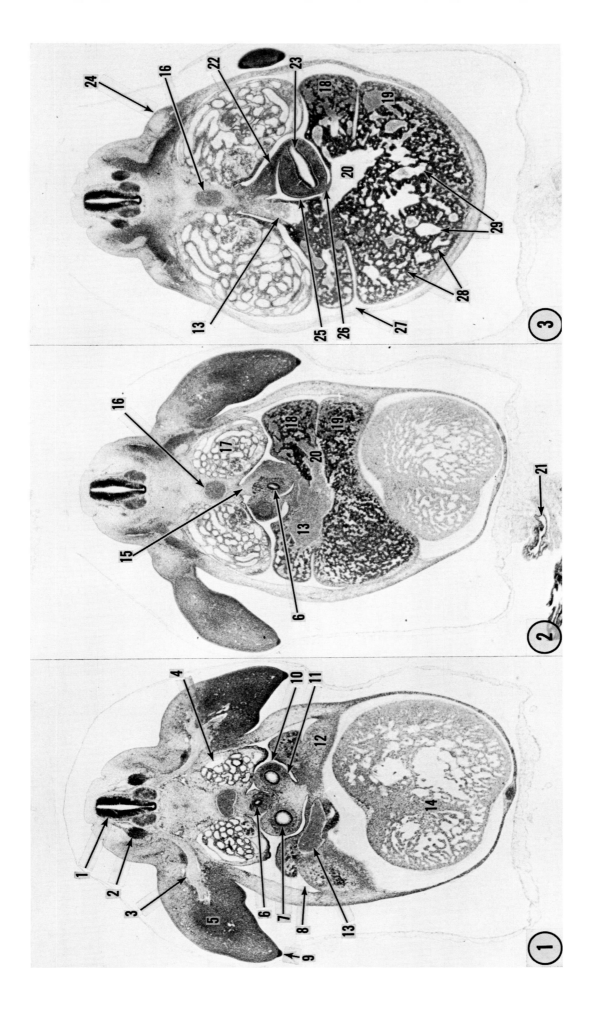

PLATE 50

10-MM PIG EMBRYO SERIAL TRANSVERSE SECTIONS

1. Descending aorta
2. Mesonephric kidney
3. Inferior vena cava
4. Omental bursa
5. Portal vein
6. Duodenum
7. Hepatoduodenal ligament
8. Right dorsal lobe of liver
9. Hepatic duct
10. Right ventral lobe of liver
11. Falciform ligament
12. Temporary umbilical hernia
13. Gonad rudiment
14. Epiploic foramen
15. Parietal peritoneum
16. Visceral peritoneum
17. Common bile duct
18. Cystic duct
19. Right umbilical vein
20. Left umbilical vein
21. Common vitelline vein
22. Cranial limb of the intestinal loop
23. Caudal limb of the intestinal loop
24. Mesonephric tubules
25. Glomeruli
26. Dorsal pancreatic rudiment
27. Germinal epithelium
28. Ventral pancreatic rudiment
29. Dorsal pancreatic duct
30. Gall bladder
31. Hepatic cords
32. Hepatic sinusoids
33. Glomerular capsule

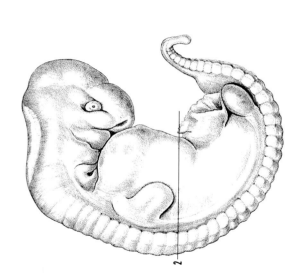

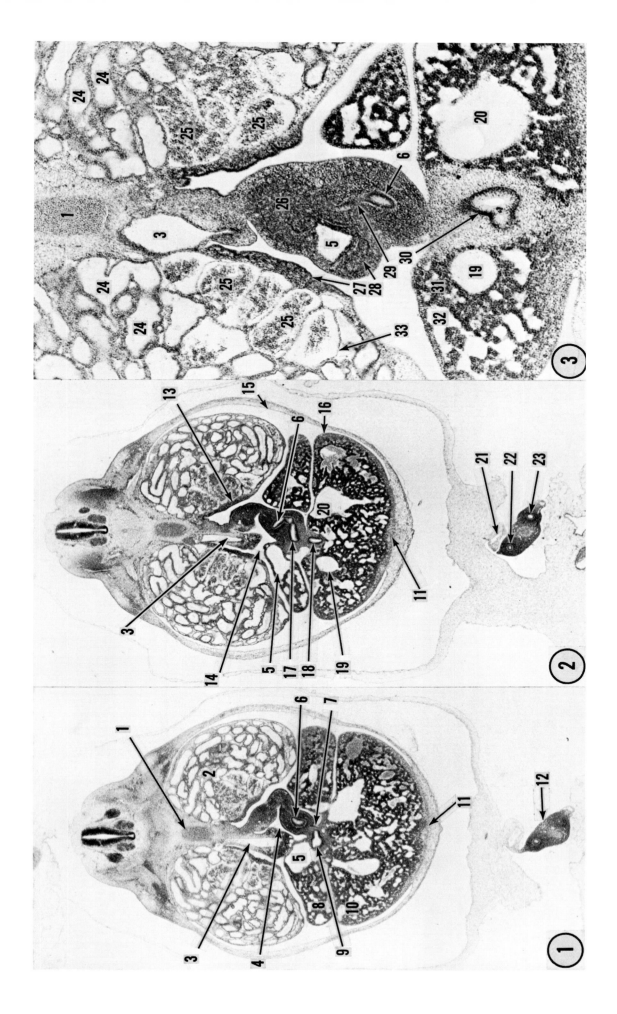

PLATE 51

10-MM PIG EMBRYO SERIAL TRANSVERSE SECTIONS

1. Descending aorta
2. Mesonephric kidney
3. Subcardinal vein
4. Superior mesenteric vein
5. Duodenum
6. Mesonephric duct
7. Gall bladder
8. Wharton's jelly of umbilical cord
9. Common vitelline vein
10. Umbilical vein
11. Cranial limb of the intestinal loop
12. Superior mesenteric artery
13. Umbilical artery
14. Tail
15. Marginal zone
16. Intermediate zone
17. Ventricular zone
18. Roof plate

19. Alar plate
20. Dorsal root axons
21. Spinal ganglion
22. Basal plate
23. Motor horn
24. Dorsal root dendrites
25. Spinal nerve—dorsal ramus
26. Ventral root
27. Floor plate
28. Notochord
29. Sclerotome
30. Spinal nerve—ventral ramus
31. Spinal nerve—visceral ramus
32. Sympathetic chain ganglion
33. Mesonephric tubules
34. Gonad rudiment
35. Caudal limb of the intestinal loop
36. Allantois

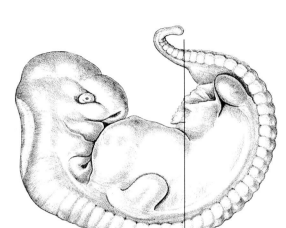

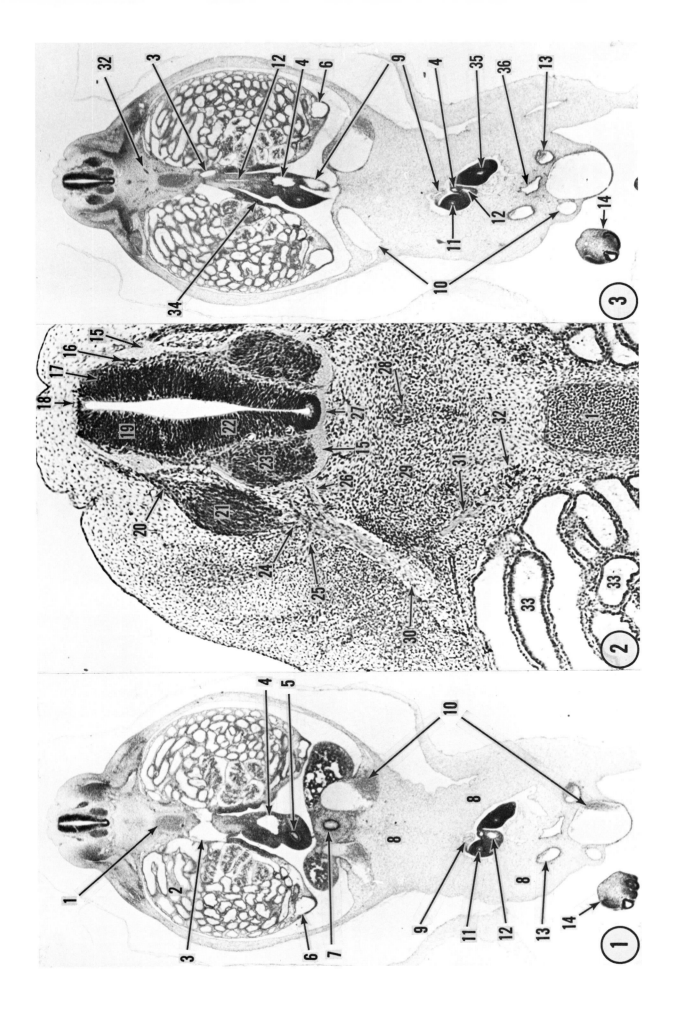

PLATE 52

10-MM PIG EMBRYO SERIAL TRANSVERSE SECTIONS

1. Mesonephric tubules
2. Subcardinal anastomosis
3. Glomerular capsule
4. Mesonephric duct
5. Continuity between the duodenum (above arrow) and cranial limb of the intestinal loop (below arrow)
6. Superior mesenteric vein
7. Caudal limb of the intestinal loop
8. Umbilical vein
9. Umbilical artery
10. Tail
11. Extraembryonic coelom
12. Descending aorta
13. Glomeruli
14. Gonad rudiment

15. Superior mesenteric artery
16. Mammary ridge
17. Genital eminence
18. Cloacal membrane
19. Tail gut
20. Mesocolon
21. Caudal limb of the intestinal loop (forms part of adult colon)
22. Allantois
23. Peritoneal cavity
24. Cloaca (future urogenital sinus)
25. Cloacal septum
26. Cloaca (future rectum)
27. Spinal cord
28. Mesonephric kidney

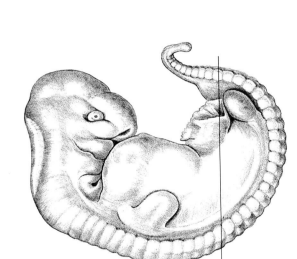

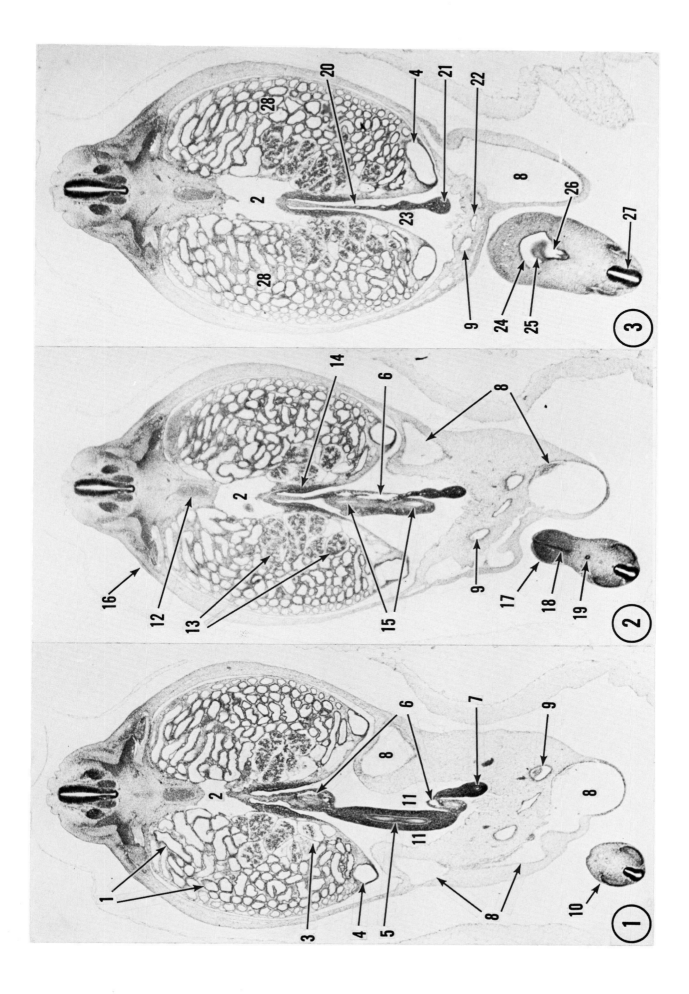

PLATE 53

10-MM PIG EMBRYO SERIAL TRANSVERSE SECTIONS

1. Subcardinal anastomosis
2. Mesocolon
3. Umbilical artery
4. Allantois (continuous below with urogenital sinus)
5. Umbilical vein
6. Mesonephric duct
7. Urogenital sinus
8. Colon
9. Descending aorta
10. Mesonephric kidney
11. Caudal limb of the intestinal loop

12. Peritoneal cavity
13. Spinal cord
14. Motor horn
15. Spinal ganglion
16. Mammary ridge
17. Apical ectodermal ridge of hindleg bud
18. Somatic mesoderm of hindleg bud
19. Ureters
20. Postcardinal vein
21. Caudal artery
22. Notochord

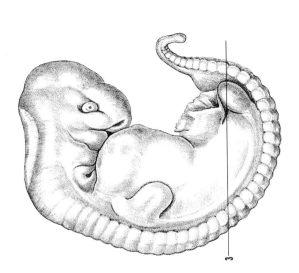

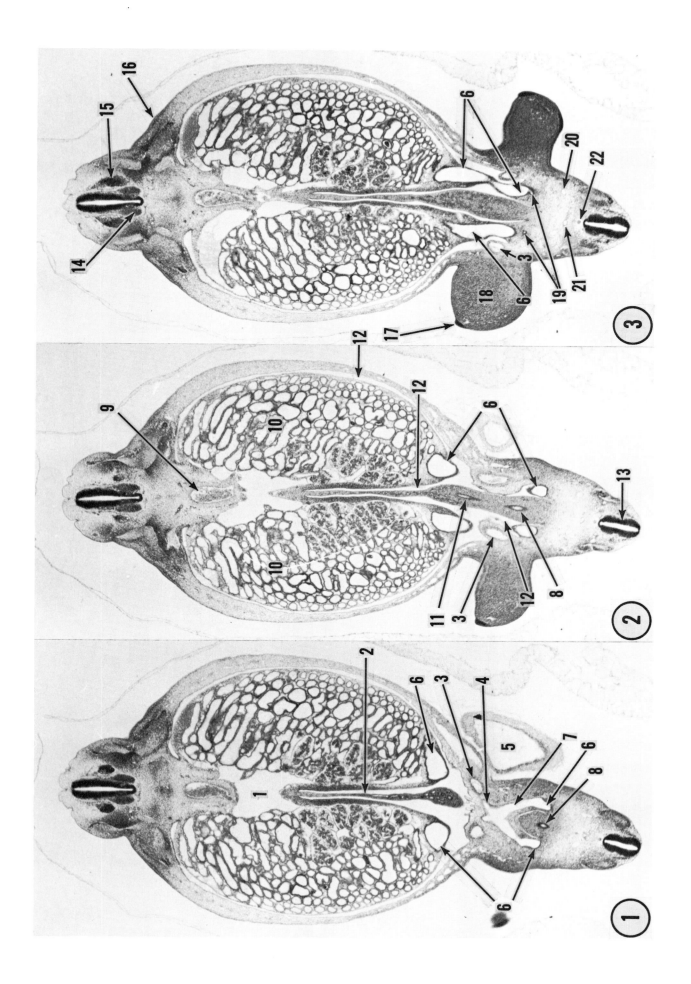

PLATE 54

10-MM PIG EMBRYO SERIAL TRANSVERSE SECTIONS

1. Umbilical artery
2. External iliac artery
3. Renal pelvis
4. Caudal artery
5. Nephrotome
6. Descending aorta
7. Mesonephric kidney
8. Peritoneal cavity
9. Postcardinal vein
10. Notochord

11. Spinal ganglion
12. Spinal cord
13. Skin ectoderm
14. Myotome
15. Dermatome
16. Ventral root
17. Sclerotome—dense caudal portion
18. Sclerotome—less dense cranial portion
19. Cavity of the spinal cord

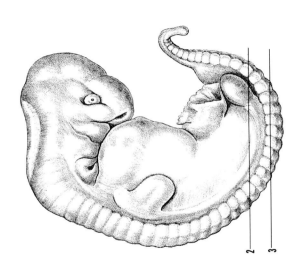

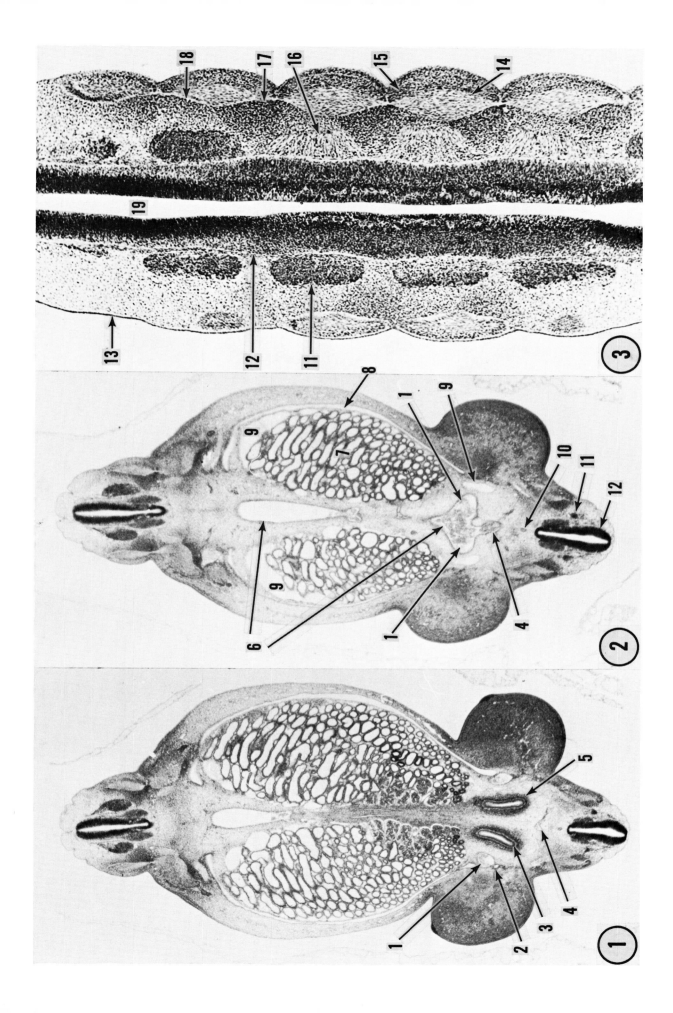

INDEX

This index contains every term listed in the text in **boldface** and every page number on which the boldfaced term appears. Also listed are structures labeled in text figures (A–X) or in plates (P1-P54).

Abducens (VI) cranial nerves, 88, S, P43
Acoustic ganglia, 76, 88, S, P42, P43
Acousticofacialis ganglia, 66, 72, 75, 76, P22, P23, P27, P30, P32, P33
Adenohypophysis (*see* Pituitary gland, anterior)
Adhesive glands, 22, P3
Alar plate, 91, P51
Albumen, 38
Allantoic arteries (*see* Umbilical arteries)
Allantoic veins (*see* Umbilical veins)
Allantois, 67, 69, 75, 79, 82, 94, P, T, P30, P38, P51, P52, P53
Allantois rudiment, 67, 69, 73, P, P26, P28
Amnion, 64, 69, 72, 73, 75, 79, 81, 82, Q, P22, P23, P24, P25, P27, P28, P33, P34, P37, P38, P40, P41, P47
Amniotic cavity, 72, 73, 81, 87, Q, P24, P25, P27, P28, P32, P33, P38, P39, P40, P42, P47
Amniotic fluid, 69
Amniotic fold, caudal or posterior, 75
Amniotic fold, cranial or anterior, 64, 72, 75, P28
Amniotic folds, boundary of the, 63, P20, P30
Amniotic folds, lateral, 64, 69, 72, 75, Q, P25, P28, P38
Animal hemisphere, 7, 9
Animal pole, 7, 9, 61, C, E, P1, P5
Anus, 23, F
Aorta, arch of the, 96, U
Aorta, ascending (*see* Aortic trunk)
Aorta, descending, 64, 68, 75, 79, 80, 99, P21, P24, P25, P32, P34, P35, P36, P37, P38, P49, P50, P51, P52, P53, P54
Aortae, dorsal, 23, 34, 35, 36, 64, 68, 72, 73, 75, 79, 80, 81, 96, H, U, P3, P4, P8, P9, P11, P12, P21, P22, P23, P24, P25, P27, P28, P29, P32, P33, P34, P38, P40, P45, P46, P47, P48

Aortae, ventral, 23, 34, H, P8
Aortic arches, first, 23, 34, 64, 68, 72, 73, 75, 79, 96, H, P3, P8, P21, P22, P23, P26, P27, P29, P32, P33, P34
Aortic arches, second, 64, 68, 75, 79, 96, P21, P23, P32, P33, P34
Aortic arches, third, 64, 68, 75, 79, 96, U, P21, P24, P32, P33, P34, P44, P45
Aortic arches, fourth, 75, 79, 96, U, P32, P34, P45
Aortic arches, fifth, 96
Aortic arches, sixth, 96, U, P46, P47
Aortic sac, 64, 68, 75, 79, 81, P21, P23, P24, P26, P32, P35, P40
Aortic trunk, 96, U, P45, P46, P47
Apical ectodermal ridges, 79, 91, P38, P49, P53
Arch of the aorta (*see* Aorta, arch of the)
Archenteron, 11, 12, 61, E, P1, P2
Area opaca, 26, 39, 44, G, P16
Area pellucida, 26, 39, 44, G, K, L, P7, P13, P16
Area vasculosa, 26, G, P7
Area vitellina, 26, G
Arterial circle of Willis (*see* Circle of Willis)
Arytenoid cartileges, 94
Arytenoid swellings, 94, P45
Atria, 28, 64, 68, 75, 79, 81, 99, P21, P24, P29, P30, P35, P36, P40, P47, P48
Atrioventricular canals, 99, P48
Auditory (VIII) cranial nerves, 66, 88, S
Auditory placodes, 32, 35, 36, 66, H, P9, P10, P11
Auditory vesicles, 22, 36, 63, 66, 75, 76, 88, S, P3, P11, P20, P22, P23, P30, P32, P41, P42, P43
Auricles (*see* Pinnae)
Autonomic nervous system, 89, 91

Axons, 22, 77, 87, 88, 89, 90
Axons, preganglionic, 89
Azygos vein, 103

Basal plate, 91, P51
Basilar artery, 98, V, P42, P43, P44
Bicuspid valve, 99
Blastocoel, 8, 9, 11, 12, 61, E, P1
Blastoderm, 26, 39, 61, 63, J, N
Blastodisc, 26, 38, 61
Blastomeres, 8, 9, 24, 39, 61, P1, P5
Blastomeres, central, 39
Blastomeres, marginal, 39
Blastoporal lip, dorsal, 10, 11, 24, C, E, P1, P6
Blastoporal lip, ventral, 10, 11, 24, E, P1
Blastoporal lips, lateral, 10, 24, P6
Blastopore, 10, 11, 15, 24, C, D, E, P1
Blastula, 8, 9, C, D, E, P1, P5
Blastulation, 8
Blood cells, primitive, 26
Blood islands, 26, G, P7
Body of the embryo, 26, G
Body folds (see Body folds, lateral; Head fold
  of the body; Tail fold of the body)
Body folds, lateral, 47, 69, 72, 79, Q, P19, P25,
  P28
Body, plan 61
Bottle cells, 44, N
Bowman's capsules (see Glomerular capsules)
Brachial plexus, 91, P49
Brain, (see also the specific divisions of), 27, 72,
  80, A, V
Branchial arches, first (see also Mandibular
  processes; Maxillary processes), 64, 72, 75, 76,
  78, 83, P27, P34
Branchial arches, second, 64, 72, 75, 76, 83, R,
  P20, P27, P30, P31, P33, P34, P44, P45
Branchial arches, third, 64, 75, 76, 83, R, P20,
  P30, P33, P34, P45
Branchial arches, fourth, 76, P34, P45
Branchial clefts, first, 78, P33
Branchial clefts, second, 78, 94
Branchial grooves, first, 64, 67, 72, 75, 78, 83,
  94, R, P20, P22, P23, P27, P30, P33, P43
Branchial grooves, second, 64, 67, 75, 78, 83,
  94, R, P20, P30, P34, P44
Branchial grooves, third (see also Cervical
  sinuses), 64, 67, 75, 78, 83, 94, P20, P30
Branchial grooves, fourth (see also Cervical
  sinuses), 78, 83, 94
Bulbar ridges, 96, P47
Bulbar septum, 96, P47
Bulbus cordis, 23, 28, 34, 35, 64, 68, 75, 79, 81,
  96, H, P3, P7, P8, P9, P11, P20, P21, P24,
  P26, P30, P32, P35, P36, P37, P40, P47, P48

C cells, 94
Calcitonin, 94
Calyces, major, 96
Calyces, minor, 96
Cardiac jelly, 34, 35, P11

Cardiac primordia, 47, 59, P17
Cardinal veins, caudal or posterior (see
  Postcardinal veins)
Cardinal veins, common, 64, 68, 69, 75, 80, 102,
  O, P21, P24, P35, P36, P48
Cardinal veins, cranial or anterior (see
  Precardinal veins)
Carotid arteries, common, 96
Carotid arteries, external, 96
Carotid arteries, internal, 75, 79, 96, U, V, P32,
  P33, P43, P44
Caudal arteries, 80, 99, P53, P54
Caudal end (see Tail end)
Celiac artery, 99
Cell bodies, 77, 87, 88, 89
Cell marker, 9, 41
Central nervous system, 27
Centrum, 91
Cerebellum, 85
Cerebral aqueduct, 85, P41, P42
Cerebral artery, anterior, 97, V, P44, P45
Cerebral hemispheres, 75, 77, 81, 87, S, P30,
  P31, P36, P37, P40, P46, P47, P48
Cerebral peduncles, 85
Cerebrospinal fluid, 32, 85
Cerebrum, 87
Cervical sinuses, 83, 94, R, P45
Chain ganglia, 90, P47, P51
Cheeks, 75
Chimera, 41
Chorioallantoic membrane, 69, 82
Chorion, 64, 69, 72, 75, 82, Q, P22, P23, P24,
  P25, P27, P34, P37, P38
Chorionic gonadotropin, 13
Choroid, 87
Choroid plexus, 85
Ciliary tufts, 24, P6
Circle of Willis, 98
Cleavage, 8, 26, 39, 61, J, P5
Cleavage, discoidal, 39
Cleavage, partial or meroblastic, 39
Cleavage, total or holoblastic, 8
Cleavage furrows, 8, 24, 39, J, P5
Cloaca, 79, 93, P, T, P38, P52
Cloacal membrane, 23, 79, 93, P, P38, P52
Cloacal septum, 93, T, P52
Cloacal valves, 13
Closing plates, first, 67, 72, 78, 94, P22, P33,
  P43
Closing plates, second, 67, 78, 94, P23, P33
Closing plates, third, 67, 78, 94, P24, P34, P45
Closing plates, fourth, 78, P34
Clutch, 39
Cochleae, 88, P43
Cochlear ganglia (see Spiral ganglia)
Coelom (see also the specific divisions of), 12,
  23, 32, 33, 34, 36, 47, 72, 73, P8, P9, P11,
  P17, P19, P28
Coelom, extraembryonic, 69, 72, 92, P, Q, P25,
  P26, P27, P33, P35, P38, P52
Coelom, intraembryonic, 69, Q